Introduction

This is the second of two textbooks covering Higher Tier GCSE. Students following a two year course would expect to take one year on each book, those on a one year course half that time. The books cover the requirements of Higher Tier GCSE and so are suitable for use with any syllabus. The division of material between them is made on the basis of the modules within the MEI syllabus.

This book is divided into 17 chapters. The first 12 of these follow on from *Hodder Mathematics Higher 1* and complete the new work in Higher Tier GCSE. The order of these chapters is designed to form a logical progression but teachers may prefer to vary it. Each chapter is divided into a number of sections, or teaching units, ending with an exercise. The chapters end with mixed exercises covering all of their content. Further exercise sheets and tests are provided in the Teacher's Resource. The remaining 5 chapters are essentially revision, designed to help students in their final weeks of preparation for the GCSE examination.

The instruction pages have been designed to help teachers engage their students in whole class discussion. The symbol ⌘ is used to indicate a Discussion Point; teachers should see it as an invitation.

Many of the exercises end with a starred question. These are designed to be more thought provoking, in many cases introducing students to ideas that they will follow up later (at A Level or in other subjects). In addition there are several past GCSE examination questions from the various boards.

Where knowledge is assumed, this is stated at the start of the chapter. Questions indicated with a calculator icon ▦ need to be answered with a calculator. The 'no calculator' icon ▨ indicates that a calculator should definitely not be used.

Although students are to be encouraged to use I.T., particularly spreadsheets, specific guidance is limited to the Teacher's Resource. Otherwise, the book would have been based on one particular package to the frustration of those using all the others.

The authors would like to thank all those who helped in preparing this book, particularly Mike Jones for long hours working through the typescript, and Terry Heard for his thoughtful and invaluable advice.

How to use this book

 This symbol next to a question means you need to use your calculator.

 This symbol next to a question means you are not allowed to use your calculator.

 This symbol means you will need to think carefully about a point and may want to discuss it.

 Caution. You will need to think carefully about this point. There may well be a mistake which is easily made.

The Quadratic Equation

The roots of $ax^2 + bx + c = 0$, where $a \neq 0$, are given by $x = \dfrac{-b \pm \sqrt{(b^2 - 4ac)}}{2a}$

Triangles

Area of a triangle = $\dfrac{1}{2}$ × base × height

Quadrilaterals

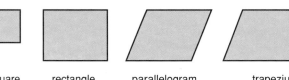

square   rectangle   parallelogram   trapezium   kite   rhombus

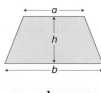

Area = base × vertical height   **Area = $\dfrac{1}{2}\,(a + b)\,h$**

D

Maths workshop

atics

2

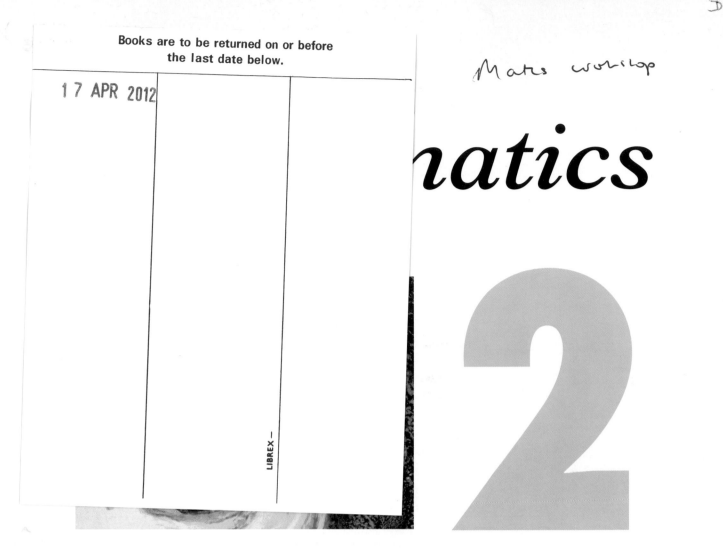

Series editor: **Roger Porkess**

MEI author team:
Catherine Berry
Diana Cowey
Dave Faulkner
Nigel Green
Christine Wood

Hodder & Stoughton

A MEMBER OF THE HODDER HEADLINE GROUP

Acknowledgements

The authors and publishers would like to thank the following companies, institutions and individuals who have given permission to reproduce copyright material: London Examinations, a division of Edexcel Foundation, Midland Bank, NatWest Bank, OCR, SEG. The publishers will be happy to make arrangements with any copyright holder whom it has not been possible to contact.

Illustrations were drawn by Tom Cross, Jeff Edwards, Phil Ford and Joseph McEwan.

Photos supplied by Bruce Coleman Collection (p.2), Life File (p.19) and Science Photo Library (p.158).

Page design and cover design by Lynda King.

Orders: please contact Bookpoint Ltd, 39 Milton Park, Abingdon, Oxon OX14 4TD.
Telephone: (44) 01235 400414, Fax: (44) 01235 400454. Lines are open from 9.00 – 6.00,
Monday to Saturday, with a 24 hour message answering service. Email address: orders@bookpoint.co.uk

Edexcel Foundation, London Examinations accepts no responsibility whatsoever for the accuracy or method of working in the answers given at the back of this book. The answers at the end of this book are the sole responsibility of the publishers and have not been provided or approved by SEG.

British Library Cataloguing in Publication Data

A catalogue record for this title is available from The British Library

ISBN 0 340 711949

First published 1999
Impression number   10 9 8 7 6 5 4 3 2 1
Year   2005 2004 2003 2002 2001 2000 1999

Cover photo from Photonica

Typeset by Multiplex Techniques Ltd, Orpington, Kent.

Printed in Italy for Hodder & Stoughton Educational, a division of Hodder Headline Plc,
338 Euston Road, London NW1 3BH by Printer Trento.

Circles

Circumference of circle $\quad = \pi \times$ diameter
$$= 2 \times \pi \times \text{radius}$$

Area of circle $= \pi \times (\text{radius})^2$

Solid figures

Cuboid	**Volume = length $\times$ width $\times$ height**
Prism	**Volume = area of cross section $\times$ length**
Cylinder	**Volume = $\pi r^2 \times$ length**
	Curved surface area = $2\pi r \times$ length
Cone	**Volume = $\frac{1}{3}\pi r^2 \times$ height**
	Curved surface area = $\pi r \times$ slant length
Sphere	**Volume = $\frac{4}{3}\pi r^3$**
	Surface area = $4\pi r^2$

Trigonometry

$\sin \theta = \dfrac{\text{opposite}}{\text{hypotenuse}} = \dfrac{y}{h}$

$\cos \theta = \dfrac{\text{adjacent}}{\text{hypotenuse}} = \dfrac{x}{h}$

$\tan \theta = \dfrac{\text{opposite}}{\text{adjacent}} = \dfrac{y}{x}$

Pythagoras' theorem: $x^2 + y^2 = h^2$

Units

Metric system

Length

k	1 kilometre	$= 10^3$ metres	$= 1000$ metres		d	1 decimetre	$= 10^{-1}$ metres	$= \dfrac{1}{10}$ metre
h	1 hectometre	$= 10^2$ metres	$= 100$ metres		c	1 centimetre	$= 10^{-2}$ metres	$= \dfrac{1}{100}$ metre
da	1 decametre	$= 10^1$ metres	$= 10$ metres		m	1 millimetre	$= 10^{-3}$ metres	$= \dfrac{1}{1000}$ metre

The units for mass and capacity follow the same pattern. Thus:
1 kilogram = 1000 grams $\qquad$ 1 litre = 1000 millilitres.
Notice also that: 1 tonne = 1000 kg.

Imperial

12 inches = 1 foot $\qquad$ 16 ounces = 1 pound
3 feet = 1 yard $\qquad$ 14 pounds = 1 stone
1760 yards = 1 mile $\qquad$ 8 stones = 1 hundredweight (cwt)
$\qquad\qquad\qquad\qquad$ 20 cwt = 1 ton

Contents

Contents

Chapter 1

Variation

> **Before you start this chapter you should:**
>
> ★ understand the meaning of $y \propto x$, $y \propto x^2$ and $y \propto x^3$
> ★ be able to solve problems involving direct proportion.

Direct variation

Mike is designing a wildlife park. He is including a fenced enclosure for a rare breed of deer. Each deer must be allocated a certain area, so the larger the enclosure the more deer it will accommodate.

Mike plans a square enclosure, with side x metres.

? *As x is increased, what happens to*

- *the total cost of fencing the enclosure?*
- *the number of deer that the enclosure can accommodate?*

You can work out the total cost of the fencing, £F, like this:

$$£F = \text{cost per metre} \times \text{number of metres}$$
$$= \text{cost per metre} \times 4x$$
$$= (4 \times \text{cost per metre}) \times x.$$

You can write this as $F = k \times x$ where k is called the **constant of proportionality**.

In this case, k is the cost of 4 m of fencing.

For example, if fencing costs £5 per metre,

$$k = 4 \times 5 = 20.$$

When $F = kx$ you can say that

F **varies directly with** x

or F **is directly proportional to** x.

You can also write this using symbols:

$F \propto x$ ← Read this as 'is proportional to'.

? *Does the number of deer,* N, *vary directly with* x *?*

Doubling the area of the enclosure means there is room for twice as many deer, three times the area means three times as many deer and so on.

The number of deer, *N*, is directly proportional to the *area* of the enclosure, x^2 square metres, so

$$N \propto x^2$$

$$\text{or } N = cx^2$$

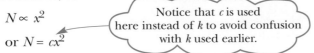

Notice that *c* is used here instead of *k* to avoid confusion with *k* used earlier.

? *What does the constant of proportionality,* c, *represent in this case?*

? *When* x *is doubled what happens to the value of* N *?*

Look at the graphs below.

- The graph of *F* against *x*, showing direct variation, is a straight line.
- The graph of *N* against *x* is a curve, not a straight line.

Example

The number of deer, *N*, is directly proportional to the area of the enclosure x^2 square metres, and $N = 8$ when $x = 40$.

Find the value of *N* when $x = 60$.

Solution

Since $N \propto x^2$, you can write $N = cx^2$, where *c* is the constant of proportionality.

When $N = 8$, $x = 40$ so

$$8 = c \times (40)^2$$

$$8 = 1600 c$$

$$c = \frac{1}{200}.$$

The relationship is

$$N = \frac{1}{200} x^2.$$

When $x = 60$

$$N = \frac{1}{200} (60)^2 = 18.$$

Exercise 1.1

1 The extension of an elastic spring is directly proportional to the mass suspended from it. A mass of 500 g produces an extension of 1 cm.

   a) What extension occurs when a mass of 1 kg is suspended?

   b) What mass is used to produce an extension of 16 mm?

2 Sara is a cricketer. She spends some time throwing a ball vertically into the air to practise her catching. The greatest height, h metres, reached by the ball on any throw is directly proportional to the square of the time, t seconds, that the ball is in the air.

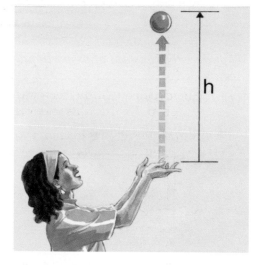

When $h = 5$, $t = 2$.

   a) When $t = 1.2$, what is the value of h?

   b) The greatest height reached by the ball is 10 m. How long is it in the air during this throw?

3 The volume, $V\,\text{m}^3$, of gas contained in a balloon varies directly as the cube of its length, $l\,\text{m}$. When $l = 2$, $V = 4$.

   a) Find V when $l = 0.5$.

   b) Find l, correct to 1 decimal place, when $V = 12$.

   c) The length l is increased by 20%. Find the percentage increase in V.

4 Copy and complete this table, given that y is directly proportional to $(x - 3)$.

x	5	9	
y		18	36

5 Terry is a biologist. He claims that for a typical adult male the mass, M kg, is directly proportional to the square of the height, h metres.

Kevin, Edward and Oliver are typical adult males. Kevin is 1.80 m tall and his mass is 64.8 kg.

   a) Edward is 1.86 m tall. What is his mass to the nearest kg?

   b) Oliver's mass is 59.3 kg. What is his height to the nearest cm?

Exercise 1.1 *continued*

6 In an experiment, pupils rolled a
ball down a ramp. They used a
stopwatch to measure the time, *t*
seconds, taken to cover a distance
d metres.

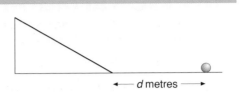

d metres

a) Sally obtained the following table of results for her ramp.

d (m)	1	2	3	4	5
t (s)	2	4	6	8	10

She decided that the time was directly proportional to the distance
travelled. Explain why she was correct.

b) Ranjit's results for his ramp were:

d (m)	1	2	3	4	5
t (s)	1.5	3	3.5	6	7.5

(i) One of his results was inaccurate. Which one, and what should it
have been?

(ii) Ranjit wanted to test the theory that *t* is directly proportional to *d*.
He predicted how far the ball should travel in 2 seconds, and
checked this.

What value should he have obtained for the distance *d* ?

SMP

7 Decide which of these sketches best illustrates each of the following
statements.

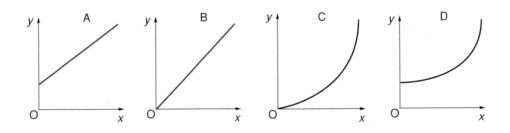

The cost £*y* is

a) directly proportional to *x*, the number of units used;

b) directly proportional to the square of the radius *x;*

c) made up of (i) a fixed charge and (ii) a variable charge which is
directly proportional to *x*, the number of units used.

8 The value of *r* varies with the square root of *A*, and *A* = 9 when *r* = 15.

a) Find the value of *r* when *A* = 25.

b) Find the value of *A* when *r* = 6.

Inverse variation

Ben is setting up as a market trader, selling earrings. He has a fixed sum of money, £k, to spend on his initial stock of earrings.

He looks at the types available.

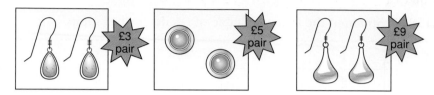

Ben's initial stock will consist of one type.

 How will the number of pairs of earrings that Ben can buy be affected if he chooses the most expensive ones rather than the cheaper ones?

You can see that if Ben buys the most expensive earrings, he can afford fewer pairs.

The total cost of the earrings is to be £k, so putting the cost per pair as £C and the number of pairs as N,

$$N \times C = k.$$

Rearranging this, to make N the subject:

$N = \dfrac{k}{C}$, (or $N = k \times \dfrac{1}{C}$) where k is the constant of proportionality.

When $N = \dfrac{k}{C}$ you can say that

N varies inversely with C

or **N is inversely proportional to C.**

You can write this as $N \propto \dfrac{1}{C}$.

Part of the graph of N against C is shown below. (k is assumed to be positive.)

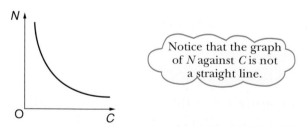

Notice that the graph of N against C is not a straight line.

You can see that the number of pairs of earrings Ben can buy decreases as the cost per pair increases.

 What does the graph look like for negative values of C? Does this have a meaning from Ben's point of view?

What happens to the graph when C = 0?

Example

Given that y varies inversely with x, and $y = 5$ when $x = 6$, find the value of y when $x = 8$.

Solution

Since y varies inversely with x, you can write $y \propto \dfrac{1}{x}$.

This means that

$$y = k \times \dfrac{1}{x}.$$

When $y = 5$, $x = 6$ so

$$5 = k \times \dfrac{1}{6}$$

$$k = 30.$$

The relationship between x and y is therefore

$$y = 30 \times \dfrac{1}{x}.$$

When $x = 8$ $\quad y = 30 \times \dfrac{1}{8} = 3.75.$

Example

Given that y is inversely proportional to the square of x, and $y = 800$ when $x = 3$, find the value of y when $x = 4$.

Solution

Since y is inversely proportional to the square of x, you can write $y \propto \dfrac{1}{x^2}$.

This means that

$$y = k \times \dfrac{1}{x^2}.$$

When $y = 800$, $x = 3$ so

$$800 = k \times \dfrac{1}{(3)^2}$$

$$k = 7200.$$

The relationship between x and y is therefore

$$y = 7200 \times \dfrac{1}{x^2}.$$

When $x = 4$ $\quad y = 7200 \times \dfrac{1}{(4)^2} = 450.$

What does the graph of y *against* x *look like in this case?*

Exercise 1.2

1 The value of y varies inversely as x^2. When $x = 5$, $y = 40$.

 a) Find the formula connecting y and x.

 b) Find the value of y when $x = 2$.

 c) For what value of x are x and y equal?

2 In a factory the number of items, N, produced each day is inversely proportional to the amount of time, T minutes, taken to make each item. When $T = 5$, $N = 600$.

 a) Find the value of N when $T = 6$.

 b) What is the maximum time that can be spent on each item if 900 items are to be produced in a day? Give your answer in minutes and seconds.

 c) Draw a graph of N against T, for values of T from 1 to 10.

3 A see-saw is 6 metres long. Jack sits on one side. He is balanced by a child of mass M kg sitting x metres from the centre on the other.

 M varies inversely with x. Jack is balanced by Katie sitting 2.5 m from the centre. Katie's mass is 20 kg.

 a) Tim has mass 25 kg. Where must he sit to balance Jack?

 b) Noemia sits 1.8 m from the centre to balance Jack. Find Noemia's mass to the nearest tenth of a kilogram.

 c) Ben has mass 15 kg. Explain why he cannot balance Jack.

4 Jenny is designing a package in the shape of a cylinder.

 Its volume is to be 125 cm^3.

 a) Explain why the height, h, is inversely proportional to the square of the radius, r.

 b) Jenny records in a table some of the possible dimensions.

 Copy and complete the table, giving measurements correct to two significant figures.

r (cm)	2.0		3.0
h (cm)	10.0	6.5	

Exercise 1.2 *continued*

5 The wavelength of radio waves is inversely proportional to their frequency.

  a) Copy and complete the following table giving your answers to the nearest whole number.

Station	Wavelength (m)	Frequency (kHz)
Talk Radio	1089	
Radio 4	1515	198
Radio 5		433
Virgin	1215	

  b) Draw a graph of frequency against wavelength.

  Mark each of the radio stations on your graph.

6 The gravitational force, F, between two objects is inversely proportional to the square of the distance, d, between them. When $d = 20$, $F = 0.00625$.

  a) Find a formula connecting F and d.

  b) Find F when $d = 5$.

  c) Find d when $F = 0.00025$.

7 The value of y varies inversely as the square root of x.

  When $x = 225$, $y = 60$.

  a) Find the value of y when $x = 144$.

  b) Find the value of x when $y = 300$.

  c) What change in x leads to the y value doubling?

  d) State the range of values of x for which y exceeds 100.

Investigation

The table below gives the values of z for different values of x and y.

For example when $x = 2$ and $y = 3$ then $z = 60$.

y \ x	1	2	3	4	5
1	5	20	45	80	125
2	10	40	90	160	250
3	15	60	135	240	375
4	20	80	180	320	500

Find the formula giving z in terms of x and y.

  a) How would you describe the relationship between x and y in words?

  b) How would you represent the information in the table on a graph?

Finishing off

> **Now that you have finished this chapter you should be able to:**
>
> ★ understand and use direct and inverse proportion.

Use the questions in the next exercise to check that you understand everything.

Mixed exercise 1.3

1 The table shows the price, £P, of a single railway journey of distance d miles. It is thought that $P \propto d$.

a) Write the statement $P \propto d$ in words.

b) Write the statement $P \propto d$ as an equation.

Price (£P)	1.35	3.60	9.00	19.50
Distance (*d* miles)	3	8	20	50

c) Is $P \propto d$ for the data given?

Show how you make your decision.

MEI

2 The volume, V, of a gas is inversely proportional to its pressure P. When $V = 520$, $P = 630$.

a) Find the formula connecting V and P.

b) (i) Find V when $P = 1950$

(ii) Find P when $V = 504$.

MEI

3 The mass, m, of a disk is directly proportional to the square of its diameter, d.

When $d = 3$, $m = 360$.

a) Find a formula connecting m and d.
b) Find m when $d = 4$.
c) When the diameter is increased by 50% what is the percentage increase in the mass?

4 The number, N, of square tiles needed to tile a floor varies inversely as the square of the length, L, of the side of the tile.

When $L = 0.4$ m, $N = 2000$.

a) Find a formula connecting N and L.

b) Calculate the number of tiles needed when $L = 0.6$ m.

SEG

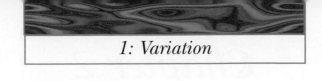
Mixed exercise 1.3 *continued*

5   The cost, *C*, of making a solid rubber ball varies directly as the cube of the radius, *r*.
     When $r = 2$, $C = 28$.
     a)   Calculate the value of *C* when $r = 2.5$.
     b)   Calculate the value of *r* when $C = 120$.

6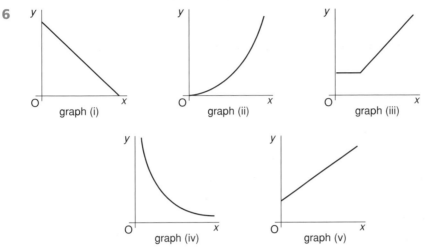

     graph (i)   graph (ii)   graph (iii)

     graph (iv)   graph (v)

     Select from the five graphs one which illustrates each of the following statements.

     a)   The time (*y*) taken for a journey is inversely proportional to the average speed (*x*).

     b)   The surface area (*y*) of a sphere is proportional to the square of the radius (*x*).

     c)   The cost (*y*) of an electricity bill consists of a fixed charge plus an amount proportional to the number of units used (*x*).

                                                                          MEG

7   The number of coins, *N*, with diameter *d* cm and with a fixed thickness, that can be made from a given volume of metal can be found by using the formula $N = \dfrac{k}{d^2}$ where *k* is a constant.

     a)   Given that 5000 coins of diameter 2.5 cm can be made from the volume of metal, find the value of *k*.

     b)   Calculate how many coins of diameter 2 cm can be made from an equal volume of metal.

     c)   Rearrange the formula $N = \dfrac{k}{d^2}$ to make *d* the subject.

     d)   2000 coins are to be made using an equal volume of metal.

          Calculate the diameter of these coins.

                                                                          MEG

8   The time of swing, *T* seconds, of a pendulum is proportional to the square root of the length, *L* centimetres, of the pendulum.

     A pendulum of length 64 cm has a time of swing 1.6 seconds.

     Find a formula for *T* in terms of *L*.

                                                                          MEG

Chapter 2

Indices, rationals and irrationals

> **Before you start this chapter you should be able to:**
>
> ★ work with indices
>
> ★ work with numbers in standard form.

Reminder

Indices

- $x^m \times x^n = x^{m+n}$ e.g. $3^4 \times 3^2 = 3^{4+2} = 3^6$

- $x^m \div x^n = x^{m-n}$ e.g. $5^7 \div 5^3 = 5^{7-3} = 5^4$

- $(x^m)^n = x^{mn}$ e.g. $(2^3)^4 = 2^{3 \times 4} = 2^{12}$

- $x^0 = 1$ e.g. $6^0 = 1$

- $x^{-n} = \dfrac{1}{x^n}$ e.g. $4^{-2} = \dfrac{1}{4^2}$

- $x^{\frac{1}{n}} = \sqrt[n]{x}$ e.g. $9^{\frac{1}{2}} = \sqrt[2]{9} = 3$

- $x^{\frac{m}{n}} = \sqrt[n]{x^m}$ or $\left(\sqrt[n]{x}\right)^m$ e.g. $16^{\frac{3}{2}} = \left(\sqrt[2]{16}\right)^3 = (4)^3 = 64$

Standard form

$3.57 \times 10^8 = 357\,000\,000$

$9.2 \times 10^{-4} = 0.000\,92$

> These are in standard form: the number in front is at least 1 and less than 10, and the power of 10 is a whole number.

Review exercise 2.1

1   Write the following as ordinary numbers.

a) 3^4 b) 2^{-1} c) 7^0 d) $25^{\frac{1}{2}}$

e) $4^{\frac{3}{2}}$ f) 6^{-2} g) $64^{\frac{1}{3}}$ h) $100^{-\frac{1}{2}}$

i) 5^{-3} j) $27^{\frac{2}{3}}$ k) $8^{\frac{5}{3}}$ l) $25^{-\frac{3}{2}}$

2   Work out the following. Give your answers in index form.

a) $(6^2)^3$ b) $\dfrac{5^2 \times 5^9}{5^3}$ c) 81×3^{-1} d) $2^5 + 2^5$

e) $7\sqrt{7}$ f) $4\sqrt{2}$ g) $9\sqrt{3}$ h) $\left(\sqrt[3]{4}\right)^2$

Review exercise 2.1 *continued*

3 Work out the value of n in each of the following.

  a) $3^n = 27$ **b)** $4^n = 8$ **c)** $5^{-n} = \dfrac{1}{25}$ **d)** $(2^n)^2 = 256$

4 Work out $10^{\frac{1}{2}} - 12^{\frac{1}{3}}$.

5 The number x is positive, and less than 1.

  Arrange these terms in order of size starting with the smallest.

  $$x^{-1} \qquad \sqrt{x} \qquad x \qquad x^0 \qquad \dfrac{1}{x^2}$$

6 Give your answers to these calculations in standard form.

  a) $2.8 \times 10^{11} + 3.1 \times 10^{10}$ **b)** $5 \times 10^{-8} - 4.7 \times 10^{-9}$

  c) $9.3 \times 10^{21} \times 4 \times 10^{-14}$ **d)** $3.6 \times 10^{18} \div (4 \times 10^8)$

  e) $7.8 \times 10^{-24} \times 2 \times 10^{19}$ **f)** $\sqrt{2.5 \times 10^{17}}$

  g) $\dfrac{(4.8 \times 10^{12}) \times (3 \times 10^{19})}{1.8 \times 10^{21}}$ **h)** $\dfrac{(2.8 \times 10^{17})}{(2 \times 10^{-7}) \times (3.5 \times 10^{12})}$

7 My computer can carry out 2.7×10^8 calculations in one hour. Work out how many of these calculations my computer can carry out in one second. Give your answer in standard form.

London

8 A crystal has rectangular cross-section of length 5.2×10^{-3} mm and width 8.7×10^{-4} mm.

  a) (i) Calculate the area of cross-section. Give your answer in standard form.

  (ii) Calculate the perimeter of the cross-section. Give your answer in standard form.

  b) The thickness of the crystal is 4×10^{-5} mm.

  Calculate how many such crystals would be needed to give a total thickness of 1 mm.

MEG

9 Last year the population of the United Kingdom was approximately 5.3×10^7.

  a) An average of £680 per person was spent on food last year in the United Kingdom.

  What was the total amount spent on food last year in the United Kingdom? Give your answer in standard form.

  b) Last year there were 1.4×10^7 car drivers in the United Kingdom.

  They spent a total of £1.5 $\times 10^{10}$ on their cars.

  What was the average amount spent by each car driver?

  Give your answer to a suitable degree of accuracy.

NEAB

Surds

Numbers like $\sqrt{2}$, $\sqrt{3}$, $\sqrt[3]{5}$ and $10^{\frac{3}{4}}$ are all examples of **surds**. You have worked with one type of surd, the square root, before.

Without using a calculator, find the roots of

$$x^2 - 6x + 4 = 0.$$

Give your answer in the form $\dfrac{p \pm \sqrt{q}}{r}$.

*Without using a calculator,
find the length of the hypotenuse
in this triangle.*

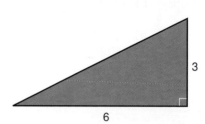

In this section you will learn how to simplify expressions involving square roots.

Addition and subtraction

You can add and subtract numbers involving surds by combining the ordinary numbers, and if possible the surds.

For example

- $3 + \sqrt{2} + 5 + 4\sqrt{2} = 8 + 5\sqrt{2}$;

- $7 + 6\sqrt{5} - \sqrt{3} - 2\sqrt{5} = 7 + 4\sqrt{5} - \sqrt{3}$

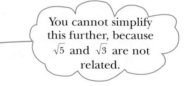

You cannot simplify
this further, because
$\sqrt{5}$ and $\sqrt{3}$ are not
related.

Can you simplify $9\sqrt{5} - \sqrt{20}$ *?*

In fact, you can write $\sqrt{20}$ in terms of $\sqrt{5}$, and this helps you to simplify the expression.

$\sqrt{20}$ can be written as $\sqrt{4 \times 5}$ or $\sqrt{4} \times \sqrt{5}$ $\sqrt{m} \times \sqrt{n} = \sqrt{mn}$

Since $\sqrt{4} = 2$, you have

$$\sqrt{20} = 2\sqrt{5}.$$

So $9\sqrt{5} - \sqrt{20} = 9\sqrt{5} - 2\sqrt{5}$

$$= 7\sqrt{5}$$

It is often helpful to convert a surd from one form to another like this.

Write $\sqrt{45}$ *in terms of* $\sqrt{5}$.

The process can also be reversed, for example

$$2\sqrt{7} = \sqrt{4} \times \sqrt{7} = \sqrt{28}.$$

Write $3\sqrt{11}$ *in the form* $\sqrt{n}$.

Multiplication

You already know that

- $\sqrt{2} \times \sqrt{2} = 2$, or more generally $\sqrt{n} \times \sqrt{n} = n$;
- $\sqrt{2} \times \sqrt{3} = \sqrt{6}$, or more generally $\sqrt{m} \times \sqrt{n} = \sqrt{mn}$.

Sometimes you will meet expressions involving brackets and surds.

Example

Simplify **a)** $\sqrt{3}(5 - 2\sqrt{3})$

  b) $(4 + 3\sqrt{5})(9 - \sqrt{5})$

  c) $(7 + \sqrt{2})(3 + \sqrt{5})$

Solution

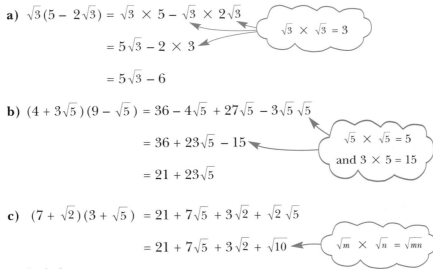

a) $\sqrt{3}(5 - 2\sqrt{3}) = \sqrt{3} \times 5 - \sqrt{3} \times 2\sqrt{3}$

$\sqrt{3} \times \sqrt{3} = 3$

$\qquad\qquad = 5\sqrt{3} - 2 \times 3$

$\qquad\qquad = 5\sqrt{3} - 6$

b) $(4 + 3\sqrt{5})(9 - \sqrt{5}) = 36 - 4\sqrt{5} + 27\sqrt{5} - 3\sqrt{5}\sqrt{5}$

$\qquad\qquad = 36 + 23\sqrt{5} - 15$

$\sqrt{5} \times \sqrt{5} = 5$
and $3 \times 5 = 15$

$\qquad\qquad = 21 + 23\sqrt{5}$

c) $(7 + \sqrt{2})(3 + \sqrt{5}) = 21 + 7\sqrt{5} + 3\sqrt{2} + \sqrt{2}\sqrt{5}$

$\qquad\qquad = 21 + 7\sqrt{5} + 3\sqrt{2} + \sqrt{10}$

$\sqrt{m} \times \sqrt{n} = \sqrt{mn}$

Division

To simplify expressions involving surds and division, you need to look for common factors and cancel them (as in algebra).

Example

Simplify **a)** $\dfrac{3\sqrt{14}}{\sqrt{21}}$ **b)** $\dfrac{6 + \sqrt{20}}{2}$

Solution

a) $\dfrac{3\sqrt{14}}{\sqrt{21}} = \dfrac{3\sqrt{2} \times \sqrt{7}}{\sqrt{3} \times \sqrt{7}}$

$\qquad = \dfrac{\sqrt{3} \times \sqrt{3} \times \sqrt{2}}{\sqrt{3}}$

$\qquad = \sqrt{3} \times \sqrt{2} = \sqrt{6}$

b) $\dfrac{6 + \sqrt{20}}{2} = \dfrac{6 + 2\sqrt{5}}{2}$

$\qquad = \dfrac{2(3 + \sqrt{5})}{2}$

$\qquad = 3 + \sqrt{5}$

Exercise 2.2

1 Write these numbers in the form $p\sqrt{q}$ where p and q are integers and q is as small as possible.

a) $\sqrt{18}$ b) $\sqrt{60}$ c) $\sqrt{48}$ d) $\sqrt{63}$

e) $\sqrt{54}$ f) $\sqrt{98}$ g) $\sqrt{128}$ h) $\sqrt{75}$

i) $\sqrt{200}$ j) $\sqrt{294}$ k) $\sqrt{180}$ l) $\sqrt{338}$

2 Write these numbers in the form $\sqrt{n}$.

a) $2\sqrt{3}$ b) $3\sqrt{7}$ c) $5\sqrt{2}$ d) $4\sqrt{5}$

e) $6\sqrt{3}$ f) $7\sqrt{10}$ g) $2\sqrt{6}$ h) $3\sqrt{15}$

3 Simplify these expressions.

a) $4 + 5\sqrt{3} - 1 + 2\sqrt{3}$ b) $(4 + 3\sqrt{2}) - (5 + \sqrt{2})$

c) $2\sqrt{5} + 3 - 3(1 + \sqrt{5})$ d) $5\sqrt{6} + 4 - (2\sqrt{6} - 1)$

e) $2(\sqrt{3} + 1) - 2(\sqrt{3} - 1)$ f) $4\sqrt{3} - 2 + \sqrt{3} - \sqrt{2}$

g) $5\sqrt{3} + \sqrt{2} - 2\sqrt{2} + 3\sqrt{3}$ h) $2\sqrt{5} - 4\sqrt{3} - (\sqrt{5} + 2\sqrt{3})$

i) $7\sqrt{2} - \sqrt{8}$ j) $6\sqrt{27} - 17\sqrt{3}$

4 Multiply out and simplify these expressions.

a) $\sqrt{5}(4 + 3\sqrt{5})$ b) $(2 + \sqrt{3})(5 - \sqrt{3})$

c) $(9 + \sqrt{2})(5 + 3\sqrt{2})$ d) $(11 - 2\sqrt{6})(4 + \sqrt{6})$

e) $(\sqrt{5} - 1)(4\sqrt{5} + 3)$ f) $(7 - 2\sqrt{2})(6 - \sqrt{2})$

g) $(3 + 4\sqrt{7})(8 - 3\sqrt{7})$ h) $(8 + 3\sqrt{3})(5 - 2\sqrt{3})$

i) $(7 + 3\sqrt{5})(2\sqrt{5} - 1)$ j) $(3 + \sqrt{3})(1 - \sqrt{12})$

5 Simplify these expressions.

a) $\dfrac{\sqrt{10}}{\sqrt{2}}$ b) $\dfrac{2\sqrt{15}}{\sqrt{6}}$ c) $\dfrac{\sqrt{72}}{6}$ d) $\dfrac{2\sqrt{15}}{7\sqrt{30}}$

e) $\dfrac{\sqrt{24}}{2}$ f) $\dfrac{(4\sqrt{5})^2}{2\sqrt{5}}$ g) $\dfrac{8 - \sqrt{12}}{2}$ h) $\dfrac{6 - 2\sqrt{3}}{\sqrt{3}}$

6 a) Work out $(5 + \sqrt{2})(5 - \sqrt{2})$

    ☆ b) Work out $(5 + \sqrt{2})^2(5 - \sqrt{2})^2$

    ☆ c) What is the value of $(5 + \sqrt{2})^n(5 - \sqrt{2})^n$?

7 The integers a and b are positive, and

$$(a + \sqrt{b})(a - \sqrt{b}) = 97$$

    ☆ a) Write down one possible pair of values of a and b.

    ☆ b) How many possible answers are there?

The number system

 What is the value of a) $\sqrt{25}$ *?* *b)* $\sqrt{0.36})$ *?* *c)* $\sqrt{\dfrac{1}{9}}$ *?* *d)* $\sqrt{2}$ *?*

How does your answer to d) differ from the other three answers?

In this section you will see how different types of numbers are defined and how they fit into the number system.

Integers

When you first learned to count you used the **positive integers**

    1,   2,   3,   4, ...

The set of positive integers is denoted by $\mathbb{Z}^+$.

Then you began to include zero:

    0,   1,   2,   3,   4, ...

These are often called the **natural numbers** and denoted by $\mathbb{N}$.

More recently you learned about the negative integers (denoted by $\mathbb{Z}^-$) so you now have

    ... −4, −3, −2, −1, 0, 1, 2, 3, 4, ...

This is the **set of integers** and is denoted by $\mathbb{Z}$.

Rational numbers

Not everything is counted in whole numbers so, the system needs to be extended again. Fractions like , $\dfrac{1}{2}$, $\dfrac{3}{10}$, $\dfrac{54}{7}$, $-\dfrac{19}{5}$, are introduced. This extended set is called the **rational numbers** and is denoted by $\mathbb{Q}$.

Rational numbers can be written in the form p/q where p and q are both integers. A number that cannot be written in this form is **irrational**.

Explain why 5 is a rational number.

How can 0.6 be written as a rational number?

Is 0.6125 a rational number?

Are all terminating decimals rational numbers?

Are all recurring decimals irrational?

What about $0.\dot{3}$ *?*

Now look at a less familiar recurring decimal, such as $0.27777\ldots (= 0.2\dot{7})$. You can work out what fraction it represents like this.

Let $x = 0.27777\ldots$

Then $10x = 2.7777\ldots$

Now subtract $\quad x = 0.27777$

$9x = 2.5$

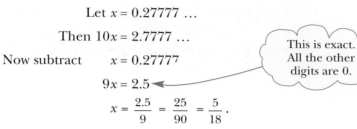

This is exact. All the other digits are 0.

$$x = \frac{2.5}{9} = \frac{25}{90} = \frac{5}{18}.$$

So $0.2\dot{7} = \frac{5}{18}$, and it is therefore a rational number.

Now use exactly the same method to try to convert $0.\dot{6}\dot{3}$ into a fraction.

What happens?

How can you adapt the method to make it work?

The power of 10 by which you multiply x depends on the length of the recurring cycle.

Example

Work out $0.5\dot{7}\dot{1}$ as a fraction in its lowest terms.

Solution

Let $x = 0.5717171\ldots$

Then $100x = 57.17171\ldots$

Now subtract $\quad x = 0.57171\ldots$

$99x = 56.6$

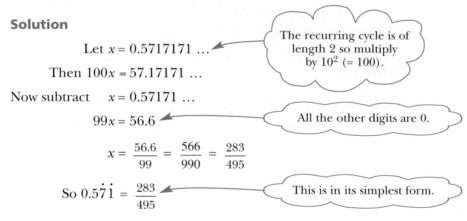

The recurring cycle is of length 2 so multiply by $10^2 (= 100)$.

All the other digits are 0.

$$x = \frac{56.6}{99} = \frac{566}{990} = \frac{283}{495}$$

So $0.5\dot{7}\dot{1} = \frac{283}{495}$

This is in its simplest form.

What types of decimals can be written as rational numbers?

Irrational numbers

An irrational number is one that is not rational. It cannot be expressed as one integer divided by another.

The rational numbers together with the irrational numbers make up the **set of real numbers**. The set of real numbers is denoted by $\mathbb{R}$.

The Venn diagram summarises the relationships between the different parts of the number system.

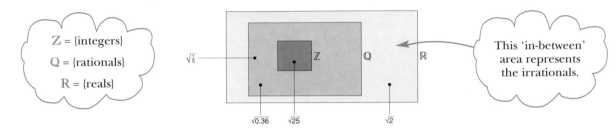

$\mathbb{Z} = \{\text{integers}\}$

$\mathbb{Q} = \{\text{rationals}\}$

$\mathbb{R} = \{\text{reals}\}$

This 'in-between' area represents the irrationals.

$\sqrt{\tfrac{1}{9}}$ $\mathbb{Z}$ $\mathbb{Q}$ $\mathbb{R}$

$\sqrt{0.36}$ $\sqrt{25}$ $\sqrt{2}$

 Check that you understand why the numbers in the diagram are in the positions shown.

Work out $\sqrt{2}$. A calculator with a ten digit display shows

 Is this exact?

Is it a recurring decimal?

In fact, $\sqrt{2}$ is an example of an irrational number. It cannot be written in the form p/q. A proof of this is given on the next page.

 Which of these numbers do you think are irrational?

$$\sqrt{3},\ \sqrt{4},\ \sqrt{5},\ \sqrt{6},\ldots$$

Other, more complex, surds such as $\sqrt[3]{5}$, $\sqrt[4]{12}$, and so on, are also irrational.

Is $\sqrt[4]{81}$ rational or irrational?

Not all irrational numbers are surds. One irrational number that you have met is $\pi = 3.141592653\ldots$, which cannot be expressed as a surd.

Numbers like $5 - \pi$ and $4 + \sqrt{3}$ are also irrational.

PROOF THAT $\sqrt{2}$ IS IRRATIONAL

Assume that $\sqrt{2}$ is rational, and that

$$\sqrt{2} = \frac{p}{q}$$

where p and q are integers, and $\frac{p}{q}$ is in its simplest form.

Squaring both sides and rearranging gives

$$2q^2 = p^2 \qquad \text{(1)}$$

Since q is an integer, $2q^2$ must be even.
So p^2 must be even.
But p^2 is only even when p is even, (2)

If p is even, we can write $p = 2r$ where r is also an integer, so in (1)

$$2q^2 = (2r)^2 = 4r^2$$
$$q^2 = 2r^2$$

Now, repeating the earlier argument, $2r^2$ is even, so q^2 must be even.
But q^2 is only even when q is even. (3)
Results (2) and (3) show that p and q are both even. This means that $\frac{p}{q}$ is not in its simplest form.
This contradicts the original assumption, so the original assumption must be false.

$\sqrt{2}$ cannot be written in the form $\frac{p}{q}$, so $\sqrt{2}$ is irrational.

Exercise 2.3

1 Write each of the following numbers as a fraction in its lowest terms.

   a) $0.\dot{2}$ **b)** $0.\dot{5}\dot{4}$ **c)** $1.\dot{0}\dot{8}$ **d)** $0.8\dot{5}$

   e) $2.4\dot{3}\dot{8}$ **f)** $0.11\dot{3}$ **g)** $0.\dot{9}6\dot{3}$ **h)** $0.\dot{1}42857\dot{7}$

   > $0.\dot{9}6\dot{3}$ means
   > 0.963963963 …

2 Which of the following numbers are rational and which are irrational?

   a) $\sqrt{7}$ **b)** $\sqrt{81}$ **c)** $\left(\sqrt{10}\right)^2$ **d)** $\sqrt[3]{11}$

   e) $9^{\frac{3}{2}}$ **f)** 2π **g)** $5 - \sqrt{3}$ **h)** $\sqrt{18} \times \sqrt{2}$

   i) $\dfrac{1}{\sqrt{3}}$ **j)** $\left(\sqrt{2}\right)^4$ **k)** $\dfrac{1}{\pi}$ **l)** $\dfrac{\sqrt{12}}{\sqrt{3}}$

3 Write down a value of y where $3 < y < 4$ for which $\sqrt{y}$ is

   a) an irrational number   **b)** a rational number.

4 Write down a value of x, where $x > 5$, for which $\sqrt{5} \times \sqrt{x}$ is

   a) rational   **b)** irrational.

5 **a)** Write down and add together two irrational numbers which will give an answer that is also an irrational number.

   b) Write down and add together two irrational numbers which will give an answer that is a rational number.

   MEG

6 **a)** Is the recurring decimal $0.\dot{6}$ rational or irrational? Give a reason for your answer.

   b) Write down one example of each of the following:

   (i) a rational number between $\dfrac{3}{4}$ and $\dfrac{4}{5}$;

   (ii) an irrational number x such that x^3 is rational;

   (iii) an irrational number less than 1.

   MEI

7 The numbers a and b are irrational and not equal.

   $a + b$ is rational.

   a) Write down possible values of a and b.

   Two other numbers c and d are also irrational and not equal.

   cd is rational.

   b) Write down possible values for c and d.

   London

8 Write down an irrational number between 4 and 5 which, when squared, is also irrational.

Finishing off

Now that you have finished this chapter you should be able to:

★ work with surds

★ write a recurring decimal as a fraction in its simplest form

★ identify rational and irrational numbers.

Use the questions in the next exercise to check that you understand everything.

Mixed exercise 2.4

1 The speed of sound is 3.3×10^2 metres per second.

How long does sound take to travel a distance of 1.2×10^4 metres?

Give your answer to the nearest second.

MEI

2 $p^{1.5} \times \sqrt{p} \times p^{-5} = p^x$

Work out the value of x.

3 a) Find the value of n in the equation $2^n = \sqrt{8}$.

Triangle ABC has an area of $32\ \text{cm}^2$.

b) Calculate the value of k.

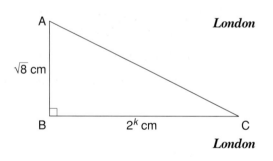

London

London

4 Given $c = 5 + 2\sqrt{3}$ and $d = 7 - \sqrt{3}$ work out the following giving your answers in the form $a + b\sqrt{3}$ where a and b are integers.

a) $c - d$ **b)** cd **c)** c^2

5 a) Write $0.\dot{2}\dot{7}$ as a fraction in its simplest form.

b) Evaluate the following.

(i) $2^{-1} + \left(\dfrac{1}{16}\right)^{\frac{1}{2}}$

(ii) $9^{\frac{3}{2}} \div 8^{\frac{2}{3}}$

c) Simplify $\sqrt{3} + \sqrt{12}$.

SEG

6 a) Write down a number greater than 17 and less than 18 that has a rational square root.

b) Give an example of two different irrational numbers c and d such that $c \times d$ is a rational number.

London

Mixed exercise 2.4 *continued*

7   **a)** Give an example of two different irrational numbers q and r such that

   $\dfrac{q}{r}$ is a rational number.

   b) Write down a number which is greater than 15 and less than 16 and which has a rational cube root.

London

8   **a)** Write down the irrational numbers from the following list.

   $144^{\frac{1}{2}},\quad 72^{\frac{1}{2}},\quad 36^{\frac{1}{2}},\quad 18^{\frac{1}{2}},\quad 9^{\frac{1}{2}}.$

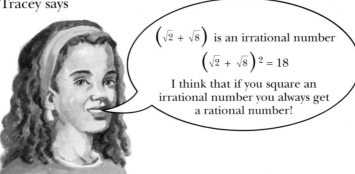

   b) The midpoints of the sides of a square of side 12 cm are joined to form another square. The process is repeated so that a nest of five squares is formed.

   Each square is labelled at one vertex only.

   The area of square B is half the area of square A.

   The area of square C is half the area of square B and so on.

   (i) Calculate the perimeter of square C.

   (ii) Is the perimeter of square D rational or irrational?

   Explain your answer.

MEG

9   **a)** Explain what a rational number is.

   b) Using $(a + b)^2 = a^2 + 2ab + b^2,$ or otherwise, show that

   $\left(\sqrt{2} + \sqrt{8}\right)^2 = 18$

 You must not use a calculator to do this question.

   c) Tracey says

$\left(\sqrt{2} + \sqrt{8}\right)$ is an irrational number

$\left(\sqrt{2} + \sqrt{8}\right)^2 = 18$

I think that if you square an irrational number you always get a rational number!

Tracey is wrong.

Use an example to show that Tracey is wrong.

NEAB

Chapter 3

Manipulating expressions

Before you start this chapter you should be able to:

★ multiply out brackets

★ factorise expressions

★ add, subtract, multiply and divide fractions

★ solve linear equations.

Reminder

Multiplying out brackets

Each term in the bracket is multiplied by $3a$.

- $3a(2a + 3b) = 3a \times 2a + 3a \times 3b$

$$= 6a^2 + 9ab$$

- $(x + 2)(2x - 3) = 2x^2 - 3x + 4x - 6$

Each term in the second bracket is multiplied by each term in the first bracket.

$$= 2x^2 + x - 6$$

Factorising

2 and p are factors of both terms.

- $2p^2 - 6pq = 2p(p - 3q)$

Fractions

- $\dfrac{2}{3} + \dfrac{1}{4} = \dfrac{8}{12} + \dfrac{3}{12} = \dfrac{11}{12}$

- $\dfrac{3}{5} \times \dfrac{1}{6} = \dfrac{3}{5} \times \dfrac{1}{6_2} = \dfrac{1}{10}$

- $\dfrac{7}{8} \div \dfrac{5}{6} = \dfrac{7}{8} \times \dfrac{6}{5} = \dfrac{7}{4\,8} \times \dfrac{^3 6}{5} = \dfrac{21}{20}$

Linear equations

Example

Solve   **a)** $\dfrac{3 - 2x}{4} = 2$ **b)** $5x - 3 = 2x + 9$

Solution

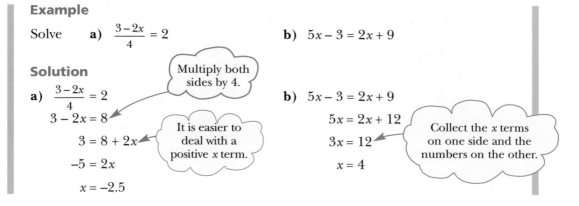

a) $\dfrac{3 - 2x}{4} = 2$

Multiply both sides by 4.

$3 - 2x = 8$

$3 = 8 + 2x$

It is easier to deal with a positive x term.

$-5 = 2x$

$x = -2.5$

b) $5x - 3 = 2x + 9$

$5x = 2x + 12$

$3x = 12$

Collect the x terms on one side and the numbers on the other.

$x = 4$

Use the questions in the next exercise to check that you remember these topics.

Review exercise 3.1

1 Multiply out the brackets.

a) $3(x + 2y)$　　　　　　　　　　**b)** $5(3p - 2q)$

c) $4(2r + 3s - t)$　　　　　　　　**d)** $x(y + z)$

e) $a(a - b)$　　　　　　　　　　　**f)** $3c(2d - 3e)$

g) $2p(p + 2q - 3r)$　　　　　　　**h)** $3ab(2a - 3b + 4c)$

2 Factorise these expressions.

a) $4a + 6b$　　　　　　　　　　　**b)** $pq - pr$

c) $x^2 - 2xy$　　　　　　　　　　**d)** $2rs + s^2 - s$

e) $3cd + 6c^2 + 9c$　　　　　　　**f)** $2a^2b - 3ab^2$

g) $4p^2qr + 8pq^2r$　　　　　　　**h)** $9x^3y^2 - 12x^2y^2$

i) $5pq - 10p^2q$　　　　　　　　**j)** $10f^2g - 15fgh + 25fg^2$

3 Multiply out the brackets.

a) $(x + 3)(y - 2)$　　　　　　　　**b)** $(a + 4)(a + 1)$

c) $(p - 5)(p + 2)$　　　　　　　　**d)** $(x - 4)^2$

e) $(a - 3)(a - 4)$　　　　　　　　**f)** $(z + 3)(z - 3)$

g) $(2p + 1)(q - 3)$　　　　　　　**h)** $(2x + 3)(x - 2)$

i) $(3a + 4)(2a + 1)$　　　　　　　**j)** $(4c - 3)(3c + 5)$

4 Multiply out the brackets and simplify.

a) $3(2a + 1) - 2(a - 3)$　　　　　　**b)** $2p(q + 2) + 4q(2p - 3)$

c) $(x + 1)(x - 3) - (x + 2)(x - 1)$　　**d)** $(2y - 1)^2 + (y + 2)^2$

5 Work these out.

a) $\dfrac{1}{3} + \dfrac{2}{5}$　　**b)** $\dfrac{3}{4} - \dfrac{1}{6}$　　**c)** $\dfrac{5}{8} + \dfrac{2}{3}$　　**d)** $\dfrac{5}{7} - \dfrac{2}{5}$

e) $\dfrac{4}{9} + \dfrac{5}{6}$　　**f)** $\dfrac{11}{12} - \dfrac{3}{8}$　　**g)** $\dfrac{2}{3} \times \dfrac{6}{7}$　　**h)** $\dfrac{3}{5} \times \dfrac{5}{9}$

i) $\dfrac{3}{4} \div \dfrac{9}{10}$　　**j)** $\dfrac{5}{6} \div \dfrac{3}{8}$　　**k)** $\dfrac{4}{5} \times \dfrac{7}{12}$　　**l)** $\dfrac{8}{15} \div \dfrac{7}{10}$

6 Solve these equations.

a) $2x + 3 = 10$　　　　　　　　　**b)** $\dfrac{x}{3} - 1 = 4$

c) $5 - 4x = 12$　　　　　　　　　**d)** $\dfrac{1 - 3x}{4} = 4$

e) $2x + 1 = x + 6$　　　　　　　　**f)** $3x - 2 = 5x + 4$

g) $4x - 1 = 6 - x$　　　　　　　　**h)** $2(3x - 1) = 3(x + 4)$

i) $\dfrac{2x + 1}{2} = \dfrac{3 - 2x}{5}$　　　　**j)** $(x - 2)(x + 3) = (x + 1)^2$

k) $\dfrac{6}{x - 1} = 5$　　　　　　　　**l)** $\dfrac{2x - 1}{3 - 2x} = 3$

m) $\dfrac{2}{1 - x} = \dfrac{5}{3x + 1}$　　　　**n)** $\dfrac{2x - 3}{x + 1} = \dfrac{4x + 5}{2x + 1}$

Algebraic fractions

Simplifying fractions

Numerical fractions can sometimes be simplified, or cancelled down.

e.g. $\dfrac{12}{16} = \dfrac{3}{4}$ ← Divide both the top and the bottom by 4.

Sometimes algebraic fractions can be simplified in a similar way.

e.g. $\dfrac{x^2}{xy} = \dfrac{x}{y}$ ← Divide both the top and the bottom by x.

Here is some work in which George has cancelled down some fractions.

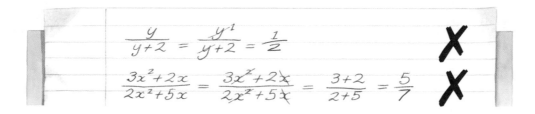

$$\frac{y}{y+2} = \frac{y^1}{y+2} = \frac{1}{2} \quad \times$$

$$\frac{3x^2+2x}{2x^2+5x} = \frac{3x^2+2x}{2x^2+5x} = \frac{3+2}{2+5} = \frac{5}{7} \quad \times$$

Why is George's work wrong?

(You may find it helpful to substitute numbers for y and x.)

What should he have done in each question?

When you can factorise the top line or the bottom line (or both) you may be able to cancel down the fraction.

Example

Simplify these fractions.

a) $\dfrac{a}{a^2 + 3a}$

b) $\dfrac{x^2 + 3x + 2}{x^2 - 1}$

Solution

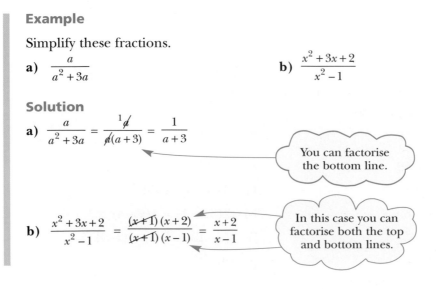

a) $\dfrac{a}{a^2 + 3a} = \dfrac{{}^1\cancel{a}}{\cancel{a}(a+3)} = \dfrac{1}{a+3}$

You can factorise the bottom line.

b) $\dfrac{x^2 + 3x + 2}{x^2 - 1} = \dfrac{\cancel{(x+1)}(x+2)}{\cancel{(x+1)}(x-1)} = \dfrac{x+2}{x-1}$

In this case you can factorise both the top and bottom lines.

Multiplying algebraic fractions

You multiply two numerical fractions like this.

You multiply algebraic fractions in the same way.

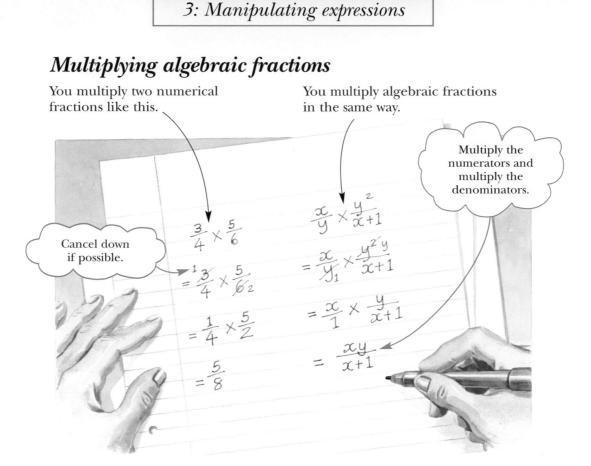

Cancel down if possible.

Multiply the numerators and multiply the denominators.

$$\frac{3}{4} \times \frac{5}{6}$$

$$= \frac{{}^1\cancel{3}}{4} \times \frac{5}{\cancel{6}_2}$$

$$= \frac{1}{4} \times \frac{5}{2}$$

$$= \frac{5}{8}$$

$$\frac{x}{y} \times \frac{y^2}{x+1}$$

$$= \frac{x}{\cancel{y}_1} \times \frac{y^{\cancel{2}} y}{x+1}$$

$$= \frac{x}{1} \times \frac{y}{x+1}$$

$$= \frac{xy}{x+1}$$

Dividing algebraic fractions

You divide two numerical fractions like this.

You divide algebraic fractions in the same way.

Invert the second fraction then multiply them together.

$$\frac{5}{8} \div \frac{7}{12}$$

$$= \frac{5}{8} \times \frac{12}{7}$$

$$= \frac{5}{\cancel{8}_2} \times \frac{\cancel{12}^3}{7}$$

$$= \frac{5}{2} \times \frac{3}{7}$$

$$= \frac{15}{14}$$

$$\frac{2a}{3a+1} \div \frac{6a}{2a-1}$$

$$= \frac{2a}{3a+1} \times \frac{2a-1}{6a}$$

$$= \frac{\cancel{2a}^a}{3a+1} \times \frac{2a-1}{\cancel{6a}_3}$$

$$= \frac{a}{3a+1} \times \frac{2a-1}{3}$$

$$= \frac{a(2a-1)}{3(3a+1)}$$

Example

Simplify   **a)** $\dfrac{p}{q^2} \times \dfrac{q^5}{p+1}$ **b)** $\dfrac{d+1}{d} \div \dfrac{d+2}{d^2-d}$

Solution

a) $\dfrac{p}{\cancel{q^2}} \times \dfrac{\cancel{q^5}^{q^3}}{p+1} = \dfrac{p}{1} \times \dfrac{q^3}{p+1} = \dfrac{pq^3}{p+1}$

b) $\dfrac{d+1}{d} \div \dfrac{d+2}{d^2-d} = \dfrac{d+1}{d} \times \dfrac{d^2-d}{d+2} = \dfrac{d+1}{\cancel{d}} \times \dfrac{\cancel{d}(d-1)}{d+2}$

$$= \frac{(d+1)(d-1)}{d+2} \qquad = \frac{d^2-1}{d+2}$$

Exercise 3.2

1   Simplify these fractions, where possible.

a) $\dfrac{x}{3x}$

b) $\dfrac{y^2}{y^3}$

c) $\dfrac{2a^2}{4a}$

d) $\dfrac{6pq}{9q^2}$

e) $\dfrac{s^2+2s}{st}$

f) $\dfrac{c+d}{2c+d}$

g) $\dfrac{2g-6}{4g}$

h) $\dfrac{4x}{2x-xy}$

i) $\dfrac{6y^2z-3yz}{9yz^2}$

2   Simplify these fractions, where possible.

a) $\dfrac{x+2}{x^2+x-2}$

b) $\dfrac{a+1}{a^2-2a+1}$

c) $\dfrac{p^2-3p}{p^2-5p+6}$

d) $\dfrac{c^2+4c+3}{2c^2-c-1}$

e) $\dfrac{2t^2-6t+4}{t^3-3t^2+2t}$

f) $\dfrac{2b^2+b-3}{2b^2-b-3}$

3   Write these as a single fraction, simplifying if possible.

a) $\dfrac{2}{3}\times\dfrac{4}{5}$

b) $\dfrac{3}{4}\times\dfrac{8}{9}$

c) $\dfrac{5}{6}\div\dfrac{1}{3}$

d) $\dfrac{7}{8}\div\dfrac{5}{12}$

e) $\dfrac{x}{2}\times\dfrac{2x}{3}$

f) $\dfrac{3a}{b}\times\dfrac{a}{2b}$

g) $\dfrac{3}{y}\div\dfrac{4}{y^2}$

h) $\dfrac{c^2}{2d}\div\dfrac{4c}{3d^2}$

i) $\dfrac{2p^2}{q}\times\dfrac{q+1}{p}$

4   Write these as a single fraction, simplifying if possible.

a) $\dfrac{z+1}{z}\div\dfrac{2}{z}$

b) $\dfrac{3s^3}{2t}\div\dfrac{6s^5}{t^2}$

c) $\dfrac{(2a)^2}{b}\times\dfrac{b+1}{3a}$

d) $\dfrac{2p+1}{p}\times\dfrac{3p}{4p+2}$

e) $\left(\dfrac{x}{2y}\right)^2\div\dfrac{2x}{y}$

f) $\dfrac{a^3}{b^2}\div\dfrac{a^5}{b^4}$

5   a)   A cuboid made of solid lead has dimensions $\dfrac{a}{2}$ m, $\dfrac{a}{3}$ m and $\dfrac{2a}{3}$ m. Find an expression for the volume of the cuboid.

b)   The cuboid is melted down and some small cylinders of lead are made from it. Each cylinder has radius $\dfrac{a}{50}$ cm and height b cm.

Find an expression for the number of cylinders that can be made.

c)   How many cylinders can be made if $b=3a$?

Adding and subtracting algebraic fractions

When you add or subtract numerical fractions, you start by finding a common denominator.

e.g. $\dfrac{1}{6} + \dfrac{3}{4} = \dfrac{2}{12} + \dfrac{9}{12} = \dfrac{11}{12}$

In the same way, when you add or subtract algebraic fractions you start by finding a common denominator. You should use the simplest algebraic expression that is a multiple of both denominators.

Example

Simplify **a)** $\dfrac{2}{x} + \dfrac{3}{x^2}$ **b)** $\dfrac{b-1}{b} - \dfrac{b}{b+1}$ **c)** $\dfrac{p}{6q} + \dfrac{p+1}{8pq}$

Solution

a) The simplest expression that is a multiple of both x and x^2 is x^2.

$$\dfrac{2}{x} + \dfrac{3}{x^2} = \dfrac{2x}{x^2} + \dfrac{3}{x^2} = \dfrac{2x+3}{x^2}$$

Multiply top and bottom by x.

b) The simplest expression that is a multiple of both b and $b+1$ is $b(b+1)$.

$$\dfrac{b-1}{b} - \dfrac{b}{b+1} = \dfrac{(b+1)(b-1)}{b(b+1)} - \dfrac{b^2}{b(b+1)}$$

Multiply top and bottom by b.

$$= \dfrac{b^2 - 1 - b^2}{b(b+1)}$$

$$= \dfrac{-1}{b(b+1)}$$

Multiply top and bottom by $b+1$.

c) The lowest common multiple of 6 and 8 is 24.

The simplest expression which is a multiple of both q and pq is pq.

So the common denominator is $24pq$.

$$\dfrac{p}{6q} - \dfrac{p+1}{8pq} = \dfrac{4p^2}{24pq} + \dfrac{3(p+1)}{24pq}$$

Multiply top and bottom by 3.

$$= \dfrac{4p^2 + 3p + 3}{24pq}$$

Multiply top and bottom by $4p$.

Exercise 3.3

1 Write each of these as a single fraction and simplify if possible.

a) $\dfrac{2}{3} + \dfrac{1}{4}$

b) $\dfrac{4}{5} - \dfrac{1}{3}$

c) $\dfrac{2}{7} + \dfrac{3}{5}$

d) $\dfrac{x}{3} + \dfrac{2x}{5}$

e) $\dfrac{3y}{4} - \dfrac{2y}{7}$

f) $\dfrac{a+1}{2} + \dfrac{3a-2}{4}$

g) $\dfrac{2c-1}{4} - \dfrac{c-2}{3}$

h) $\dfrac{3p-2}{6} - \dfrac{1-p}{8}$

i) $\dfrac{5x+6y}{5} - 2x$

2 Write each of these as a single fraction and simplify if possible.

a) $\dfrac{3}{a} + \dfrac{1}{2a}$

b) $\dfrac{4}{z} + \dfrac{3}{z^2}$

c) $\dfrac{1}{a} - \dfrac{2}{b}$

d) $\dfrac{3}{p} - \dfrac{2}{p+1}$

e) $\dfrac{4}{x+1} + \dfrac{2}{x-2}$

f) $\dfrac{3y}{y+1} - \dfrac{2y}{y-1}$

g) $\dfrac{2a-1}{a+2} + \dfrac{1-3a}{2a+1}$

h) $\dfrac{3p+1}{q-1} - \dfrac{2p-1}{q+3}$

i) $\dfrac{2w-z}{w+z} + \dfrac{3w+z}{z-2w}$

j) $\dfrac{2}{a} - \dfrac{3}{a-1} + \dfrac{1}{a+1}$

3 a) Write $\dfrac{x}{x+1} + \dfrac{x-2}{x+2}$ as a single fraction.

b) Hence solve the equation $\dfrac{x}{x+1} + \dfrac{x-2}{x+2} = 2$

4 a) Write $\dfrac{2}{x} - \dfrac{1}{x-1}$ as a single fraction.

b) Hence solve the equation $\dfrac{2}{x} - \dfrac{1}{x-1} = \dfrac{1}{x+3}$

5 Simplify these fractions.

(Hint: factorise the denominator of each fraction first.)

a) $\dfrac{1}{x^2+3x+2} + \dfrac{1}{x^2+x} - \dfrac{1}{x^2+2x}$

b) $\dfrac{1}{a^2-1} - \dfrac{1}{2a^2+3a+1} - \dfrac{1}{2a^2-a-1}$

Rearranging a formula

In this section you revise the work on rearranging formulae that you covered in Book 1.

Reminder

- When you rearrange a formula you must do the same to each side of it, just as you do when you are solving an equation.

- Think about the order of operations on x in the formula. You must 'undo' them in reverse order.

- Isolate squared and square root terms before dealing with them.

Example

Make x the subject of these formulae.

a) $\dfrac{ax + b}{c} = d$

b) $\dfrac{p}{q - x} = r$

c) $r(x^2 + s) = t$

d) $\sqrt{\dfrac{x}{w}} + y = z$

Solution

a) $\dfrac{ax + b}{c} = d$ — Multiply both sides by c.

$ax + b = cd$ — Subtract b from both sides.

$ax = cd - b$ — Divide both sides by a.

$x = \dfrac{cd - b}{a}$

b) $\dfrac{p}{q - x} = r$ — Get rid of the fraction by multiplying both sides by $q - x$.

$p = r(q - x)$

$\dfrac{p}{r} = q - x$

$\dfrac{p}{r} + x = q$ — If you have a negative x term, add it to both sides so that you are working with a positive x term.

$x = q - \dfrac{p}{r}$

c) $r(x^2 + s) = t$

$x^2 + s = \dfrac{t}{r}$

$x^2 = \dfrac{t}{r} - s$ — Isolate the x^2 term before square rooting.

$x = \sqrt{\dfrac{t}{r} - s}$

d) $\sqrt{\dfrac{x}{w}} + y = z$

$\sqrt{\dfrac{x}{w}} = z - y$ — Isolate the square root term before squaring.

$\dfrac{x}{w} = (z - y)^2$ — Notice the use of brackets.

$x = w\,(z - y)^2$

Formulae in which the new subject appears more than once

Suppose you want to make x the subject of the formula

$$ax - b = cx + d.$$

Notice that there are two x terms in the formula. To make x the subject, you need first to collect the x terms together. It is a bit like solving an equation such as

$$5x - 1 = 3x + 7.$$

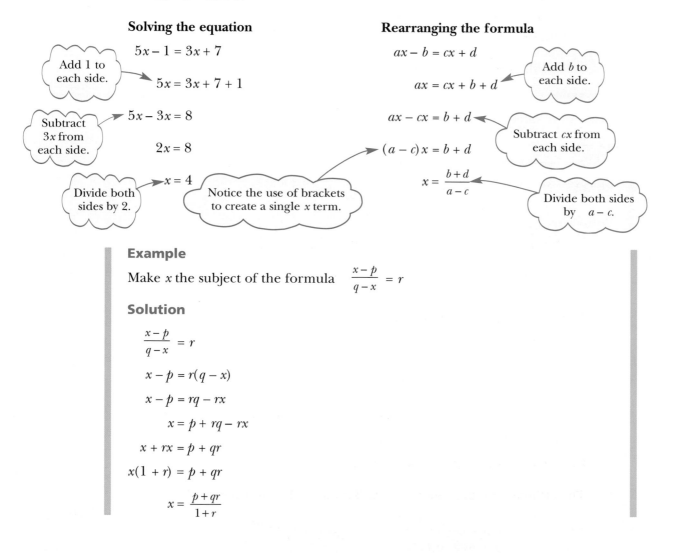

Solving the equation

$$5x - 1 = 3x + 7$$

Add 1 to each side.

$$5x = 3x + 7 + 1$$

Subtract $3x$ from each side.

$$5x - 3x = 8$$

$$2x = 8$$

$$x = 4$$

Divide both sides by 2.

Notice the use of brackets to create a single x term.

Rearranging the formula

$$ax - b = cx + d$$

Add b to each side.

$$ax = cx + b + d$$

Subtract cx from each side.

$$ax - cx = b + d$$

$$(a - c)x = b + d$$

$$x = \frac{b + d}{a - c}$$

Divide both sides by $a - c$.

Example

Make x the subject of the formula $\dfrac{x - p}{q - x} = r$

Solution

$$\frac{x - p}{q - x} = r$$

$$x - p = r(q - x)$$

$$x - p = rq - rx$$

$$x = p + rq - rx$$

$$x + rx = p + qr$$

$$x(1 + r) = p + qr$$

$$x = \frac{p + qr}{1 + r}$$

Exercise 3.4

1 Make x the subject of each of these formulae.

a) $wx + y = z$

b) $s - x = t$

c) $\dfrac{x}{a} - b = c$

d) $\dfrac{y}{x} = z$

e) $\dfrac{p - x}{q} = r$

f) $\dfrac{r}{s - x} = t$

g) $\dfrac{x^2 + a}{b} = c$

h) $\sqrt{cx - d} = e$

i) $p - \sqrt{\dfrac{x}{q}} = r$

j) $\dfrac{f}{(x - h)^2} = g$

k) $\dfrac{w}{\sqrt{x + y}} = z$

l) $a - \dfrac{b}{x^2} = c$

2 Make x the subject of each of these formulae.

a) $ax + b = cx + d$

b) $px - q = qx$

c) $xy + z = y - xz$

d) $\dfrac{cx + d}{e} = x$

e) $\dfrac{x - a}{b} = \dfrac{x + b}{c}$

f) $\dfrac{x + p}{x - q} = p$

g) $\dfrac{x}{s} + \dfrac{x}{t} = r$

h) $\dfrac{a}{x} + \dfrac{b}{ax} = b$

i) $\sqrt{\dfrac{x - y}{x + w}} = z$

j) $\dfrac{x + c}{x + d} = \dfrac{x - d}{x + 2c}$

k) $\dfrac{\sqrt{x^2 + p}}{x} = p$

l) $(ax + b)^2 = (bx + a)^2 + a^2$

3 The formula for the surface area of a cone is

$$A = \pi r^2 + \pi r \sqrt{h^2 + r^2}.$$

Make h the subject of the formula.

4 The formula $\dfrac{1}{R} = \dfrac{1}{R_1} + \dfrac{1}{R_2}$ is used to find resistance in an electric circuit.

a) Make R the subject of the formula.

b) Make R_1 the subject of the formula.

5 The cylinder and the cuboid shown both have the same height, h.

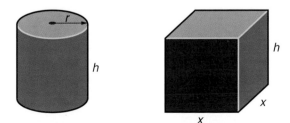

a) Find an expression for the surface area of the cuboid.

b) Find an expression for the surface area of the cylinder.

c) The two surface areas are equal. Find an expression for h in terms of r and x.

Finishing off

> **Now that you have finished this chapter you should be able to:**
>
> ★ simplify algebraic fractions
>
> ★ add, subtract, multiply and divide algebraic fractions
>
> ★ rearrange a formula.

Use the questions in the next exercise to check that you understand everything.

Mixed exercise 3.5

1 Write each of these as a single fraction, and simplify where possible.

a) $\dfrac{4a}{9b} \times \dfrac{3b}{2a^2}$

b) $\dfrac{p+1}{p} \times \dfrac{2p^2}{5}$

c) $\dfrac{x^2+2x}{y} \div \dfrac{x+2}{y+1}$

d) $\dfrac{(2z)^2}{z-1} \div \dfrac{3z}{z^2-1}$

e) $\dfrac{1}{x} + \dfrac{2}{x+1}$

f) $\dfrac{2}{a} - \dfrac{1}{a^2}$

g) $\dfrac{3}{ab} + \dfrac{1}{2ac}$

h) $\dfrac{3}{x+2} - \dfrac{2}{2x-1}$

i) $\dfrac{y}{y+1} - \dfrac{y+3}{y-1}$

j) $\dfrac{2p-1}{q+2} + \dfrac{3-2p}{q-1}$

2 a) Write $\dfrac{2x-1}{x+2} + \dfrac{3x+2}{x+1}$ as a single fraction.

b) Hence solve the equation $\dfrac{2x-1}{x+2} + \dfrac{3x+2}{x+1} = 5$

3 Make x the subject of each of these formulae.

a) $\dfrac{x}{a} - b = c$

b) $\dfrac{p-qx}{r} = p$

c) $\dfrac{c}{x-d} = e$

d) $rx + s = sx - r$

e) $\dfrac{x^2+w}{z} = y$

f) $a - \sqrt{\dfrac{x}{b}} = b$

g) $\dfrac{p}{x-q} = \dfrac{q}{p+x}$

h) $\left(\dfrac{y}{z-x}\right)^2 = z$

i) $\sqrt{m - \dfrac{n}{x}} = n$

j) $\dfrac{f}{g-x} = \dfrac{g+x}{h}$

4 This formula gives the energy E of a moving object:

$$E = mgh + \frac{1}{2}mv^2.$$

a) Make m the subject of the formula.

b) Make v the subject of the formula.

Mixed exercise 3.5 *continued*

5   The heat setting of a gas oven is called its Gas Mark.

A Gas Mark, *G*, may be converted to a temperature, *F*, in degrees Fahrenheit, using the formula $F = 25G + 250$.

a) Factorise completely $25G + 250$.

A Gas Mark, *G*, may be converted to a temperature, *C*, in degrees Celsius, using the formula $C = 14G + 121$.

b) Make *G* the subject of the formula $C = 14G + 121$.

c) Use the formulae $F = 25G + 250$ and $C = 14G + 121$ to express *F* in the form

$$F = kC + d$$

Give the values of *k* and *d* correct to 2 significant figures.

Edexcel

6   A flower bed is cut out of a square piece of lawn.

The unshaded part of the diagram shows the part of the lawn which is cut away. The boundary of the flower bed consists of four circular quadrants, each of radius *r*.

a) Show that the unshaded area, *A*, is given by the formula

$$A = 4r^2 - \pi r^2.$$

b) Rearrange this formula to obtain *r* in terms of *A*.

c) Hence, or otherwise, find the value of *r* required to make a flower bed of area 25 m².

NEAB

7   A cylinder of radius *R* cm and height *h* cm has a central cylindrical hole of radius *r* cm drilled through it. Its volume *V* cm³ is given by the formula

$$V = \pi(R^2 - r^2)h.$$

a) Find the value of *V* when

$$\pi = \frac{22}{7}, \quad R = 4, \quad r = 0.5, \quad h = 2\frac{3}{4}.$$

The surface area, *A* cm², of the shape can be written as

$$A = 2\pi(R + r)(R - r + h).$$

For a particular solid of this type the numerical value of the surface area is twice the numerical value of the volume.

b) For this particular shape express *h* in terms of *R* and *r*.

Edexcel

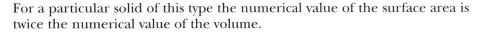

Chapter 4

Similarity and congruence

Similarity

The image produced by an enlargement is the same shape as the object but a different size: the object and image are said to be **similar**.

With an enlargement, the object and image have other properties too.

For example, each line joining a point on an object A, and its image, A_1, passes through the centre of enlargement, O, and corresponding lines AB and A_1B_1 are parallel.

The object and image are said to be **similarly situated**.

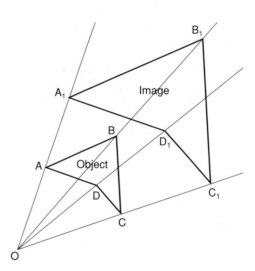

Two shapes can be similar without being similarly situated.

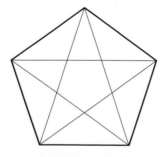

The diagram shows a regular pentagon with its diagonals.

Check that you can find 30 triangles in this figure. How many different shapes of triangles are there?

For each shape of triangle find a pair of triangles that are similarly situated (i.e. are the object and image of an enlargement) and a pair of triangles that are not similarly situated.

Properties of similar figures

Suppose that $A_1B_1C_1D_1$ is the image of the quadrilateral ABCD under an enlargement scale factor k. These similar quadrilaterals have two important properties.

① The object and image have the same shape, so that

$$\angle A_1 = \angle A, \quad \angle B_1 = \angle B, \quad \angle C_1 = \angle C, \quad \angle D_1 = \angle D.$$

Therefore **corresponding pairs of angles are equal**.

② $A_1B_1 = k \times AB$, so that $\dfrac{A_1B_1}{AB} = k$,

and similarly $\dfrac{B_1C_1}{BC} = \dfrac{C_1D_1}{CD} = \dfrac{D_1A_1}{DA} = k.$

Therefore **corresponding pairs of sides are in the same ratio**.

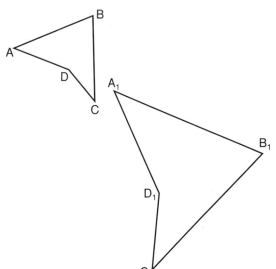

Properties 1 and 2 remain true for similar quadrilaterals which are not similarly situated. They are also true (for the same reasons) for similar triangles, similar pentagons, and all other similar polygons.

The converse is also true: if two polygons have both properties 1 and 2 then they are similar.

By considering a) a square and a rectangle, b) a square and a rhombus, prove that, for a quadrilateral, properties 1 and 2 are independent *(i.e. that neither property implies the other).*

Similar triangles

Since the shape of a triangle is completely determined by its angles or by the ratio of its sides, triangles have the very convenient special feature that each of the properties 1 and 2 given above implies the other one. This gives two ways of proving that triangles are similar.

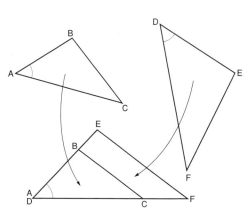

There is also a third 'mixed' way to prove similarity.

Two triangles ABC, DEF in which $\dfrac{AB}{DE} = \dfrac{AC}{DF}$ and $\angle A = \angle D$ can be superimposed so that A and D coincide, and DE, DF lie along AB, AC respectively.

Then the enlargement with centre D and scale factor $\dfrac{AB}{DE}$ maps E to B and F to C, which shows that the original triangles are similar.

Therefore to show two triangles are similar you need only to show one of these:

- the pairs of angles are equal
- all three corresponding pairs of sides are in the same ratio
- two pairs of sides are in the same ratio and the included angles are equal.

Example

In the diagram AB = 7, BD = 3, AC = 4 and $\angle ABC = \angle AED$.

Calculate CE.

Solution

In triangles ABC, AED

$\angle ABC = \angle AED$ (given)

$\angle BAC = \angle EAD$ (same angle)

Therefore the triangles are similar (pairs of angles are equal).

Therefore $\dfrac{AE}{AB} = \dfrac{AD}{AC}$ (corresponding pairs of sides are in the same ratio).

i.e. $\dfrac{AE}{7} = \dfrac{7+3}{4}$

so $AE = 7 \times \dfrac{10}{4} = 17.5$ and $CE = 17.5 - 4 = 13.5$.

Example

Use similar triangles to prove Pythagoras' theorem.

Solution

Let ABC be a triangle in which $\angle C$ is a right angle and CD is the perpendicular from C to AB.

Let a, b, c, x, y be the lengths of BC, CA, AB, AD, BD respectively.

In the triangles ACD, ABC

$\angle A$ is common

$\angle ADC = \angle ACD$ (right angles)

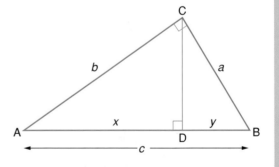

Therefore the triangles are similar (pairs of angles are equal).

Therefore $\dfrac{x}{b} = \dfrac{b}{c}$, and so $xc = b^2$.

Similarly triangles BCD, BAC are similar.

Therefore $\dfrac{y}{a} = \dfrac{a}{c}$, and so $yc = a^2$.

Adding these results $\quad xc + yc = b^2 + a^2$

so that $\quad (x + y)c = b^2 + a^2$.

But $\quad x + y = c$.

Therefore $\quad c^2 = b^2 + a^2$, which is Pythagoras' theorem.

Exercise 4.1

1 Prove that these pairs of triangles are similar. Then copy and complete the statement below each figure. (Lines marked with arrows are parallel.)

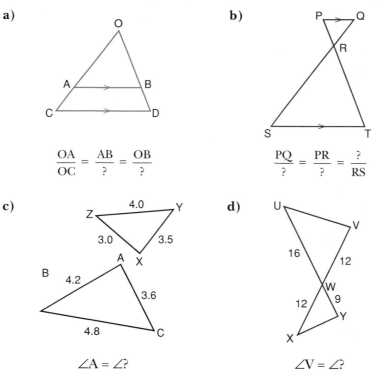

a)

$$\frac{OA}{OC} = \frac{AB}{?} = \frac{OB}{?}$$

b)

$$\frac{PQ}{?} = \frac{PR}{?} = \frac{?}{RS}$$

c)

$$\angle A = \angle?$$

d)

$$\angle V = \angle?$$

2 Use similar triangles to find the lengths p, q, r, s.

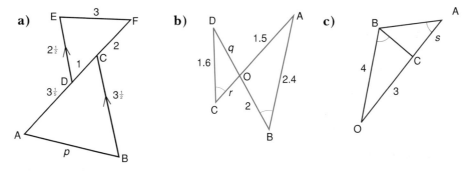

a)

b)

c)

3 Find the perpendicular height x of this right-angled triangle, and hence find the area of the triangle.

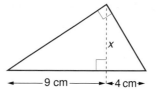

9 cm   4 cm

Exercise 4.1 *continued*

4 The diagram shows the side of a house with a garage attached. Beyond the garage is a path and boundary fence. How high above the ground is the lowest point of the house wall that can be reached using a straight ladder?

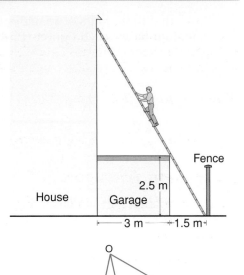

House

Garage

2.5 m

Fence

3 m ┈ 1.5 m

5 The diagram shows a framework for supporting the overhead wire on an electric railway.
OC = OD = 8 m, OB = AB = 5 m, CD = 3 m, and AB is parallel to CD. Find the length of CA.

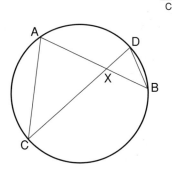

6 The diagram shows chords AB, CD intersecting at X.
   a) Prove that triangles AXC, DXB are similar.

   b)(i) If AX = 8, BX = 3, CX = 12, find DX.

   (ii) If AB = 45, AX = 24, CX = 56, find CD.

7 Use similar triangles to prove that the line joining the mid-points of two sides of a triangle is parallel to and half as long as the third side.

Congruence

The images under translations, reflections and rotations are exactly the same size and shape as the object. Two figures which are exactly the same size and shape are said to be **congruent**. You could cut out one and fit it exactly over the other.

? *What is different about reflected shapes?*

? *Can the object and image of an enlargement ever be congruent? If so, when?*

Congruent triangles

Congruent triangles are similar triangles which are also the same size, so that the ratio of corresponding sides is 1. This gives three ways of showing that triangles are congruent.

① The pairs of angles and one pair of **corresponding** sides are equal.

   This is abbreviated to angle, angle, side or AAS (only two pairs of angles are needed).

② All three pairs of sides are equal. Abbreviation SSS.

③ Two pairs of sides and the **included** angles are equal. Abbreviation SAS.

? *A developer describes a triangular plot of land ABC to his surveyor by telephone, saying: 'Angle A is 40°, side AB is 74 m and side BC is 53 m. Please calculate the area for me.' What reply should the surveyor give?*

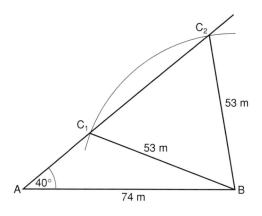

This question illustrates why it is essential to use the included angle in 3 above. If the surveyor sketches the field from the information, he gets two possible triangles, ABC_1 and ABC_2, which are clearly not congruent (and have different areas). This is called the **ambiguous case**.

There is a useful special case when two pairs of sides and a non-included angle will prove congruence. This is when the angle is a right angle. For example, suppose that $\angle A = 90°$, $AB = 7$ and $BC_1 = 9$.

Constructing the triangle again gives two possibilities, ABC_1 and ABC_2, but this time each is the reflection of the other in AB, so the size and shape of the triangle is fixed by the information without ambiguity.

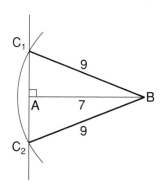

This gives the fourth way of showing that triangles are congruent.

④ Both triangles are right-angled, and the hypotenuses and one other pair of sides are equal. Abbreviation RHS.

4: Similarity and congruence

Once you have shown that two triangles are congruent you can deduce that all their corresponding pairs of sides and angles, are equal. Other corresponding lengths (e.g. corresponding altitudes) are equal too, and so are the areas of the triangles. You can use congruent triangles to prove many geometrical results.

Example

A parallelogram is defined as a quadrilateral with opposite pairs of sides parallel. Prove that opposite pairs of sides are also equal.

Diagram

ABCD is a parallelogram with AB parallel to DC and BC parallel to AD. Diagonal AC is drawn.

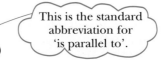

Proof

In triangles ABC, CDA

$\angle$BAC = $\angle$DCA (alternate angles AB // DC)

$\angle$ACB = $\angle$CAD (alternate angles, BC // AD)

AC is common to both triangles.

Therefore the triangles are congruent (AAS).

Therefore AB = CD and BC = DA (corresponding pairs of sides).

This is the standard abbreviation for 'is parallel to'.

What other well-known property of a parallelogram can be deduced using the same triangles?

Example

Prove that the two tangents drawn from a point to a circle are equal in length.

Diagram

The tangents from T touch the circle at P and Q,

C is the centre of the circle, and CT is drawn.

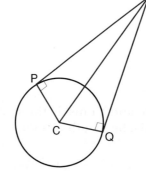

Proof

In triangles CPT, CQT

$\angle$CPT = CQT = 90° (angle between radius and tangent)

CP = CQ (radii)

CT is common.

Therefore the triangles are congruent (RHS).

Therefore TP = TQ (corresponding sides of congruent triangles).

Deduce also that CT bisects both $\angle$PTQ and $\angle$PCQ.

Exercise 4.2

1 In each case, decide whether triangles ABC, XYZ drawn with the following properties are congruent. If so, state which case of congruency applies.

    a) AB = XY, BC = ZX, CA = YZ   **b)** AB = ZX, ∠B = ∠Y, ∠A = ∠Z

    c) AB = XY, ∠A = ∠Y, ∠B = ∠X   **d)** AB = YZ, BC = ZX, ∠B = ∠Z

    e) AB = XY, BC = YZ, ∠B = ∠Z   **f)** AB = ZX, BC = YX, CA = YZ

    g) ∠B = ∠Z = 90°, AC = YZ, BC = XY

2 ABC is an isosceles triangle with AB = AC, and AD is the perpendicular from A to BC. Without assuming any other properties of isosceles triangles, prove that triangles ABD, ACD are congruent. Deduce that

    a) ∠B = ∠C

    b) D is the midpoint of BC

    c) AD bisects ∠BAC.

3 A rectangle is defined as a parallelogram in which one angle is a right angle. Without assuming any other properties of rectangles prove that the diagonals of a rectangle are equal.

4 The diagonals of a quadrilateral are perpendicular and bisect each other. What can you deduce about the quadrilateral?

5 **a)** The diagram shows the bisector of angle ABC, constructed with straight edge and compasses. Use congruent triangles to prove that ∠DBA = ∠DBC.

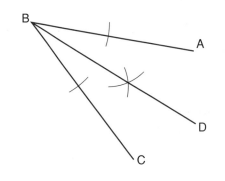

    b) Justify the straight edge and compasses construction for drawing a perpendicular to a line BC from a point A not on BC.

6 ABCD is a square and triangles XAB, YBC are both equilateral, with X inside and Y outside the square. Use triangles ABC, XBY to prove that XY equals the length of a diagonal of the square.

7 ABC is a triangle in which AB is longer than AC. The bisector of ∠A meets the perpendicular bisector of BC at K, the perpendicular from K to AB meets AB at P, and the perpendicular from K meets AC produced at Q. Prove that

    a) KP = KQ   **b)** KC = KB   **c)** BP = CQ.

Finishing off

Now that you have finished this chapter you should be able to:

★ recognise similarity and prove similarity of triangles

★ use properties of similar shapes in calculations

★ recognise congruence and prove congruence of triangles

★ use congruent triangles to prove geometrical results.

Use the questions in the next exercise to check that you understand everything.

Mixed exercise 4.3

1

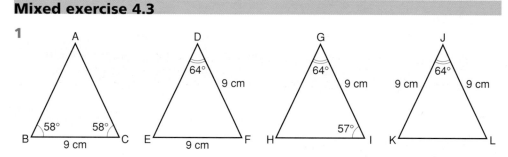

Which of the following statements about these triangles is/are true?

a) All the triangles are congruent.

b) Three of the triangles are similar.

c) Triangles ABC and JKL are congruent.

d) Triangles DEF and GHI are similar but not congruent.

e) Triangles ABC and JKL are similar but not congruent.

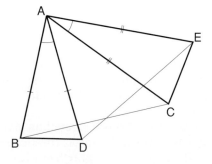

2 ABD and ACE are similar isosceles triangles with a common vertex A. Prove that BC = DE.

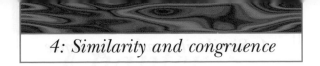
Mixed exercise 4.3 *continued*

3 Craig used the following method to find the width of a straight canal.
He placed a stake at B directly opposite a tree A on the opposite bank of
the canal. He walked 10 metres along the canal to point C where he
placed another stake.
He walked another 2 metres to point D. He then walked at right angles to
the canal until he reached a point E directly in line with A and C.

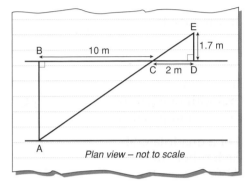

Plan view – not to scale

a) Explain clearly why triangle ABC is similar to triangle EDC.

b) Given that the distance DE = 1.7 metres, find the width AB of the canal.

MEI

4 In the diagram, PQ = PS and
PR = PT. Angle RPT = angle SPQ.

a) Show that triangles PRQ and
PTS are congruent.

b) Hence show that PS bisects
angle QST.

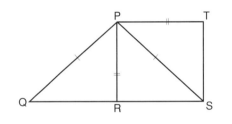

London

5 These triangles are congruent.

a) What is the value of *x*?

b) What is the length, *y*?

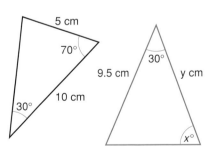

NEAB

6 Given the information in
the diagram

a) prove that triangles XAD,
XCB are similar;

b) prove that quadrilateral
ABCD is cyclic (i.e. all four
vertices are on the
circumference of a circle).

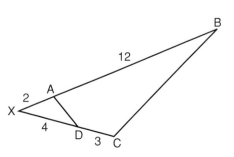

Cumulative frequency

It is often helpful to display a large amount of data on a cumulative frequency graph, as shown in the following example.

Example

A scientist is investigating the extent to which a pesticide has been taken up by the fox population.

She measures the quantity x micrograms (abbreviated to µg) in 120 foxes.

The results are shown in the table, and on the frequency chart, below.

Amount of pesticide	$0 \leq x < 5$	$5 \leq x < 10$	$10 \leq x < 15$	$15 \leq x < 20$	$20 \leq x < 25$	$25 \leq x < 30$
Frequency	14	22	32	28	16	8

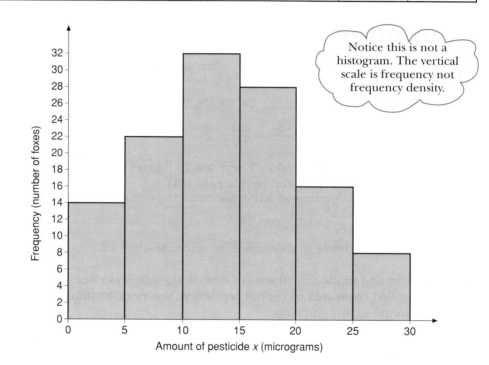

Notice this is not a histogram. The vertical scale is frequency not frequency density.

Amount of pesticide x (micrograms)

The corresponding cumulative frequency table and graph are as follows.

Amount of pesticide	< 0	< 5	< 10	< 15	< 20	< 25	< 30
Frequency	0	14	36	68	96	112	120

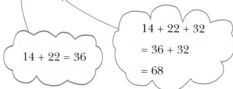

$14 + 22 = 36$

$14 + 22 + 32$
$= 36 + 32$
$= 68$

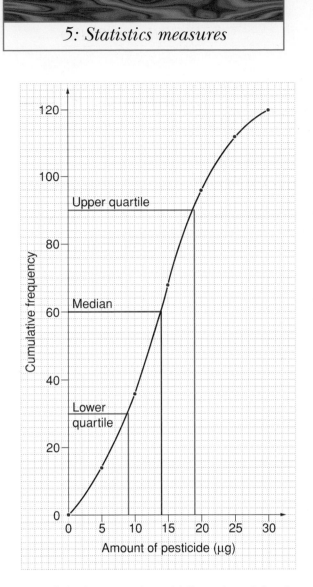

The red line on the graph is drawn at the middle point of the data. It shows you that the median is about 14 micrograms.

The green lines give the upper and lower quartiles

Upper quartile: $\frac{3}{4} \times 120 = 90$ Value   19

Lower quartile: $\frac{1}{4} \times 120 = 30$ Value   9

So the interquartile range = 19 − 9 = 10

Like range, interquartile range is a measure of spread. Interquartile range is not affected by the extreme values. By contrast, it is the extreme values that you use when working out the range.

You may have noticed that when finding the median of 10 data values on page 47, we took the value mid-way between numbers 5 and 6, that is at $5\frac{1}{2}$. Using the same logic we should have found the median of the 120 values at $6\frac{1}{2}$ and not at 60. However with large data sets it is usual to take the median point at $\frac{1}{2}n$ and the quartiles at $\frac{1}{4}n$ and $\frac{3}{4}n$.

The cumulative frequency table from page 48 is given again here.

Amount of pesticide (µg)	< 0	< 5	< 10	< 15	< 20	< 25	< 30
Frequency	0	14	36	68	96	112	120

Another way of writing the table is:

Amount of pesticide (µg)	5	10	15	20	25	30
Cumulative frequency	14	36	68	96	112	120

What are the differences between these two ways of writing a cumulative frequency table?

Working with grouped data

The data in the previous example about the foxes were grouped. How can you calculate the various measures when your data are grouped?

Median   The best way to estimate the median is to draw the cumulative frequency curve as above. It gave us the answer 14 µg.

Mode   You cannot state a single value for the mode but you can see from the table, and from the frequency chart, that the **modal class** is 10–15 µg, since this has the highest frequency (the largest number of foxes).

Mean   To estimate the mean, take the mid-point of each interval, as follows

$$\frac{(14 \times 2.5) + (22 \times 7.5) + (32 \times 12.5) + (28 \times 17.5) + (16 \times 22.5) + (8 \times 27.5)}{14 + 22 + 32 + 28 + 16 + 8}$$

$$= \frac{35 + 165 + 400 + 490 + 360 + 220}{120} = \frac{1670}{120}$$

$$= 13.9 \text{ µg (to 1 decimal place)}.$$

 Why are the median and the mean estimates and not accurate values?

What can you say about the range of the amount of pesticide in the foxes?

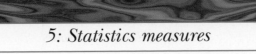

Use the questions in the next exercise to check that you remember these topics.

Review exercise 5.1

1 Andrew throws two dice and records their total many times over.
The results are shown on the tally.

a) How many times did he throw the dice?

b) What score was

   (i) the mode

   (ii) the median

   (iii) the mean?

Total of two dice	Tally
2	//
3	ЖҢ ///
4	ЖҢ ЖҢ /
5	ЖҢ ЖҢ ///
6	ЖҢ ЖҢ ЖҢ //
7	ЖҢ ЖҢ ЖҢ ЖҢ /
8	ЖҢ ЖҢ ////
9	ЖҢ ЖҢ ///
10	ЖҢ ////
11	ЖҢ ///
12	////

2 In their last 10 matches, a football team have scored the following number of goals

0, 0, 0, 0, 1, 1, 2, 2, 2, 12

a) Find the mode, median and mean of these numbers.

b) Which of these measures would you use in the following situations?

   (i) You are the manager of the club and are looking for sponsorship.

   (ii) You are a member of the team and want to decide what is a reasonable score.

   (iii) You are the captain of another team which is about to play them, and are giving a talk to your players.

3 Sheila found the mode, median and mean of sets of five numbers. Her results are shown in the table.

Numbers	Mode	Median	Mean
1, 1, 2, 3, 4	1	2	2.2
1, 2, 3, 4, 4	4	3	2.8
1, 3, 4, 5, 5	5	4	3.6
1, 2, 2, 3, 4	2	2	2.4
2, 2, 4, 6, 7	2	4	4.2

Sheila said: 'The mean can never be between the mode and the median.'

Investigate whether she is correct by considering other sets of five numbers.

MEI

Review exercise 5.1 *continued*

4   The Staffordshire Blue Cat is famous for its mousing.
     In a survey over the 31 days in January the numbers of mice caught by 80
     of these cats were counted and recorded.

Mice caught per cat	0–9	10–19	20–29	30–39	40–49	50–59	60–69	70–79	80–89
Frequency (no. of cats)	0	2	5	22	21	13	10	6	1

    a) State whether these data are discrete or continuous.

    b) Draw up the cumulative frequency table and draw the cumulative
       frequency graph.

    c) Estimate the median and interquartile range of the number of mice
       caught per cat.

    d) A top class mouser averages over two mice a day.
       How many top class mousers were in this group?

    e) What percentage of cats caught less than 25 mice in the month?

    f) Estimate the mean number of mice caught per cat in the month.

5   A gardener weighs the cabbages he grows in one year.

Mass (m kg)	$0.5 \leq m < 0.6$	$0.6 \leq m < 0.7$	$0.7 \leq m \leq 0.8$	$0.8 \leq m < 0.9$
Frequency	6	12	22	40

Mass (m kg)	$0.9 \leq m < 1.0$	$1.0 \leq m < 1.1$	$1.1 \leq m < 1.2$	$1.2 \leq m < 1.3$
Frequency	55	35	20	10

    a) State whether these data are discrete or continuous.

    b) Draw up the cumulative frequency table and draw the cumulative
       frequency graph.

    c) Estimate the median and interquartile range of the mass of the cabbages.

    d) The cabbages under 0.75 kg are fed to his goats. How many do they get?

    e) He sells his heaviest 40 cabbages to a local shop.
       What is the minimum mass of one of these cabbages?

Review exercise 5.1 *continued*

6   An inspector buys a portion of
chips from each of the shops in
one town.

He weighs each one. The results
are shown in the frequency chart.

What can you say about the
mean, median, mode and range
of the masses of the portions
of chips?

Give each answer as precisely as
you can.

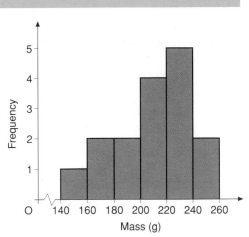

7   In an ice-skating competition two judges give the competitors the
following scores.

	A	B	C	D	E	F	G	H	I	J
Judge 1	5.2	5.1	4.9	5.1	5.0	5.3	5.0	5.3	5.1	5.0
Judge 2	5.6	5.0	4.6	5.2	4.7	5.8	5.1	5.3	4.9	4.8

There are complaints about the differences in the judges' scoring and so
the competition referee is called in to investigate them.

a)   Compare the mean scores given by the two judges.

b)   Compare the ranges of the scores given by the two judges.

The referee decides to adjust the scores awarded by Judge 1 in such a
way that their mean remains the same but they have the same range as
those of Judge 2.

c)   Copy and complete this table showing what the referee does.

	A	B	C	...
Original score	5.2	5.1	4.9	...
- 5.1	0.1	0.0	-0.2	...
x 3	0.3	0.0	-0.6	...
Adjusted score: + 5.1	5.4	5.1	4.5	...

d)   Show that the adjusted scores have the same mean and range as those
of Judge 2.

e)   The scores from the two judges are added together. Rank the
competitors using
(i) the original scores and
(ii) the adjusted scores.

How many competitors' positions are affected by the mark adjustments?

Measures of spread

Mel and Viv go ten-pin bowling. The figures below give the number of pins (skittles) they knock over on their first roll of each round.

Mel	6	5	7	10	0	7	6	6	7	6
Viv	0	10	10	1	2	9	8	3	10	7

Both sets of figures have mean 6.

However, if you look at the figures you will see that they are different sorts of players. Mel is very consistent; apart from one 10 and one 0 his scores are all close to 6.

By contrast Viv's scores are very spread out; she has more high scores and more low ones.

How can you express this mathematically?

The measures of spread you have used so far are range and interquartile range.

Range does not help because for both players

Range = 10 − 0 = 10.

Interquartile range is really a measure for large data sets. It is not good practice to use it on small sets like these. You need a new measure of spread.

What problems can arise using interquartile range with small data sets?

Mean absolute deviation

The first step is to write down the **deviation**, d, of each score from the mean. Deviation is given by the equation

$$d = x - \bar{x}$$

and in the case of Mel's scores, $\bar{x}$ (the mean) is 6.

Mel

Score	6	5	7	10	0	7	6	6	7	6
Deviation	0	-1	1	4	-6	1	0	0	1	0

Notice that if you add the deviations of Mel's scores you get 0. This is a useful check before you go onto the next step.

Why do you get 0 when you add the deviations together? Write down the deviations for Viv's scores and check that when you add them you also get 0.

Now ignore all the minus signs and add the absolute values of the deviations. For Mel's scores this give a total of

$$0 + 1 + 1 + 4 + 6 + 1 + 0 + 0 + 1 + 0 = 14$$

and the mean is

$$\frac{14}{10} = 1.4$$

This is called the **mean absolute deviation** and written as

$$\frac{\sum |d|}{n} \quad \text{or} \quad \frac{\sum |x - \bar{x}|}{n}.$$

> Notice the symbol $|d|$. This means the positive, or absolute, value of d.

 Work out the mean absolute deviation for Viv's scores.

You should get the answer 3.6. This confirms that Viv's scores are indeed more spread out than Mel's, 3.6 compared to 1.4.

Standard deviation

While mean absolute deviation is a perfectly good measure of spread, it is not actually very widely used. Instead a different procedure is followed in which you square the deviations, rather than take their absolute values, leading to the measure called **standard deviation** and denoted by s.

The steps are illustrated using Mel's scores.

Score	x	6	5	7	10	0	7	6	6	7	6
Deviation	$d = x - \bar{x}$	0	-1	1	4	-6	1	0	0	1	0
Deviation²	$d^2 = x - \bar{x}$	0	1	1	16	36	1	0	0	1	0

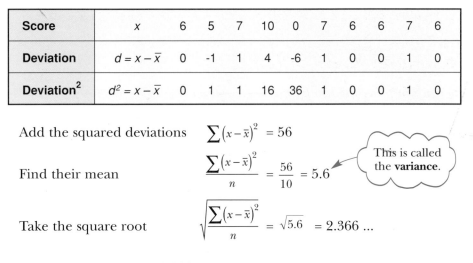

Add the squared deviations $\sum (x - \bar{x})^2 = 56$

Find their mean $\dfrac{\sum (x - \bar{x})^2}{n} = \dfrac{56}{10} = 5.6$

> This is called the **variance**.

Take the square root $\sqrt{\dfrac{\sum (x - \bar{x})^2}{n}} = \sqrt{5.6} = 2.366 \ldots$

Standard deviation $s = 2.366\ldots$

 Follow the same procedure to find the standard deviation of Viv's scores. You should get 3.847…

Why is standard deviation often used instead of mean absolute deviation?

The reason is that standard deviation turns out to have an important place in more advanced statistics theory, whereas mean absolute deviation does not.

For basic statistics work you may well be better using the mean absolute deviation, since it is much simpler to work out.

It is usual to set out a calculation of standard deviation in a table with the values x down, rather than across, the page as shown in this example.

Example

Find the standard deviation of the numbers 5, 6, 8, 9.

x	$x - \bar{x}$	$(x - \bar{x})^2$
5	-2	4
6	-1	1
8	1	1
9	2	4
Σ 28	0	10

$$\bar{x} = \frac{28}{4} = 7$$

$$\sum (x - \bar{x})^2 = 10$$

$$s = \sqrt{\frac{\sum (x - \bar{x})^2}{n}} = \sqrt{\frac{10}{4}} = \sqrt{2.5} = 1.581 \approx 1.58$$

Calculation form

Because the mean is often not a whole number, the numbers involved in calculating $(x - \bar{x})^2$ can become rather messy. An alternative formula is often used to do the calculations.

This is $\qquad s = \sqrt{\dfrac{\sum x^2}{n} - \bar{x}^2}$

How can you prove the two formulae are equivalent? (The proof is given in the answers at the back of the book.)

The calculation for the example above becomes

x	x^2
5	25
6	36
8	64
9	81
Σ 28	206

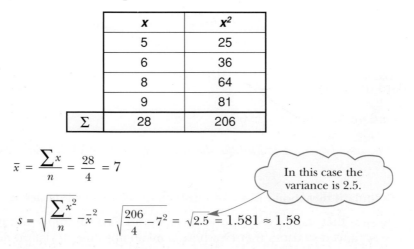

$$\bar{x} = \frac{\sum x}{n} = \frac{28}{4} = 7$$

$$s = \sqrt{\frac{\sum x^2}{n} - \bar{x}^2} = \sqrt{\frac{206}{4} - 7^2} = \sqrt{2.5} = 1.581 \approx 1.58$$

In this case the variance is 2.5.

In the next example this formula is adapted for use with data in a grouped frequency table.

Example

A firm is replacing the Luminese light bulbs in its factory. Information is collected on the lifetimes, in hours, of Everlux bulbs that could be used as replacements.

Lifetime in hours, l	700– 800	800– 900	900– 1000	1000– 1100	1100– 1200	1200– 1300	1300– 1400
Frequency	2	6	11	15	10	5	1

In this table, 700–800 means $700 \leq l < 800$.

(i) Estimate the mean and standard deviation of the lifetime of the Everlux light bulbs.

(ii) The Luminese brand has a mean of 1080 hours and standard deviation of 410 hours, and costs less than the Everlux. Which brand would you advise the factory to use, and why?

Solution

(i) This is again best done in a table. Remember when dealing with grouped data that the mid-point of each interval is used.

	Mid-point, x	Frequency, f	fx	fx^2
$700 \leq l < 800$	750	2	1 500	1 125 000
$800 \leq l < 900$	850	6	5 100	4 335 000
$900 \leq l < 1000$	950	11	10 450	9 927 500
$1000 \leq l < 1100$	1050	15	15 750	16 537 500
$1100 \leq l < 1200$	1150	10	11 500	13 225 000
$1200 \leq l < 1300$	1250	5	6 250	7 812 500
$1300 \leq l < 1400$	1350	1	1 350	1 822 500
	Σ	50	51 900	54 785 000

Notice that $n = 50$, the sum of the frequencies.

Mean $\bar{x} = \dfrac{51\,900}{50} = 1038$ hours

Standard deviation $s = \sqrt{\dfrac{\sum x^2}{n} - \bar{x}^2}$

$= \sqrt{\dfrac{54\,785\,000}{50} - 1038^2}$

$= \sqrt{18\,256} \approx 135$ hours

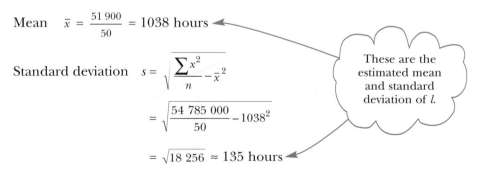

These are the estimated mean and standard deviation of l.

(ii) Luminese brand has a higher mean, and costs less so this suggests that it is the better buy. However the Everlux brand has a much lower standard deviation and so is more predictable. It depends on the situation in which the bulb will be used and the cost of replacing the bulb. The more important it is that the bulbs are working and the more the unexpected replacement costs then the more important it is to use the bulb with the lower standard deviation.

Using a calculator to find mean and standard deviation

Although most calculators work in a similar way, there are differences between the ways in which you use their statistical functions. When you get a new calculator make sure your read the manufacturer's instructions.

A useful check is to have a simple example with a few numbers where you know the right answers, such as that used earlier.

5, 6, 8, 9 gives $\bar{x} = 7$, $s^2 = 2.5$ and $s \approx 1.58$.

The main steps in using a calculator are:

1. Put the calculator into statistics or SD mode.

2. Enter the data.

3. Recall, and note the answers.

There is no need to do any calculations, the calculator automatically does them as each item of data is entered.

You have to be careful when recalling the standard deviation. Your calculator gives you the option of dividing by n or dividing by $n - 1$. For the formula we are using you want to divide by n. Notice that if your calculator gives a standard deviation of 1.825 then you have the 'wrong' standard deviation.

Why do calculators give two standard deviations?

Notice also that you can get Σx and Σx^2 from your calculator.

Data given in a frequency table

The only difference for data given in a frequency table is in the method of entry.

Use the data from the light bulb example, to check that you know how to enter the data. The appropriate figures are:

Mid-point	Frequency
750	2
850	6
950	11
1050	15
1150	10
1250	5
1350	1
	50

Your answers should be: mean 1038, standard deviation 135.114…

Exercise 5.2

1 **a)** Calculate the mean and standard deviation of these sets of numbers

    (i)   2, 2, 3, 3, 5, 5, 8, 8, 9, 10

    (ii) 12, 12, 13, 13, 15, 15, 18, 18, 19, 20

    (iii) 102, 102, 103, 103, 105, 105, 108, 108, 109, 110.

  b) Comment on your answers.

2 **a)** Calculate the mean and standard deviation of these sets of numbers.

    (i) 0, 0, 2, 4, 8, 16   (ii) 0, 0, 20, 40, 80, 160

    (iii) 0, 0, 1, 2, 4, 8.

  b) Comment on your answers.

3 **a)** Calculate the mean and standard deviation for these data.

(i)

x	1	2	3	4	5	6
f	5	12	18	21	16	8

(ii)

x	1	2	3	4	5	6
f	18	12	5	8	16	21

  b) Comment on your results.

4 **a)** Estimate the mean and standard deviation for these data.

    Explain why your answers are estimates rather than accurate values.

x	$0 \leq x < 10$	$10 \leq x < 20$	$20 \leq x < 30$	$30 \leq x < 40$	$40 \leq x < 50$
f	8	23	44	21	4

  b) The figures refer to the salaries, in thousands of pounds, of the employees in a company, but do not include that of the managing director. He earns £226,000 per year.

    Find the percentage increase in

    (i) the mean   (ii) the standard deviation

    when his salary is included in the calculations.

5 In an experiment, Nazia measured the time it took for a ball bearing to sink down to the bottom of a tube of oil. She made 5 measurements. Her results are given below.

    2.4 s, 2.5 s, 2.4 s, 2.6 s, 2.7 s

  a) Calculate the standard deviation of these times.

    Give your answer correct to 3 decimal places.

  Nazia found that her timing had been 0.2 seconds too short each time.

  b) For these corrected times, find

    (i) the mean time,   (ii) the standard deviation.

London

5: Statistics measures

Exercise 5.2 *continued*

6   The heights of a random sample of 100 eleven year old boys are given in the table.

Height, h (cm)	Frequency
$140 \leq h < 144$	5
$144 \leq h < 148$	10
$148 \leq h < 152$	20
$152 \leq h < 156$	40
$156 \leq h < 160$	14
$160 \leq h < 164$	8
$164 \leq h < 168$	3

An estimate of the mean height of these eleven year old boys is 153.36 cm.

a) Calculate an estimate of the standard deviation of the heights of these eleven year old boys. Give your answer correct to two decimal places.

The mean and standard deviation of the heights of a random sample of 100 sixteen year old boys were 174.25 cm and 4.23 cm respectively.

b) Compare the mean and the dispersion of the heights of the eleven year old boys with those of the sixteen year old boys.

SEG

7   The following sets of marks were scored by ten candidates in two examinations, *A* and *B*.

A 62, 54, 56, 63, 55, 61, 53, 69, 62, 65

B 52, 59, 38, 87, 64, 59, 51, 43, 84, 63

a) Calculate the mean mark for each examination, and verify that these are the same.

b) Calculate the standard deviation for each examination.

c) It is required to scale the marks for examination *A* so that the standard deviation is the same as for *B*. Suggest how this could be done, and produce the scaled set of marks.

MEI

8   Range, interquartile range, mean absolute deviation and standard deviation are all measures of spread. Which one would you use in each of the following situations?

a) You are conducting medical research into the variability of the level of a particular chemical in people's blood. Your data are the measurements from a sample of 500 specimens of blood.

b) You are grading an examination paper in which the middle half of the candidates will be given a pass grade. Your data are the marks from the 25 000 candidates who took the examination.

c) You are the captain of a golf team and want to choose the more reliable of two players of about the same standard to play in a match. Your data are their last 12 scores on the course.

d) You are investigating the heights of the tides on a remote island. Your data are 4500 measurements of the water level, taken at hourly intervals over several months.

Finishing off

★ calculate standard deviation

★ work with measures of spread and measures of central tendency.

Use the questions in the next exercise to check that you understand everything.

Mixed exercise 5.3

1

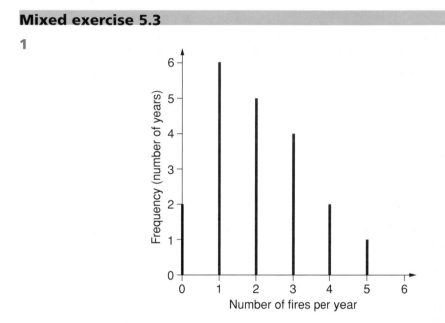

The vertical line chart shows the frequency of fires in a small town over a period of 20 years. Which of the following statements are true and which false?

a) The mode is 6.

b) The upper quartile is 3.

c) The chart shows that fires were more frequent during the first 10 years than during the second 10 years.

d) There is a probability of 0.4 that, in a year chosen at random, the number of fires is less than the median.

SMP (adapted)

2 Find the mean absolute deviation and the standard deviation of:

a) 2, 4, 6, 8, 10

b) 10, 10, 9, 8, 3

c) 23, 22, 22, 21, 20, 20, 20, 19, 19, 14

d) 3, 8, 3, 4, 2, 6, 1, 9, 8, 10, 4, 2

e) 3, 5, 8, 11, 9, 4, 6, 1, 3, 8, 7.

3 The table shows the distribution of scores obtained by 100 people taking an aptitude test.

Score	0	1	2	3	4	5	6	7	8
Frequency	7	9	6	12	17	31	10	4	4

Calculate **a)** the mean score and **b)** the standard deviation of the scores.

MEI

4

Type of operation	Number of operations	Cost per operation (£)
Plastic surgery	3	2000
Varicose veins	3	4500
Knee replacements	1	5200
Hip operations	3	7800

The table shows the numbers and costs of some operations in a hospital over one month.

The mean cost of an operation was £4810.

a) Calculate the standard deviation of the cost of an operation. Give your answer correct to the nearest £100.

The hospital later realised that each operation cost £200 more than originally thought.

b) Write down

(i) the true mean cost of an operation

(ii) the true standard deviation of the cost of an operation.

London

5 The lengths of telephone calls, in minutes, received at a switchboard during the first hour of one day were recorded, with the following results:

Length of calls	Frequency
0–5	2
5–8	5
8–11	10
11–14	10
14–18	3

Note: 5–8 means at least 5 and less than 8.

a) On squared paper draw a histogram of these data.

b) Calculate an estimate of the mean length of the calls and explain briefly why this is only an approximation.

c) Calculate an estimate of the standard deviation.

d) On your histogram mark the mean and the points two standard deviations above and below the mean.

MEI (adapted)

Chapter 6

Trigonometry 1

Use the questions in the next exercise to check that you remember this topic.

Reminder

Pythagoras' theorem is:

$$a^2 + b^2 = c^2$$

Remember that c is the hypotenuse.

Review exercise 6.1

1 Find the value of x in these triangles.

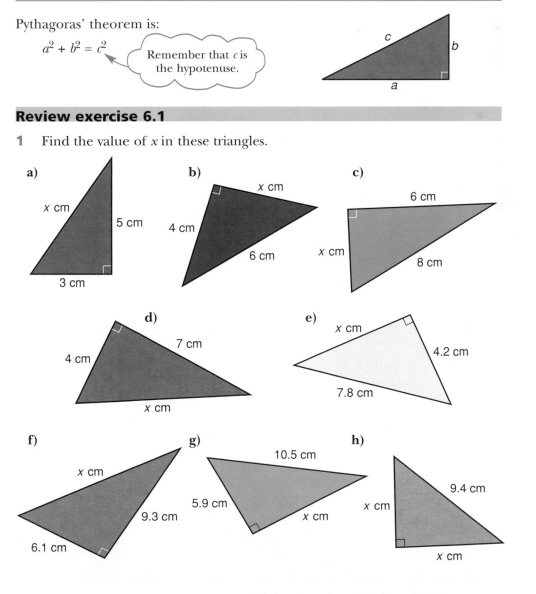

a)
x cm
5 cm
3 cm

b)
x cm
4 cm
6 cm

c)
6 cm
x cm
8 cm

d)
7 cm
4 cm
x cm

e)
x cm
4.2 cm
7.8 cm

f)
x cm
9.3 cm
6.1 cm

g)
10.5 cm
5.9 cm
x cm

h)
9.4 cm
x cm
x cm

Review exercise 6.1 *continued*

2 Use Pythagoras' theorem to find the distance between the following pairs of points.

a) (4, 3) and (1, −2) **b)** (−1, 0) and (2, 5)

c) (2, −4) and (3, −6) **d)** (−4, 2) and (3, 3)

3 A rectangular field is 120 m long and 70 m wide.

What is the diagonal distance across the field?

4 The diagram shows the cross-section of a greenhouse.

What is the height of the greenhouse?

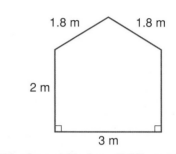

5 In this cuboid, X is the midpoint of AD, Y is the midpoint of CG and Z is the midpoint of GH.

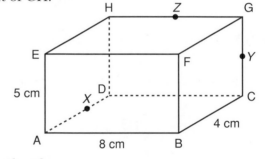

Find the lengths of

a) AG **b)** AY **c)** AZ

d) GX **e)** XY **f)** XZ

6 Find the distance between each of these pairs of points in three dimensional space.

a) (2, 1, 0) and (3, 3, −2) **b)** (1, −3, 4) and (−3, −5, 2)

7 Find the vertical height of this pyramid.

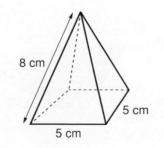

8 A cube has a diagonal of length 6 cm.

Find the length of each side of the cube.

Trigonometry review

This section revises the work on trigonometry from Book 1.

The three trigonometrical ratios are:

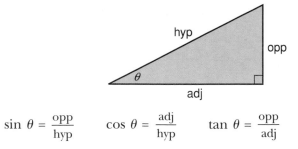

$$\sin \theta = \frac{\text{opp}}{\text{hyp}} \qquad \cos \theta = \frac{\text{adj}}{\text{hyp}} \qquad \tan \theta = \frac{\text{opp}}{\text{adj}}$$

You can use these ratios to find sides and angles in right-angled triangles.

Finding a side

Example 1

Find the value of x in this triangle.

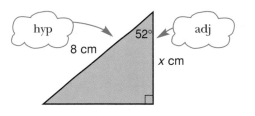

Solution

The first step is to decide whether to use sin, cos or tan.

The side that is 8 cm is the hypotenuse, and the side that is x is the adjacent side, so you use cos.

$$\cos 52° = \frac{x}{8}$$
$$x = 8 \cos 52°$$
$$x = 4.93 \text{ cm}$$

In the next example an extra step is needed, because the unknown side is the denominator of the fraction.

Example 2

Rachel is standing on top of a cliff 150 m high. She can see a boat out at sea. The angle of depression of the boat is 28°.

How far is the boat from the foot of the cliff?

Solution

$$\tan 28° = \frac{150}{d}$$
$$d \tan 28° = 150$$
$$d = \frac{150}{\tan 28°}$$
$$d = 282 \text{ (3 s.f.)}$$

This is the extra step.

This is the angle of depression.

This angle is also 28°.

150 m

d m

28°

The boat is 282 m from the foot of the cliff.

? *Check that you know how to use the sin, cos and tan functions on your calculator by working out the answers to the examples above.*

Finding an angle

To find an angle in a right-angled triangle, you need to use the inverse of sin, cos or tan. On your calculator these may be labelled arcsin, arccos and arctan, or $\sin^{-1}$, $\cos^{-1}$ and $\tan^{-1}$.

Example

Find the angle marked θ in this triangle.

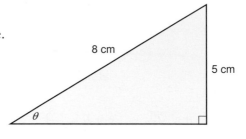

Solution

The 5 cm side is the opposite side, and the 8 cm side is the hypotenuse, so you need to use sin.

$$\sin \theta = \frac{5}{8} \qquad \theta = 38.7°$$

Three dimensional problems

When solving a problem in three dimensions, always draw a true shape diagram (so that right angles look like 90°) of the right-angled triangle you are using.

The angle between a line and a plane is the angle between the line and a line immediately below it on the plane. You may find it helpful to think of it as the shadow of the line if a light were shining from directly above.

Example

Find the angle between the edge AE and the base ABCD of this pyramid.

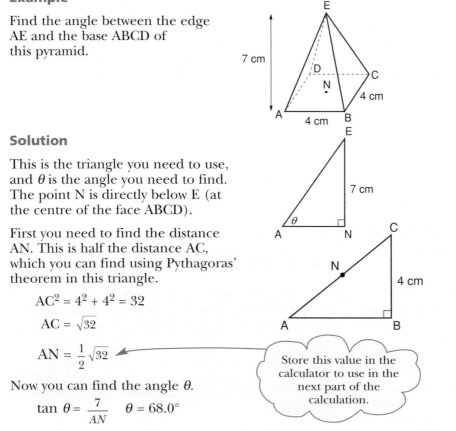

Solution

This is the triangle you need to use, and θ is the angle you need to find. The point N is directly below E (at the centre of the face ABCD).

First you need to find the distance AN. This is half the distance AC, which you can find using Pythagoras' theorem in this triangle.

$$AC^2 = 4^2 + 4^2 = 32$$

$$AC = \sqrt{32}$$

$$AN = \frac{1}{2}\sqrt{32}$$

> Store this value in the calculator to use in the next part of the calculation.

Now you can find the angle θ.

$$\tan \theta = \frac{7}{AN} \qquad \theta = 68.0°$$

Explain why the angle EAN, found in the example above, is the smallest possible angle between the line EA and the plane ABCD. (Consider some other possible angles, such as EAB.)

Exercise 6.2

1 Find the values of *a* – *h* in these triangles.

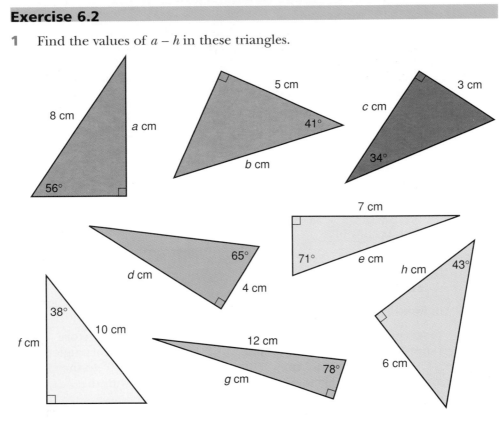

2 Find the angles marked with letters in these triangles.

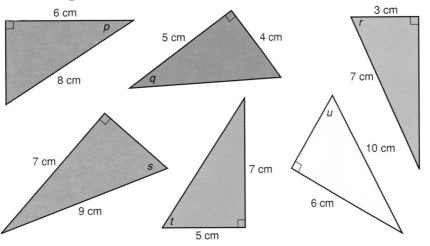

3 a) Lucy is standing 50 m from the foot of a tower. The angle of elevation of the top of the tower is 38°. How high is the tower?

b) Emily is standing on top of the tower. She can see her car which she knows is parked 350m away.

What is the angle of depression of the car from the top of the tower?

Exercise 6.2 *continued*

4 **a)** A ship sails 30 km on a bearing of 325°. How far north and how far west is it from its starting point?

   b) The ship then sails a further 40 km due east. On what bearing must it sail to get back to its starting point?

5 In this cuboid, X is the centre of the face ABCD and Y is the midpoint of the line CG. Find the angle between

   a) the diagonal AG and the horizontal;

   b) the line XG and the horizontal;

   c) the line AY and the plane ADHE;

   d) the lines HX and GX.

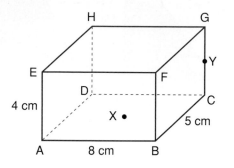

6 The diagram shows part of the roof of a new out-of-town superstore. The point X is vertically above A, and ABCD is a horizontal rectangle in which CD = 5.6 m, BC = 6.4 m. The line XB is inclined at 70° to the horizontal. Calculate the angle that the ridge XC makes with the horizontal.

MEI

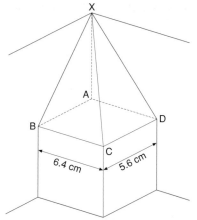

7 The diagram shows part of a tripod. It stands on horizontal ground.
Each of the three legs, TA, TB, TC is 50 cm long.
They each make the same angle with the ground.

Triangle ABC is equilateral, with each side 66 cm long.

The point O is on the ground vertically below T.

   a) Show that OB is 38 cm long, to the nearest centimetre.

   b) Taking OB as 38 cm, calculate the angle TB makes with the ground.

MEI

Angles greater than 90°

So far you have used the sine, cosine and tangent only of angles between 0° and 90°, because you have been working with right-angled triangles. In fact your calculator will give you a value for sine, cosine and tangent of any angle.

The diagram shows a circle with radius 1 unit.

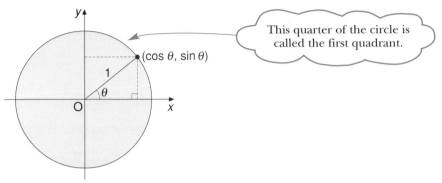

The x co-ordinate of the red point on the circumference of the circle is equal to cos θ, and the y co-ordinate is equal to sin θ.

 Explain why this is the case.

Imagine that the red point is moving anticlockwise round the circumference of the circle, so that θ increases. In the diagram below, θ is 120°.

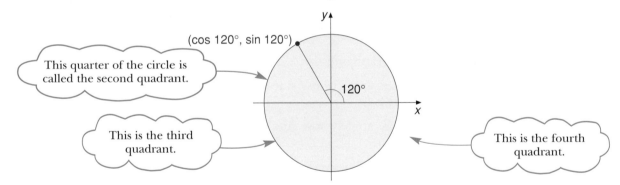

In the second quadrant, when θ is between 90° and 180°, you can see that the x co-ordinate is negative, but the y co-ordinate is positive. So cos θ is negative and sin θ is positive.

Check on your calculator that cos 120° is negative and sin 120° is positive.

Is tan 120° positive or negative? Check on your calculator.

Are sin θ, cos θ and tan θ positive or negative in the third quadrant?

What about the fourth quadrant?

Exercise 6.3

1 a) Draw a set of axes with x from 0 to 360 and y from −1 to 1. A suitable scale is 1 cm = 20 on the x axis and 1 cm = 0.2 on the y axis.

b) Use a calculator to find the values of sin $x°$ for multiples of 10° between 0° and 360°. Plot these values to draw the graph of $y = \sin x°$.

2 a) Use your graph from **1** to find:

(i) two angles with a sine of 0.6;

(ii) two angles with a sine of 0.3;

(iii) two angles with a sine of −0.2.

b) What is the relationship between the two angles in each case?

c) Use the circle diagram on the left page to explain why this is so.

3 Draw another set of axes to the same scale and plot the graph of $y = \cos x°$ for angles between 0° and 360°.

4 a) Use your graph to find:

(i) two angles with a cosine of 0.7;

(ii) two angles with a cosine of −0.4;

(iii) two angles with a cosine of −0.8.

b) What is the relationship between the two angles in each case?

c) Use the circle diagram on the left page to explain why this is so.

5 a) Compare the sine graph and the cosine graph. What do you notice?

b) (i) Find the smallest angle whose sine is 0.4 and the smallest angle whose cosine is 0.4.

(ii) Find the smallest angle whose sine is 0.7 and the smallest angle whose cosine is 0.7.

c) What is the relationship between the two angles in each case?

d) Use your answer to part a) to explain why this is so.

6 Draw another set of axes, this time with the y axis from −6 to 6.

Plot the graph of $y = \tan x°$ for values of x between 0 and 360.

7 What happens to the graphs at $x = 90$ and $x = 270$? Use the circle diagram on the left to explain why this is the case.

8 a) Use your graph to find:

(i) two angles with a tangent of 0.2;

(ii) two angles with a tangent of 0.5;

(iii) two angles with a tangent of −0.6.

b) What is the relationship between the two angles in each case?

The sine, cosine and tangent functions

In the last exercise you should have found that the graphs of the sine, cosine, and tangent functions look like this.

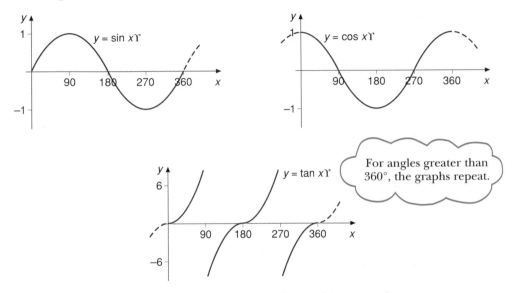

For angles greater than 360°, the graphs repeat.

You should have also found the following relationships:

$$\sin x = \sin (180 - x)$$
$$\cos x = \cos (360 - x)$$
$$\tan x = \tan (180 + x)$$

These relationships are important because they allow you to find other angles with a particular sine, cosine or tangent as well as the one your calculator gives you.

You should also have found the relationship:

$$\cos \theta = \sin (90 - \theta)$$

Example

Solve these equations for angles between 0° and 360°.

a) $\sin \theta = 0.8$ **b)** $\cos \theta = -0.1$ **c)** $\tan \theta = -0.4$

You can see from the graphs above that there are two angles to find in each case.

Solution

a) Using the inverse sine function on a calculator gives $\theta = 53.1°$.

There is one other angle: it is $180 - 53.1° = 126.9°$

b) Using the inverse cosine function on a calculator gives $\theta = 95.7°$.

There is one other angle: it is $360° - 95.7° = 264.3°$

c) Using the inverse tangent function on a calculator gives $\theta = -21.8°$ which is not in the required interval.

You can add 180° to get one angle between 0° and 360°, which is 158.2°. To find the other angle you add 180° again: $180° + 158.2° = 338.2°$.

Exercise 6.4

1 Solve the following equations for values of x between $0°$ and $360°$.

    a) $\sin x = 0.75$ **b)** $\tan x = -2.5$

    c) $\cos x = 0.81$ **d)** $\sin x = -0.34$

    e) $\cos x = -0.59$ **f)** $\tan x = 0.97$

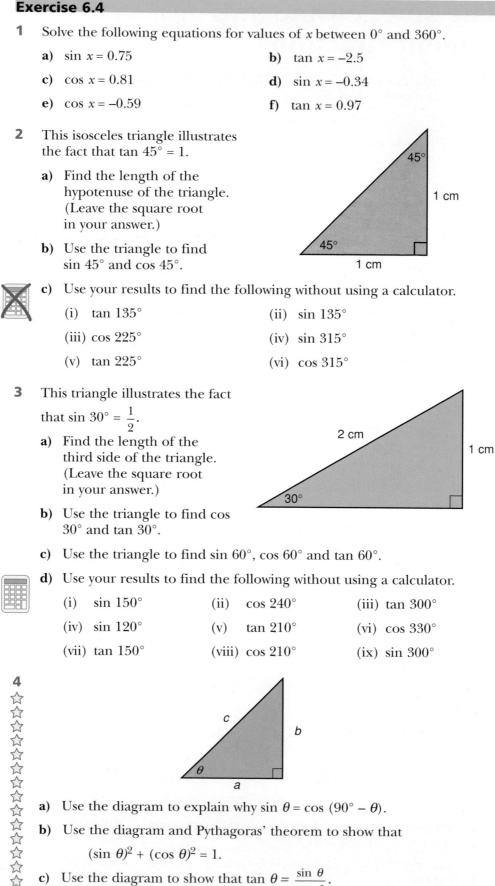

2 This isosceles triangle illustrates the fact that $\tan 45° = 1$.

    a) Find the length of the hypotenuse of the triangle. (Leave the square root in your answer.)

    b) Use the triangle to find $\sin 45°$ and $\cos 45°$.

    c) Use your results to find the following without using a calculator.

        (i) $\tan 135°$ (ii) $\sin 135°$

        (iii) $\cos 225°$ (iv) $\sin 315°$

        (v) $\tan 225°$ (vi) $\cos 315°$

3 This triangle illustrates the fact that $\sin 30° = \dfrac{1}{2}$.

    a) Find the length of the third side of the triangle. (Leave the square root in your answer.)

    b) Use the triangle to find $\cos 30°$ and $\tan 30°$.

    c) Use the triangle to find $\sin 60°$, $\cos 60°$ and $\tan 60°$.

    d) Use your results to find the following without using a calculator.

        (i) $\sin 150°$ (ii) $\cos 240°$ (iii) $\tan 300°$

        (iv) $\sin 120°$ (v) $\tan 210°$ (vi) $\cos 330°$

        (vii) $\tan 150°$ (viii) $\cos 210°$ (ix) $\sin 300°$

4

    a) Use the diagram to explain why $\sin \theta = \cos (90° - \theta)$.

    b) Use the diagram and Pythagoras' theorem to show that

        $(\sin \theta)^2 + (\cos \theta)^2 = 1$.

    c) Use the diagram to show that $\tan \theta = \dfrac{\sin \theta}{\cos \theta}$.

Finishing off

Now that you have finished this chapter you should be able to:

★ use sine, cosine and tangent to find sides and angles of right-angled triangles in two or three dimensions

★ recognise and sketch the graphs of sine, cosine and tangent functions

★ use the relationships between angles which have the same sine, cosine or tangent.

Use the questions in the next exercise to check that you understand everything.

Mixed exercise 6.5

1 Find the sides and angles marked with letters in these triangles.

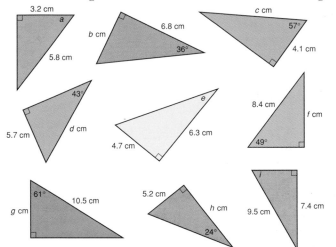

2 In this question give both answers to a sensible degree of accuracy.

The diagram shows the end ABCD of a building.

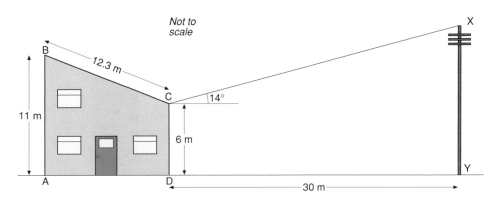

AB = 11 m, BC = 12.3 m and CD = 6 m.

a) Find the angle that CB makes with the horizontal.

b) A telegraph pole XY is 30 metres from the house.

The angle of elevation of X from C is 14°.

Find the length of the wire CX.

MEI

Mixed exercise 6.5 *continued*

3 Solve these equations for values of *x* between 0° and 360°.

    a) $\sin x = 0.81$ **b)** $\cos x = -0.64$ **c)** $\tan x = 1.6$

    d) $\cos x = 0.93$ **e)** $\sin x = -0.35$ **f)** $\tan x = -0.78$

4 The diagram shows a marquee.

A, B, C and D are four corners of a rectangle on horizontal ground.

E, F, G and H are all in the same horizontal plane and are vertically above A, B, C and D respectively.

PQ and SR are equal vertical poles such that P and S are on the ground and QE = QH = RF = RG.

AB = 18 m, BC = 10 m, AE = 2 m, QR = 12 m and PQ = 5.5 m.

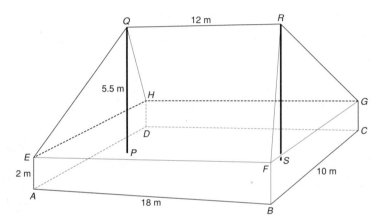

    a) Calculate the length RG.

    b) Calculate the angle between RG and the horizontal.

MEI

5 From a point P, on level ground, a surveyor measures the angle of elevation of R, the top of a building, as 32°.

He walks 12 metres towards the building to point Q and measures the angle of elevation of R as 57°.

X is the point on PR such that angle PXQ = 90°.

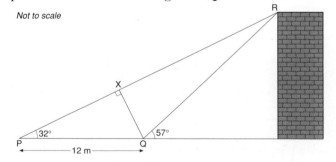

    a) Show that QX = 6.36 m

    b) (i) Explain why angle PRQ is 25°;

        (ii) hence find the length of QR.

    c) Calculate the height of the building.

MEI

Straight lines and curves

Straight line graphs

You will probably find that the work in this section is revision.

Many real-life situations give rise to straight line graphs, such as that in the following example.

Dan runs a delivery service. He has a standing charge and a cost per mile. Here is a list of his charges. They form a sequence.

How much does he charge per mile?

What is the standing charge?

Miles	Cost
1	£1.80
2	£2.10
3	£2.40
4	£2.70
5	£3.00

This can be shown in a graph of cost against distance.

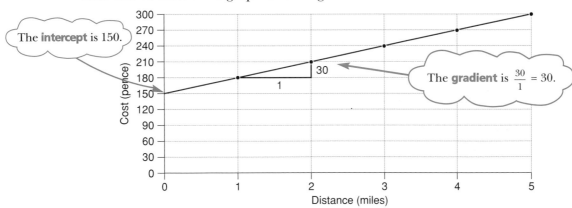

The **intercept** is 150.

The **gradient** is $\frac{30}{1} = 30$.

This line has gradient 30 and intercept 150, so its equation is $y = 30x + 150$.

How does this relate to Dan's charges?

How does it relate to the expression for the nth term of the sequence?

Exercise 7.1

1 State the gradient and the intercept of each of the following lines.

a) $y = 2x + 3$ **b)** $y = 3x - 5$

c) $y = 5x + 4$ **d)** $y = -2x - 5$

e) $2y = x - 6$ **f)** $3y = x - 4$

2 Find the equation of each of the following lines.

a) Gradient 5; intercept 3.

b) Gradient 4; intercept −1.

c) Gradient −3; intercept −2.

d) Gradient $\frac{1}{2}$; intercept 5.

e) Passing through (2, 5) and (4, 9).

f) Passing through (−1, 0) and (2, −3).

3 Find the equations of the lines in the following graphs.

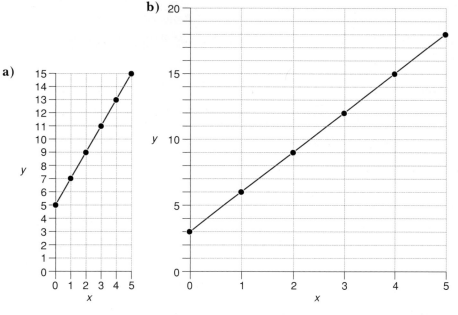

4 Nasim is a well-borer. His charges increase with the depth at which he must work, as shown in this graph.

a) How much does he charge for the third metre?

b) How much would it cost to have a well 3 metres deep?

c) How much does he charge for the nth metre?

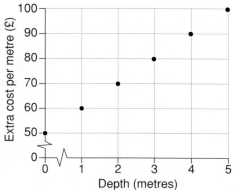

Exercise 7.1 *continued*

5 Estimate the equation of a line of best fit for the following scatter graphs.

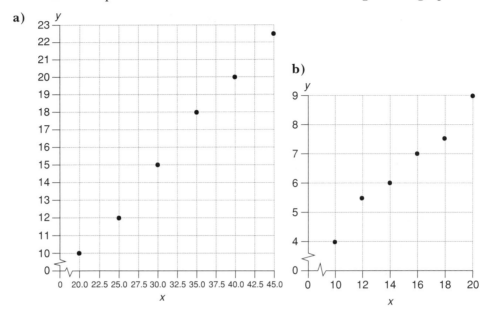

a)

b)

6 In an experiment the length of a rod is measured at different temperatures.

Temperature $T\,°C$	10	30	40	60
Length x cm	201.4	203.0	203.8	205.4

a) Plot the graph of x against T.

b) Find the numbers a and b in the equation $x = aT + b$.

c) State what the numbers a and b mean.

7 The graph shows Jamila's salary for her first 5 years of work. She received an increase in salary at the end of each year she worked.

a) What was her starting salary?

b) What was her annual increase?

c) What is her salary in year n?

d) What was Jamila's salary when she had worked for two and a half years?

e) How could you show this on the graph?

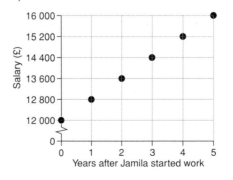

Curves

In the previous section you saw that if you have a straight line graph you can find its equation.

 What is the minimum information you need to find the equation of a straight line?

When it comes to a curve, the situation is not quite so easy. Look at this sketch through the points (0, 1) and (1, 2). These two points fit the equations

$$y = x + 1$$
$$y = x^2 + 1$$
$$y = x^3 + 1$$

among others.

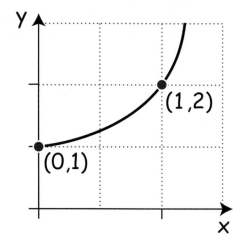

 Sketch these curves (or enter them on a calculator). Can you decide which equation refers to the sketch curve above?

State two other curves which also go through (0, 1) and (1, 2)?

Finding the equation of a curve

One way of finding the equation of a curve is to plot the points using a different quantity on the horizontal axis.

Take these points:

x	0	1	2	3	4	5
y	3	5	11	21	35	53

When y is plotted against x, the result is a curve. It could be a quadratic of the form $y = ax^2 + b$.

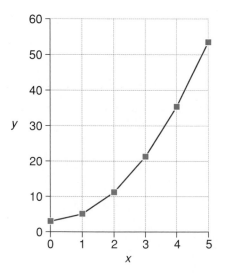

To test whether this is the case, draw the graph of y against x^2.

The first step is to make a new table of values.

x	0	1	2	3	4	5
x^2	0	1	4	9	16	25
y	3	5	11	21	35	53

The graph comes out to be a straight line and that means that the equation is indeed of the form $y = ax^2 + b$. We guessed right.

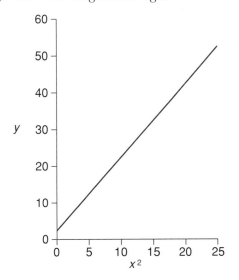

This graph contains 3 important pieces of information:

- as already mentioned, the straight line tells you the curve is of the form $y = ax^2 + b$

- the gradient gives the value of a; in this case $a = 2$

- the intercept gives the value of b; in this case $b = 3$.

So the equation of the original curve is

$$y = 2x^2 + 3.$$

Finding the right form of the equation

Notice that if the graph of y against x^2 had not been a straight line, you would know that the form $y = ax^2 + b$ was wrong.

In that case you might try plotting y against x^3, hoping the form would be $y = ax^3 + b$.

So far you would be entitled to think that finding the equation of a curve starts with guesswork; guessing the right form to try. That need not always be the case. Sometimes the situation may give you a clue; if, for instance, y is the price (in £) of a square piece of glass size x m, you would expect x^2 to be involved since this is the area of the glass.

You can also use the **method of differences** to look for quadratic, cubic, quartic etc. forms. Take the values of y in the example above (where $y = 2x^2 + 3$).

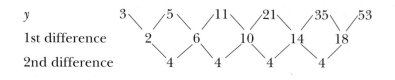

You will see that the 2nd differences are all the same and this shows you that the equation is of quadratic form, i.e. power 2.

If you have to go to the 3rd differences before they are all the same, the form is power 3, a cubic. And so on.

 Construct a table of values for $y = 2x^3 - 5$ *and show that the third differences are indeed always the same.*

Investigation

Use algebra to show that the second differences for $y = ax^2 + b$ must be the same. Take values of x of n, $n + 1$, $n + 2$ and $n + 3$.

What about $y = ax^3 + b$?

 The method you have learnt in this section depends on turning a curve into a straight line. It is useful when it works, but there are many cases when it does not. It would not, for example, help you with the curve of $y = 2x^2 - 3x + 4$.

 Find the equations of two other curves for which this method will not be helpful.

The fact that the relationship between y and x is quadratic does not mean it must be of the form $y = ax^2 + b$. It could be $y = ax^2 + bx + c$. In the same way $y = ax^3 + b$ is not the only form of a cubic relationship.

Exercise 7.2

1   In each of the following the points lie on a curve of either the form
$y = ax^2 + b$ or of the form $y = ax^3 + b$.

  a)   Make out a differences table and use it to decide which is the right
form.

  b)   Plot y against x^2 or x^3.

  c)   Find the values of a and b, and so write down the equation.

  (i)

x	1	2	3	4	5
y	10	19	34	55	82

  (ii)

x	1	2	3	4	5
y	6	34	110	258	502

  (iii)

x	1	2	3	4	5
y	4.1	4.4	4.9	5.6	6.5

  (iv)

x	1	2	3	4	5
y	7.5	9	11.5	15	19.5

  (v)

x	1	2	3	4	5
y	−3	0.5	10	28.5	59

2   A curve is believed to have an equation of the form $y = \dfrac{a}{x} + b$.

The table gives the co-ordinates of five points on the curve.

x	1	2	3	4	5
y	35	23	19	17	15.8

Plot $y = \dfrac{1}{x}$ and find the equation of the curve.

Exercise 7.2 *continued*

3 A curve is believed to have an equation of the form $y = \frac{a}{x^2} + b$.

The table gives the co-ordinates of five points on the curve.

x	1	2	3	4	5
y	45	18	13	11.25	10.44

Plot $y = \frac{1}{x^2}$ and find the equation of the curve.

4 Darren has broken a window and goes to a glazier to buy a new piece of glass. He sees this list of prices.

GLASS SQUARES
for
SHOP WINDOWS (etc.)

Length (m)	Cost (£)
1	8
2	23
3	48
4	83
5	128

a) Find the formula that the glazier has used to work out the costs.

b) Darren wants a piece 50 cm × 50 cm. How much will it cost him?

5 The Highway Code gives the following information about stopping distances.

Speed in mph v	Thinking distance in feet	Braking distance in feet	Total stopping distance in feet, d	$\frac{d}{v}$
30	30	45	75	
50	50	125	175	
70	70	245	315	

The stopping distance, d, and the speed, v, are related by the formula $d = av + bv^2$.

a) What is the formula for $\frac{d}{v}$?

b) Copy and complete the table of values.

c) Draw the graph of $\frac{d}{v}$ against v.

d) Use your graph to find a and b.

Growth and decay

AVONFORD STAR

5 January 2004		35p

DRAMA ON THE MOOR

Severe blizzards and snowdrifts have cut off the remote moorland village of Hightop. Completely cut off from the rest of the world, young Sharon Bigley (16)

and three of her friends were struck down by an infection at midday on the 2nd January. Local doctor James Allan is expressing grave concern because the

number of cases is doubling every day and he has only enough antibiotics to treat 100 patients.

According to this report the graph of the number ill against the dates should look like this.

How many people were ill by midnight on January 5th?

At what time did the doctor run out of antibiotics?

A curve like this which increases by a constant factor (in this case ×2 per day) is called an **exponential growth curve**. The factor is sometimes called the **growth factor**.

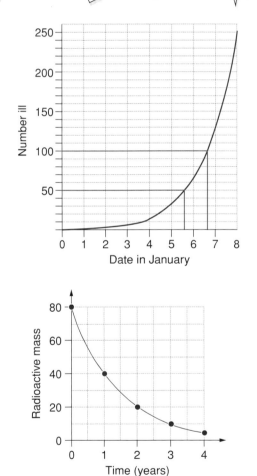

If the factor is less than 1, this curve decreases and in this case it is called an **exponential decay curve**. The factor is then sometimes called the **reducing factor**.

An example of exponential decay occurs with radioactivity. The mass of a radioactive substance decays at a rate which is proportional to the amount that is present.

In this example by the end of each year it is half of what it was at the start.

What term is used to describe the period of one year in this example?

What other situations lead to growth and decay curves?

When an equation is used to describe a real-life situation, it is said to give a **mathematical model**. Often the mathematical model is not exactly what happens, but close enough to be useful.

Trigonometrical functions

Situations where events recur regularly are called **cyclic**. These can often be modelled using a sine or cosine curve, as in the next example.

Ben works for Avonford Council and is preparing a cash flow forecast for next year. In order to calculate the amount needed to spend on street lighting, he needs to know the hours, h, when street lighting is needed for each day of the year, d.

He finds that the formula connecting h and d is given by

$$h = 12 + 5\sin\frac{360d}{365}$$

The graph shows how the number of hours of non-daylight, h, in Avonford changes during the year, where d is the number of days after 21st September.

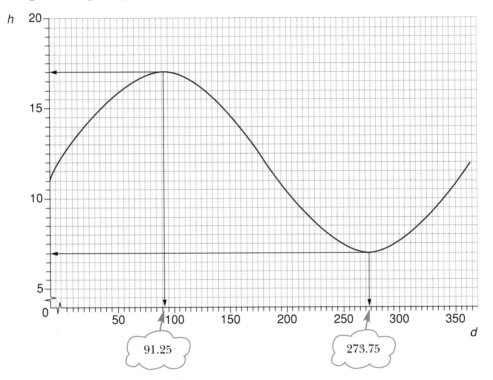

Mid-summer's day is the day with the greatest hours of daylight, and least hours of lighting up time. From the graph there are 7 hours of non-daylight on mid-summer's day, which occurs 273.75 days after 21st September.

 Mid-winter's day is the day with least hours of daylight and longest lighting up period. How many hours of lighting up time are there on mid-winter's day?

How many days after 21st September will mid-winter's day occur?

Why does d start from 21st September?

When is the springtime equivalent to 21st September?

 What other situations are cyclic?

Exercise 7.4

In this exercise use a graphical calculator or sketch the graphs and use your knowledge of trigonometry.

1 Solve the equations for $0 \le x \le 360°$ using the following graphs.

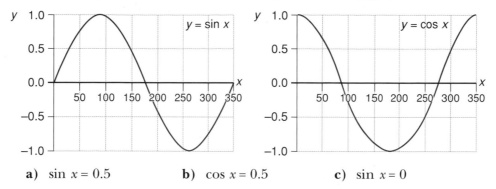

a) $\sin x = 0.5$ **b)** $\cos x = 0.5$ **c)** $\sin x = 0$

2 The depth of water in metres in a harbour entrance over a 24-hour period starting at midnight is $d = 7 - 2 \sin (30t)°$ metres where t is the number of hours after midnight on Wednesday.

The graph shows the depth of water in the harbour entrance for the first 12 hours of the 24-hour period.

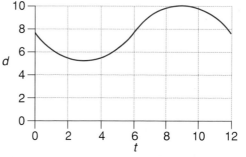

a) Copy and complete the graph for the rest of the 24-hour period.

b) What is the greatest and least depth of water in the harbour?

c) At what time is low tide on Thursday morning?

d) A fishing boat needs a depth of 6 metres to enter the harbour. Using the graph or otherwise, state the times over the 24-hour period during which it is impossible for the boat to do this.

3 The graph of $y = 5 + 3 \sin 30t$ shows the level of water in a tidal river passing under a bridge The height of the bridge is 10 metres. Draw the graph for $0 \le t \le 12$.

a) At what time is   **(i)** high tide   **(ii)** low tide?

b) How deep is the water at   **(i)** high tide   **(ii)** low tide?

c) A vessel needs 3.5 metres of water to keep it afloat. Find the times between which it cannot pass under the bridge.

d) The mast of a yacht requires a clearance of 3.5 metres. Find the times between which it can pass under the bridge.

4 A water board knows that the amount of water stored in a reservoir, W million gallons, is given by $W = 2 + \cos 30t$, where t is the number of the month in the year (i.e. $t = 1$ for January, etc.)

a) Find the volume of water in the reservoir in
   (i) February   **(ii)** August.

b) The local council would need to consider water rationing in any month in which the volume of water stored is likely to be less than 1.13 million gallons. When is this likely to be?

Finishing off

Now that you have finished this chapter you should be able to:

★ use graphs to help you express general laws in symbolic form

★ express relationships in linear form and find the connections graphically

★ use graphs to model real-life situations and solve associated problems.

Use the questions in the next exercise to check that you understand everything.

Mixed exercise 7.5

1 Wayne and Simon are carrying out an experiment in which they measure the length of an elastic band when different weights are suspended from the lower end.

Weight of body W g	0	1	2	3	4	5	6
Length of band L cm	8	9	8.9	10.5	11.3	12.3	13.3

a) Draw the graph of L against W.

b) Which point do you think might be wrong?

They repeat the experiment for that point and get a value of L of 9.7.

c) Is this new result consistent with the overall pattern?

d) Suggest an equation giving L in terms of W.

2 Water runs out of a tank so that after t minutes there are g gallons left where $g = a - bt$.

Time t in minutes	0	1	2	3	4	5	6
Water in tank g gallons	700	650	600	550	500	450	400

a) Find a and b.

b) How long does it take to empty the tank?

Mixed exercise 7.5 *continued*

3   A hose squirts a stream of water horizontally. The height of the stream, y metres, at a distance x metres from the hose is estimated to be as follows.

Horizontal distance x	0	1	2	3	4	5	6
Vertical distance y	5	4.95	4.8	4.55	4.2	3.75	3.2

a)   Use the method of differences to show that the relationship between y and x is quadratic.

b)   Draw a graph of y against x^2 and obtain an equation connecting x and y.

4   A quantity of gas is contained in a cylinder and subjected to various pressures. The volume occupied by the gas under different pressures is shown in the table.

Pressure P	1	2	3	4	5	6
Volume V	36	18	12	9	8	6

a)   Draw a graph of V against $\dfrac{1}{P}$.

b)   One value is incorrect. Which value is it and what should it be?

c)   Obtain an equation connecting P and V.

5   A voltmeter was used to test the values of the resistance R (in ohms) at various voltages V.

Voltage V	50	60	70	80	90	100	110
Resistance R	85	97	117	121	133	145	157

a)   Draw a graph of R against V.

b)   One value is incorrect. Which value is it and what should it be?

c)   Obtain an equation connecting R and V.

6   A ball was thrown into the air and its flight recorded on video. By the use of freeze frames it was possible to measure the vertical height, H, of the ball at any given time, T.

Time T in seconds	0	1	2	3	4	5	6
Vertical height H	0	45	80	105	120	125	120

a)   Use the method of differences to show that the relationship between H and T is quadratic.

b)   Draw the graph of H against T^2 and explain how this tells you that the equation is not of the form $H = aT^2 + b$.

c)   Draw the graph of $\dfrac{H}{T}$ against T for $1 \leq T \leq 6$ and use it to obtain the equation connecting H and T.

Mixed exercise 7.5 *continued*

7   The height, H metres, of a storm wave in an offshore wind, and its distance from the shore, D metres, is given in the table.

Distance D	900	1600	2000	2500	3000	3600	4900
Height H	1.5	2	2.24	2.5	2.74	3	3.5

It is suspected that $H = k\sqrt{D}$. Draw a graph to check this and find k.

8   Sharon has eaten a poisonous berry, and is being treated in hospital. The amount of poison in her body is monitored and the readings are shown in the table.

Time t (hours)	0	1	2	3	4	5
Amount of poison (units)	50	35	24.5	17.15	12	8.4

a)   Show that these figures are consistent with the amount decaying exponentially with a reducing factor of 0.7 per hour.

b)   Write down a formula for the amount of poison, A units, at time t hours.

9   Steven's cradle is hanging by a spring from the ceiling. Once it is set moving, the height H metres, of the cradle above the floor is given by $H = 1.4 - 0.2 \cos 30t$ where t is the number of seconds after starting to move.

a)   Illustrate this graphically for $0 \leq t \leq 60$.

b)   State the greatest and least values of H.

c)   Find H when $t = 8$.

d)   When is the height first 1.6 metres above the floor?

e)   How many complete cycles does the cradle go through in one minute?

10   The depth of water, d metres, in a tidal channel, is given by $d = 4 + 2 \sin 30t$, where t is the number of hours after midnight.

a)   Write down the depths of high and low water.

b)   What is the depth of water at 5 p.m.?

c)   Find the first time after 1 a.m. at which the water is 5 metres deep.

It takes a ship 45 minutes to pass through the channel.

d)   A ship requires at least 3 metres depth of water. Find the latest time before 9 a.m. that this ship can enter the channel in order to pass through.

e)   For safety reasons no ship may enter the channel until the preceding ship has left it. A convoy arrives at the channel at noon. How many ships can pass through during the afternoon?

Chapter 8

Transformations

Before you start this chapter you should be able to:

★ draw the graph of a function from its equation

★ recognise and use translations and reflections

★ understand and use function notation

★ draw and sketch graphs of sin x and cos x for any angle.

Transforming graphs

Drawing an accurate graph of $y = f(x)$ by plotting points and joining them (usually with a smooth curve) can take a long time. Sometimes there is no need for such detailed work – often just sketching the general shape and position of a curve is enough. This chapter shows how transformations can help you do this.

Translations

The blue curve is the graph of $y = x^2$. Note that it is symmetrical about $x = 0$ (the y axis), and has a minimum point at $(0, 0)$.

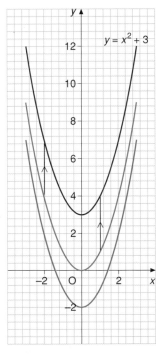

If the equation is changed to $y = x^2 + 3$ then, for every value of x, the value of y is 3 more than before. So the graph of $y = x^2 + 3$ is the same shape as $y = x^2$ but shifted up 3 units: the red curve is the image of the original blue curve when translated by $\binom{0}{3}$.

The axis of symmetry is still $x = 0$, but the minimum point is now $(0, 3)$.

 If the green curve is the image of the original blue curve when translated by $\binom{0}{-2}$, what is the equation of the green curve?

 Find the vector of the translation which maps the graph of $y = x^2$ to the graph of $y = x^2 + b$. Where is the minimum point of $y = x^2 + b$, and what is the equation of its axis of symmetry?

Working out $x^2 + 3$ is a combination of two processes: square, then add 3. If you do these in the reverse order (add 3, then square) you get $(x + 3)^2$. The way in which the graphs of $y = x^2$ and $y = (x + 3)^2$ are related is clear from this table.

x	−6	−5	−4	−3	−2	−1	0	1	2	3
x^2	36	25	16	9	4	1	0	1	4	9
$x + 3$	−3	−2	−1	0	1	2	3	4	5	6
$(x + 3)^2$	9	4	1	0	1	4	9	16	25	36

The coloured shading shows that the graph of $y = (x + 3)^2$ is the same shape as $y = x^2$, but shifted 3 units to the left, i.e. translated by $\begin{pmatrix} -3 \\ 0 \end{pmatrix}$. It may seem strange that *adding* 3 moves the curve to the *left*. To remember this, note that the minimum point is where $x + 3 = 0$, i.e. $x = −3$.

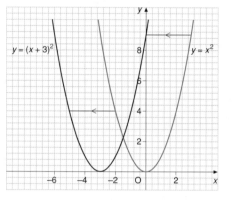

 Sketch $y = x^2$ *and its image under* $\begin{pmatrix} 5 \\ 0 \end{pmatrix}$. *What is the equation of the image curve?*

 Find the vector of the translation which maps the graph of $y = x^2$ *to the graph of* $y = (x + a)^2$. *Where is the minimum point of* $y = (x + a)^2$, *and what is the equation of its axis of symmetry?*

These horizontal and vertical shifts can be combined. For example, to sketch the graph of $y = (x − 2)^2 + 4$ you start with $y = x^2$ (blue curve), translate this by $\begin{pmatrix} 2 \\ 0 \end{pmatrix}$ (green curve), and then translate this by $\begin{pmatrix} 0 \\ 4 \end{pmatrix}$ to reach the final red curve.

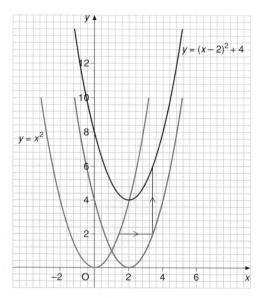

The minimum point is (2, 4), and the axis of symmetry is $x = 2$.

Does the order of the translations make any difference to the end result?

With practice you can go straight from $y = x^2$ to $y = (x − 2)^2 + 4$ by the single translation $\begin{pmatrix} 2 \\ 4 \end{pmatrix}$. The general result is that $y = x^2$ is mapped to $y = (x + a)^2 + b$ by the translation $\begin{pmatrix} -a \\ b \end{pmatrix}$.

 Where is the minimum point of $y = (x + a)^2 + b$, *and what is the equation of its axis of symmetry?*

Exercise 8.1

1   Sketch on the same axes the graphs of

   a) $y = x^2$

   b) $y = x^2 + 4$

   c) $y = x^2 - 3$

   d) $y = (x + 4)^2$

   e) $y = (x - 3)^2$.

2   Sketch the graphs with these equations.
For each one give the co-ordinates of the minimum point and the
equation of the axis of symmetry.

   a) $y = (x - 3)^2 + 4$

   b) $y = (x + 1)^2 - 1$

   c) $y = (x + 0.5)^2 + 2.3$

   d) $y = \left(x - \dfrac{5}{2}\right)^2 - 7$.

3   Each of these graphs is a translation of $y = x^2$.
Find the equation of each graph in the form

   a) $y = (x + a)^2 + b$

   b) $y = x^2 + px + q$.

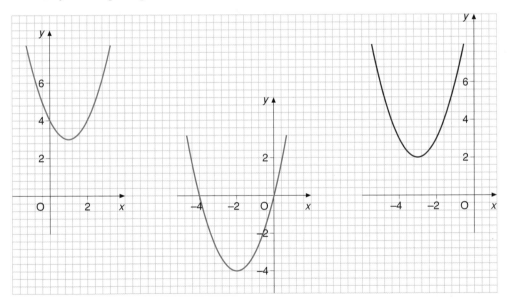

Reflections

If the equation $y = x^2$ is changed to $y = -x^2$ then the sign of each value of y is reversed: the graph of $y = x^2$ (blue curve) is mapped to the graph of $y = -x^2$ (red curve) by reflection in the x axis.

Write down the equations of the reflections of $y = x^2 - 2$ and $y = (x - 4)^2$ in the x axis. Sketch these curves.

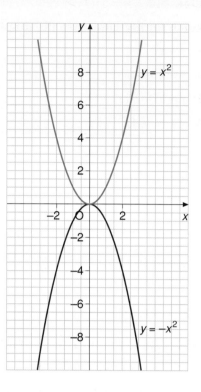

One-way stretches

If the equation $y = x^2$ is changed to $y = 2x^2$ then each value of y is multiplied by 2, so that the distance of each point of the original curve from the x axis is doubled.

The transformation which maps the blue curve to the red curve is called a **one-way stretch** with **scale factor 2** and **invariant line** the x axis.

Describe the transformation which maps the red curve to the blue curve.

The general result is that $y = x^2$ is mapped to $y = kx^2$ by the transformation in which each y co-ordinate is multiplied by k; this is called a one-way stretch with scale factor k and invariant line the x axis.

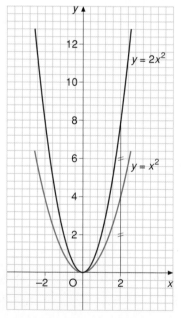

Note that if k is negative then the sign of y changes too. In particular, if $k = -1$ the one-way stretch is simply a reflection in the x axis.

How many transformations would you need to map $y = x^2$ to $y = 3x^2 + 2$? Describe them.
Do the same mapping for $y = x^2$ to $y = 3(x^2 + 2)$.
Does the order of the transformations make any difference?

Exercise 8.2

1 Sketch on the same axes the graphs of

    a) $y = x^2$ **b)** $y = -x^2 + 4$

    c) $y = 3 - x^2$ **d)** $y = -(x + 4)^2$

    e) $y = -(x - 3)^2$

2 Sketch on the same axes the graphs of

    a) $y = -x^2$ **b)** $y = 3x^2$

    c) $y = -2x^2$ **d)** $y = \frac{1}{2}(x + 4)^2$

    e) $y = 2x^2 - 3$

3 Sketch the graphs with these equations.
For each one give the co-ordinates of the minimum or maximum point and
the equation of the axis of symmetry.

    a) $y = 8 - 2x^2$ **b)** $y = 3(x + 1)^2 - 3$

    c) $y = \frac{1}{2}(x - 6)^2 - 12$ **d)** $y = 10 - \frac{1}{10}(x + 10)^2$

4 The diagram shows the path of a ball after Chris has thrown it. The level
ground is the x axis. The equation of the path is $y = 17 - \frac{1}{25}(x - 20)^2$,
where x and y are measured in metres, and the ball leaves Chris's hand at
$(0, h)$. Find

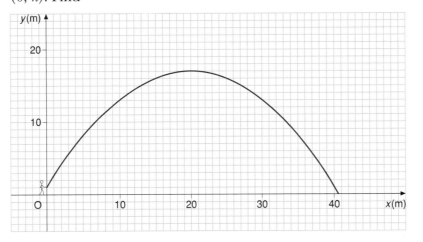

    a) the value of h

    b) the greatest height reached by the ball

    c) the horizontal distance travelled by the ball before it hits the ground.

Chris now climbs onto a platform 2 m high, and then throws the ball just
as before. Find

    d) the equation of the new path

    e) the new horizontal distance travelled by the ball.

Investigation

Investigate the ways in which the line $y = x$ can be mapped to the line
$y = mx + c$. Can you use a single transformation?

Transformations of sin x and cos x

In Chapter 6 you drew the graphs of $y = \sin x$ and $y = \cos x$. Here they are as a reminder.

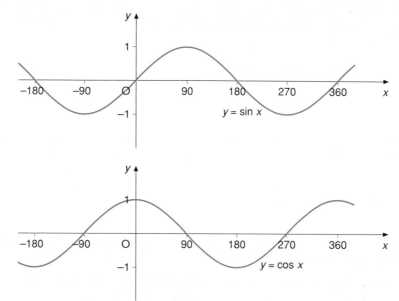

The sine and cosine curves are the same size and shape (i.e. they are congruent), but differently located on the axes. There are many ways of mapping one to the other; for example, the translation $\begin{pmatrix} -90 \\ 0 \end{pmatrix}$ maps sin x to cos x (remember that x is measured in degrees).

 Find a) a translation,   b) a reflection,   c) a rotation which maps the graph of $y = \sin x$ *to itself.*

 Sketch the graphs of $y = \sin x$ *and* $y = \cos x$ *on the same axes.*
Find a) a translation,   b) a reflection which maps cos x *to sin* x.

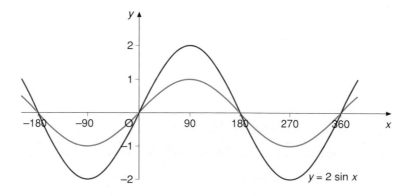

To sketch the graph of $y = 2\sin x$ you can start with $y = \sin x$ (blue curve) and double all the y values to get the red curve. You have applied the one-way stretch with scale factor 2 and invariant line the x axis. Since the maximum and minimum values of sin x are 1 and −1, the maximum and minimum values of 2sin x are 2 and −2 respectively.

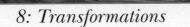
 Sketch the graphs of y = cos x *and* y = 3 cos x *on the same axes. Describe the transformation.*

Since the values of sin x and cos x are unchanged if x is changed by 360 (or any multiple of 360) the graphs of $y = \sin x$ and $y = \cos x$ go through a complete cycle every 360° and then repeat themselves. They are **periodic** functions, with **period** 360°.

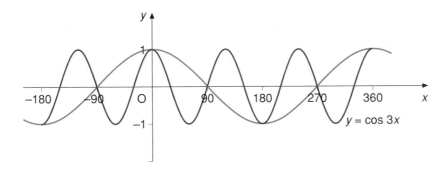

Similarly, the value of cos $3x$ is unchanged if $3x$ is changed by 360, i.e. if x is changed by 120. So cos $3x$ has period 120°.

Therefore the graph of $y = \cos 3x$ (red curve) has the same wave form as $y = \cos x$ (blue curve), but completes a cycle every 120°.

The transformation which maps $y = \cos x$ to $y = \cos 3x$ is a one-way stretch with scale factor $\frac{1}{3}$ and invariant line the y axis. (Since the scale factor is less than 1 the 'stretch' is really a 'shrink'.)

These one way stretches with different invariant lines can be combined.

The general result is that $y = \sin x$ is mapped to $y = k \sin hx$ by the one-way stretch with scale factor $\frac{1}{h}$ and invariant line the y axis followed by the one-way stretch with scale factor k and invariant line the x axis.

The same transformations map $y = \cos x$ to $y = k \cos hx$. This example shows $y = 2\cos 3x$.

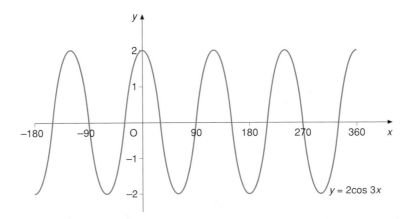

Exercise 8.3

1 Sketch the graph of $y = \sin x$ for $0 \le x \le 360$. On the same axes sketch the graphs of

a) $y = \sin 2x$

b) $y = 3\sin x$

Draw a separate sketch of $y = 3\sin 2x$.

2 These graphs are all transformations of $y = \cos x$.
For each one describe the transformation and write down the equation.

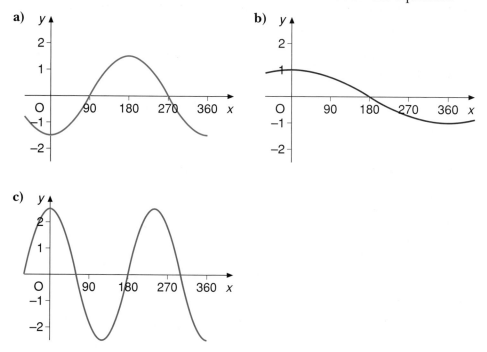

a)

b)

c)

3 The depth of water in a harbour, d metres, varies with the time, t hours, according to the formula $d = 2\sin 30t + 8$.

a) Find

(i) the greatest and least depths of water

(ii) the time from high tide to the next low tide.

b) Sketch the graph of d against t.

Transforming other functions

The ideas you have met here in connection with quadratic and trigonometric functions apply similarly to the graphs of other functions. The general results are these:

- $y = f(x)$ is mapped to $y = f(x + a)$ by the translation $\begin{pmatrix} -a \\ 0 \end{pmatrix}$

- $y = f(x)$ is mapped to $y = f(x) + b$ by the translation $\begin{pmatrix} 0 \\ b \end{pmatrix}$

- $y = f(x)$ is mapped to $y = -f(x)$ by reflection in the x axis

- $y = f(x)$ is mapped to $y = f(hx)$ by the one-way stretch with scale factor $\dfrac{1}{h}$ and invariant line the y axis

- $y = f(x)$ is mapped to $y = kf(x)$ by the one-way stretch with scale factor k and invariant line the x axis.

? *What is the equation of the reflection of* $y = f(x)$ *in the* y *axis?*

Example

The graph of $y = f(x)$ is shown.

Draw the graphs of

a) $y = -3f(x + 1)$

b) $y = f(2x) - 5$.

Solution

a)

> The transformations are translation $\begin{pmatrix} -1 \\ 0 \end{pmatrix}$ to give $f(x+1)$ followed by reflection in the x axis to give $-f(x+1)$ followed by one-way stretch, $\times 3$, x axis invariant.

b)

> The transformations are one-way stretch, $\times \frac{1}{2}$, y axis invariant to give $f(2x)$ followed by translation $\begin{pmatrix} 0 \\ -5 \end{pmatrix}$.

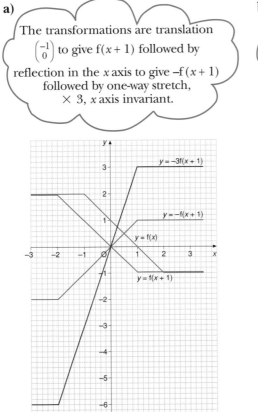

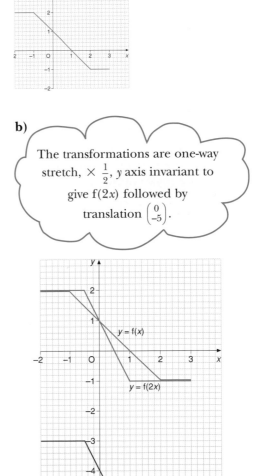

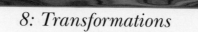

Exercise 8.4

1 The diagram shows the graph of $y = f(x)$.
Copy this graph, and on the same axes draw and label the graphs of

a) $y = -f(x)$ b) $y = f(x) + 3$ c) $y = f(x - 4)$

d) $y = 3f(x)$ e) $y = f(\frac{1}{2}x)$

2 The diagram shows the graph of $y = x^3$. Sketch this curve, and show on the same axes clearly labelled images of this curve under these transformations.

a) translation $\begin{pmatrix} 0 \\ 10 \end{pmatrix}$

b) reflection in $y = 0$

c) translation $\begin{pmatrix} 2 \\ 0 \end{pmatrix}$

d) translation $\begin{pmatrix} 2 \\ 10 \end{pmatrix}$

e) one-way stretch × 3 with $y = 0$ the invariant line.

In each case write down the equation of the image curve.

3 a) Complete the table and draw the graph of $y = \frac{2}{x}$.

x	0.1	0.2	0.3	0.4	0.5	0.6	0.7	0.8	0.9	1.0
y	20		6.67				2.86			

b) On the same axes draw these graphs

(i) $y = \frac{2}{x} + 5$ (ii) $y = \frac{1}{x}$

(iii) $y = -\frac{4}{x}$ (iv) $y = \frac{2}{x - 0.5} + 5$.

c) Describe the transformations which map $y = \frac{2}{x}$ to these graphs.

Finishing off

> **Now that you have finished this chapter you should be able to:**
>
> ★ recognise, sketch and draw images of curves under translation, reflection in the x axis and stretches
>
> ★ using graphs of sin x and cos x, sketch and draw graphs of $a \sin bx$ and $a \cos bx$, where a and b are positive integers.

Use the questions in the next exercise to check that you understand everything.

Mixed exercise 8.5

1 Sketch and label all these curves on the same axes

    a) $y = 1 - x^2$ **b)** $y = x^2 - 1$

    c) $y = 2 - 2x^2$ **d)** $y = 2x - x^2$.

    Describe the transformations which map curve **a)** to each of the other curves.

2 The diagram shows the graph of $y = (x - 1)(x - 2)(x - 3)$.

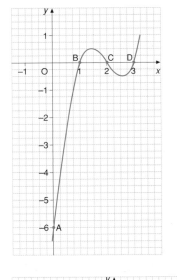

    In separate diagrams sketch the images of this curve under these transformations, giving the co-ordinates of the images of the points A, B, C, D and the equation of the image curve in each case.

    a) translation $\begin{pmatrix} -1 \\ 0 \end{pmatrix}$

    b) reflection in the x axis

    c) one-way stretch by a scale factor of 2 with the x axis invariant.

3 Copy this graph of $y = f(x)$. On the same axes draw and label the graphs of

    a) $y = f(2x)$

    b) $y = f(x + 2)$.

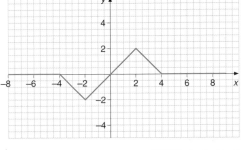

MEG (adapted)

Mixed exercise 8.5 *continued*

4   The diagram shows the curve with equation $y = f(x)$, where $f(x) = x^2 - 2x - 3$.

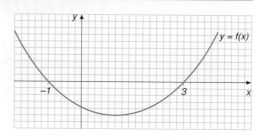

a)   On a copy of this diagram sketch the curve with equation $y = f(x - 2)$. Label the points where this curve cuts the *x* axis.

b)   The curve with equation $y = f(x)$ meets the curve with equation $y = f(x - a)$ at the point P. Calculate the *x* co-ordinate of the point P. Give your answer in terms of *a*.

c)   The curve with equation $y = x^2 - 2x - 3$ is reflected in the *y* axis. Find the equation of this new curve.

London (adapted)

5   Sketch the graph of $y = \cos x$. In separate diagrams sketch graphs of

a) $y = 2\cos x$ b) $y = -\cos x$

c) $y = -\cos 2x$ d) $y = 1 - \cos 2x$.

6   Here are sketches of the graphs $y = \sin x$ and $y = a \sin(x + b)$.

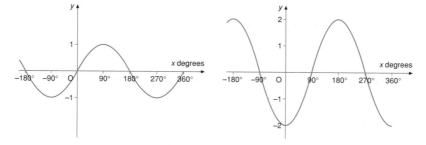

Find the values of *a* and *b*.

NEAB (adapted)

7   a)   Given that $x^2 + 4x + 8 = (x + p)^2 + q$, find the value of *p* and show that $q = 4$.

b)   The diagram shows a sketch of the curve with equation

$$y = \frac{40}{x^2 + 4}.$$

Use your result from part **a)** to sketch the curve with

equation $y = \dfrac{40}{x^2 + 4x + 8}$.

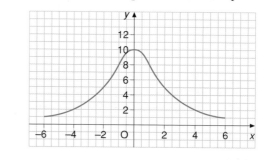

MEG

8   Given that $ax^2 + bx + c = a((x + p)^2 + q)$, show that $p = \dfrac{b}{2a}$ and find *q* in terms of *a*, *b*, *c*. By considering the graph of $y = ax^2 + bx + c$, show that the quadratic equation $ax^2 + bx + c = 0$ has no solution if $b^2 - 4ac$ is negative.

Chapter 9

Probability

Before you start this chapter you should be able to:

★ define the term 'probability'

★ understand the meanings of associated terms: 'event', 'outcome', 'fair', 'at random', 'mutually exclusive' and 'independent'

★ calculate probability from theory

★ estimate probability from past data

★ use probability to estimate the number of times an event is expected to occur

★ use tables and tree diagrams to work out probabilities.

Reminder

● Probability can be shown on a scale:

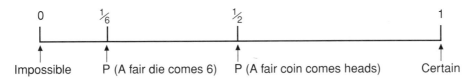

 Where would you place the probability that you will get married?

● There are two approaches to finding probability.

1. In certain situations, like tossing a coin, throwing a die, choosing a card from a pack, you can calculate probability from theory, using:

$$\text{Probability} = \frac{\text{Number of favourable outcomes}}{\text{Number of possible outcomes}}$$

This is sometimes called **relative frequency**.

So if you choose a card at random from a standard pack of 52 playing cards, the probability it is a heart is given by:

Calculated $\text{P(Heart)} = \dfrac{13}{52}$

There are 13 hearts in the pack.

$= \dfrac{1}{4}$

There are 52 cards in the pack.

2. In other situations you use data to estimate probability.

   A certain type of plant is observed to produce pink and white flowers.

   In an experiment, 100 flowers are selected; 27 are pink and the rest are white.

   Estimated $P(\text{Pink}) = \dfrac{27}{100} = 0.27$

   You may (or may not) then be able to develop a theory that allows you to explain the result.

   In the case of the flowers it may be that there are four possible combinations of two genes (AA, Aa, aA, aa). Any pair containing the dominant A gene gives white flowers. The aa combination of two recessive genes gives pink flowers. If so the probability is $\dfrac{1}{4}$ or 0.25.

 Is the probability that a coin comes down heads exactly $\dfrac{1}{2}$?

Is the probability that a baby is a girl exactly $\dfrac{1}{2}$?

 Give a situation where the possible outcomes are not equally probable.

> Not A is also sometimes written as A' or $\overline{A}$.

- The probability of an event not happening: $P(\text{Not A}) = 1 - P(A)$

- For independent events A and B:

  $P(\text{Both A and B}) = P(A) \times P(B)$

> These are often thought of as first–then events.

 A football team has won the toss in the last 10 matches. What is the probability it wins it in the next match?

A team has won its last 10 matches. What can you say about the probability of its winning the next one.

- For mutually exclusive events, X and Y:

  $P(\text{Either X or Y}) = P(X) + P(Y)$

> These are often thought of as either–or events.

 You have a pack of 52 playing cards and select one at random.

Why are the outcomes 'you draw a spade' and 'you draw a queen' not mutually exclusive?

- A tree diagram can be used to calculate the probability of two or more events.

Example

Two fair coins are tossed. What is the probability that they will come up one head and one tail?

Solution

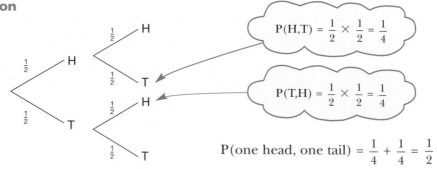

$P(H,T) = \dfrac{1}{2} \times \dfrac{1}{2} = \dfrac{1}{4}$

$P(T,H) = \dfrac{1}{2} \times \dfrac{1}{2} = \dfrac{1}{4}$

$P(\text{one head, one tail}) = \dfrac{1}{4} + \dfrac{1}{4} = \dfrac{1}{2}$

Use the questions in the next exercise to check that you remember these topics.

Review exercise 9.1

1 **a)** What is the probability of

  (i) A coin coming down heads?

  (ii) A die coming up 6?

  (iii) Selecting a spade from a pack of 52 playing cards?

  (iv) Selecting an ace from a pack of 52 playing cards?

  b) Are your answers in part **a)** calculated or estimated?

2 An ordinary die is thrown. What is the probability that it comes up

  a) An odd number

  b) A number between 1 and 6 inclusive

  c) 7

  d) not 7?

3 The numbers 0, 1, 2, … 36 are all equally likely to come up when a roulette wheel is spun.

  a) What is the probability that on any spin it comes up

  (i) 7

  (ii) not 7

  (iii) an odd number?

Septima plays roulette one evening.

Each spin she bets £20 on the number 7; if it comes up she receives £600 (and her £20 back).

The wheel is spun 200 times during the evening.

  b) How much would you expect Septima to win or lose during the evening?

4 A letter is chosen at random from those in the sentence:

  'To be or not to be, that is the question.'

  a) State the probability that the letter is

  (i) e   (ii) c   (iii) q   (iv) t   (v) any vowel.

  b) Shaun says: 'You can tell whether something is written by Shakespeare because the probability that any letter is an o in his work is $\frac{1}{6}$.'

  Explain how Shaun came to this conclusion and state, with reasons, whether you think he is right.

Review exercise 9.1 *continued*

5 Three students A, B, C were each asked to toss a coin 30 times and record whether it came down heads (H) or tails (T) each time.

They said their results were as follows:

Student A: T T T H T H T T T H T T T H T T T H T T T T H H T T T T H T T

Student B: H T H T H T H T H T H T H T H T H T H T H T H T H T H T H T

Student C: H T H T H H H H T H T T H H H H T T H T H T H T T T H H T H T T

One of the students used an unbiased coin, one used a biased coin and the remaining student did not have a coin so just made up the results.

a) (i) Which student used a biased coin?

    (ii) Estimate the probability that, the next time this coin is tossed, it will come down heads.

b) Which student just made up the results? Give a reason for your answer.

MEG

6 One summer afternoon, $\frac{3}{4}$ of the many butterflies in a garden are large whites.

a) A scientist nets a butterfly at random. What is the probability that it is not a large white?

b) The scientist nets three butterflies at random. What is the probability that

    (i) all three are large whites

    (ii) at least one is not a large white?

7 A man throws a die and tosses a coin.

a) Copy and complete this table to show the possible outcomes.

b) State the probability that:

	1	2 .	3	4	5	6
H	H1					
T			T3			

    (i) The coin comes up heads.

    (ii) The die shows 6.

    (iii) The coin comes up heads and the die shows 6.

    (iv) The coin comes up heads or the die shows six (or both).

8 A family has three children.

a) Complete the table, showing its possible composition of boys and girls.

b) Using this table, find the probability that

3 boys	BBB
2 boys, 1 girl	BBG, BGB, GBB
1 boy, 2 girls	
3 girls	

(Each entry is in the order of age)

    (i) there are no boys

    (ii) there are more boys than girls.

c) What assumption did you need to make in order to be able to do part **b)**?

Review exercise 9.1 *continued*

9 **a)** Copy and complete this diagram showing the possible totals when two fair dice are thrown.

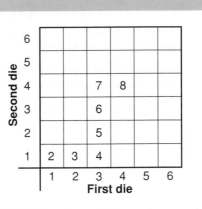

b) What is the probability of totals of:

   (i)   12

   (ii) not 12

   (iii) 7

   (iv) 4 or 6?

c) In part **a)** the dice are described as 'fair'. What does this word mean in this situation?

10 A man has two packs of 52 playing cards, one with red backs and one with blue backs. He draws one card at random from each pack.

a) By drawing a suitable tree diagram find the probabilities that

   (i)   both cards are spades

   (ii) neither card is a spade

   (iii) exactly one of the two cards is a spade.

b) Add your answers to (i), (ii) and (iii) together and explain your answer.

11 A motorist has to pass through two sets of traffic lights on his way to work. They work independently of each other. The first set has a cycle of 1 minute during which it is green for 20 seconds and not green for the remainder of the minute. The second set has a cycle of 40 seconds; it is green for 20 seconds of the cycle and not green for 20 seconds.

a) Draw a tree diagram showing whether each set of lights is green or not.

b) Find the probability that on any journey the motorist finds

   (i)   both sets green

   (ii) neither set green

   (iii) exactly one set green.

c) Explain how adding your answers to (i), (ii) and (iii) can give you a check as to whether you have made a mistake.

Conditional probability

What is the probability that you will live to the age of 90?

The answer depends on so many factors that it is almost a meaningless question. One important consideration is whether you are male or female.

The probability of reaching 90 is much greater for females. So you can give two answers to the question, namely:

P (You reach 90 if you are female)

P (You reach 90 if you are male).

Each of these is called a **conditional probability**. It is calculated or estimated in the knowledge of some condition (i.e. your gender).

What other factors affect the probability that you will live to 90?

A simple example of conditional probability arises when you draw two cards at random, without replacing the first one.

The probability that the second card is a particular card depends both on the fact that there are fewer cards to choose from, and what the first card was.

Example

Two cards are drawn at random from a pack without replacement. What is the probability that they are both aces?

Solution

This situation is shown on the tree diagram below. Notice how it only takes account of whether a card is an ace or not an ace.

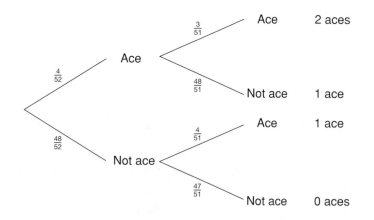

After the first ace is taken out, there are only 3 left.

When the first card is taken out there are only 51 left.

So that:

$$P(\text{Two aces}) = \frac{4}{52} \times \frac{3}{51} = \frac{12}{2652} = \frac{1}{221} \approx 0.0045$$

Notice how the probability of the second ace is conditional on what happened when the first card was drawn.

In the next example the probability is conditional on the group from which the selection is made.

Example

The figures in the table below give the number of students on different courses in the physical science department at a university (each student is on just one course), for each of the three years.

	Physics	Chemistry	Astronomy	Total
Year 1	50	70	30	150
Year 2	40	40	30	110
Year 3	40	30	30	100
Total	130	140	90	360

One student is selected, at random, to represent the university at a ceremony.

Estimate the probability that the student is from Year 1 in these cases.

a) You do not know what course the student is taking.

b) You know that the student is doing chemistry.

Solution

a) $P \text{ (Year 1)} = \dfrac{\text{Number of Year 1 students}}{\text{Total number of students}}$

$= \dfrac{150}{360}$

$= 0.42$ (to 2 decimal places)

b) P (Year 1 given that the student does chemistry)

$= \dfrac{\text{Number of Year 1 chemistry students}}{\text{Total number of chemistry students}}$

$= \dfrac{70}{140}$

$= 0.5$

Compare the probabilities of a chemistry student being selected in these two situations.

a) All the students' names are put into a hat and one is drawn out.

b) One of the years is first chosen (each with probability $\frac{1}{3}$) and then a student is chosen from that year.

Why do these two methods not give the same answer?

How is this connected to stratified sampling?

Finishing off

Now that you have completed this chapter you should be able to:

★ work with conditional probability.

Use the questions in the next exercise to check that you understand everything.

Mixed exercise 9.3

1 All female chaffinches have the same pattern of laying eggs.

The probability that any female chaffinch will lay a certain number of eggs is given in the table below.

Number of eggs	0	1	2	3	4 or more
Probability	0.1	0.3	0.3	0.2	0.1

a) Calculate the probability that a female chaffinch will lay less than three eggs.

b) Calculate the probability that two female chaffinches will lay a total of two eggs.

London

2 On Mondays, Wednesdays and Fridays, Laura and some of her friends have lunch in a particular café.

If Laura arrives at 12:30 for lunch, there is a probability of 0.7 that she is first to arrive.

One week, Laura arrives at 12:30 for lunch on all three days.

a) Find the probability that Laura will be first to arrive on all three days.

b) Find the most likely number of days in this week on which Laura will be first to arrive.

Show the calculations you do to justify your conclusion.

MEI

Mixed exercise 9.3 *continued*

3   a)

Wayne and Donna each have five cards lettered A, B, C, D and E.

Both sets of cards have been placed face down on the table.

They each pick up one of their cards at random.

(i)   What is the probability that they both pick up a card lettered B?

(ii) What is the probability that they both pick up a card with the same letter?

b) Colin and Dipak are playing a series of games each of which one of them must win.

The probability that Colin wins the first game is 0.6.

For further games the probability that Colin wins is: 0.8 if he won the previous game; 0.3 if he lost the previous game.

(i)   Calculate the probability that Dipak wins the first two games.

(ii) Calculate the probability that, in three games, Colin wins two and Dipak one.

MEG

Mixed exercise 9.3 *continued*

4   In the game of tennis a player has two serves.

If the first serve is successful the game continues.

If the first serve is not successful the player serves again. If this second serve is successful the game continues.

If both serves are unsuccessful the player has served a 'double fault' and loses the point.

Gabriella plays tennis. She is successful with 60% of her first serves and 95% of her second serves.

a)   Calculate the probability that Gabriella serves a double fault.

If Gabriella is successful with her first serve she has a probability of 0.75 of winning the point.

If she is successful with her second serve she has a probability of 0.5 of winning the point.

b)   Calculate the probability that Gabriella wins the point.

MEG

5   Peter and Asif are both taking their driving test for a motor cycle for the first time.

The table below gives the probabilities that they will pass the test at the first attempt or, if they fail the first time, the probability that they will pass at the next attempt.

	Probability of passing at first attempt	Probability of passing at next attempt if they fail the first attempt
Peter	0.6	0.8
Asif	0.7	0.7

On a particular day 1000 people will take the test for the first time.

For each person the probability that they will pass the test at the first attempt is the same as the probability that Asif will pass the test at the first attempt.

a)   Work out an estimate for how many of these 1000 people are likely to pass the test at the first attempt.

b)   Calculate the probability that both Peter and Asif will pass the test at the first attempt.

c)   Calculate the probability that Peter will pass the test at the first attempt and Asif will fail the test at the first attempt.

d)   Calculate the probability that Asif will pass the test within the first two attempts.

London

Mixed exercise 9.3 *continued*

6   Mr McTaggart lives on the island of Fluva. He walks to work but is quite often late, particularly when the weather is wet. During the last year there were 240 working days. The state of the weather, and Mr McTaggart's punctuality at work, are summarised in the table below.

		Weather	
		Dry	Wet
Mr McTaggart	On time	72	120
	Late	8	40

A day is selected at random for next year. Estimate the probability

a)   that it will be wet

b)   that Mr McTaggart will be late for work.

One day Mr McTaggart is late for work.

c)   Estimate the probability that it is wet (assuming that you do not know whether or not it really is wet).

7   A test for a disease gives a positive result 95% of the time when used on someone who has the disease. When tried on someone who does not have the disease, it gives a positive result 8% of the time. In a particular group of patients 30% of them have the disease.

a)   Copy and complete the following tree diagram:

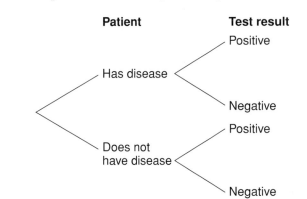

b)   Use the tree diagram to find the probability that:

(i)   a patient chosen at random has the disease and tests positive

(ii)   a patient chosen at random does not have the disease and tests negative

(iii)   the test result is correct

(iv)   the test result is wrong.

Chapter 10

Vectors

Before you start this chapter you should be able to:

★ describe and carry out a translation.

What is a vector?

Look at the diagram. It shows three points, P, Q, R and their images P′, Q′, R′ under a translation $\begin{pmatrix} 3 \\ 2 \end{pmatrix}$.

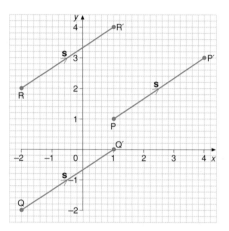

The translation is denoted by **s**. Another word for translation is **displacement**.

You will notice that **s** has a fixed length and a fixed direction but no particular position It is an example of a **vector** quantity. By contrast a quantity like volume, with size but no direction, is called a **scalar.**

 You are told 'There is a £50 note in this field'. What two questions would you ask?

Displacement is not the only vector quantity; there are many more like force and electric field.

 What other quantities are vectors?

The techniques for manipulating vectors are the same whatever they represent, so quite often you will meet examples referring to them in the abstract. Don't be confused by this; if you feel you want to get back in touch with reality, you can always think of them as displacements (or translations).

Writing vectors

There are several ways of writing a vector.

- As a letter such as **s**. Notice that bold type is used.

- As a line joining two points $\overrightarrow{PP'}$, or **PP'**.

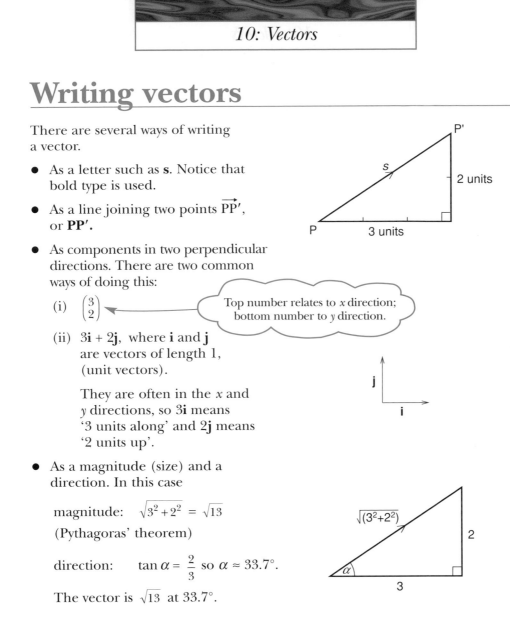

- As components in two perpendicular directions. There are two common ways of doing this:

  (i) $\begin{pmatrix} 3 \\ 2 \end{pmatrix}$ ← Top number relates to x direction; bottom number to y direction.

  (ii) $3\mathbf{i} + 2\mathbf{j}$, where **i** and **j** are vectors of length 1, (unit vectors).

  They are often in the x and y directions, so $3\mathbf{i}$ means '3 units along' and $2\mathbf{j}$ means '2 units up'.

- As a magnitude (size) and a direction. In this case

  magnitude: $\sqrt{3^2 + 2^2} = \sqrt{13}$
  (Pythagoras' theorem)

  direction: $\tan \alpha = \dfrac{2}{3}$ so $\alpha \approx 33.7°$.

  The vector is $\sqrt{13}$ at $33.7°$.

 Notice that in mathematics angles are usually measured from the x direction, anticlockwise. This is not the same convention as that for compass bearings; bearings are measured clockwise from North.

- The vector joining the origin to a point is called the **position vector** of the point.

  The position vector of a point A is $\overrightarrow{OA}$ where O is the origin.

The next two examples show you how to convert between different ways of writing the same vectors.

Exercise 10.1

*In this exercise, take the unit vectors **i** and **j** to be as shown.*

1   Look at the diagram.

Write each of these vectors in the forms $\begin{pmatrix} x \\ y \end{pmatrix}$ and $x\mathbf{i} + y\mathbf{j}$.

a) $\overrightarrow{BC}$

b) $\overrightarrow{CE}$

c) $\overrightarrow{GH}$

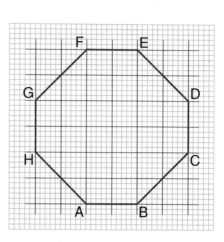

2   Look again at the diagram in Question **1**.

a) Write down two vectors that are equal to $\begin{pmatrix} 2 \\ 0 \end{pmatrix}$.

b) The vector $\mathbf{h} = 2\mathbf{j}$.

Which two lines on the diagram correspond to $\mathbf{h}$?

c) Which two points can be joined by the vector $\begin{pmatrix} -2 \\ 6 \end{pmatrix}$?

3   Write the following vectors in

(i) both component forms (i.e. $\begin{pmatrix} x \\ y \end{pmatrix}$ and $x\mathbf{i} + y\mathbf{j}$);

(ii) magnitude–direction form.

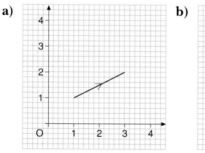
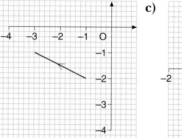

4   Write the following vectors in magnitude–direction form.

a) $\begin{pmatrix} 4 \\ 4 \end{pmatrix}$ b) $\begin{pmatrix} -4 \\ -2 \end{pmatrix}$ c) $\begin{pmatrix} -8 \\ -4 \end{pmatrix}$ d) $\begin{pmatrix} 5 \\ 0 \end{pmatrix}$

5   Write the following vectors in both component forms.

a) 14.14 at 45°   b) 5 at 117°

c) 2 at 240°   d) 4 at 330°

Operations on vectors

Addition

Look at the diagram. You can see the effect of two translations, first

$\mathbf{s} = \begin{pmatrix} 3 \\ 2 \end{pmatrix}$ and then $\mathbf{t} = \begin{pmatrix} 1 \\ -4 \end{pmatrix}$,

on a point P.

s moves P(1, 1) to P′(4, 3).

t moves P′(4, 3) to P″(5, −1).

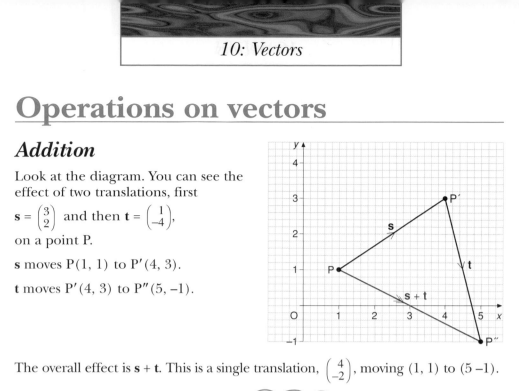

The overall effect is **s** + **t**. This is a single translation, $\begin{pmatrix} 4 \\ -2 \end{pmatrix}$, moving (1, 1) to (5 −1).

$$\mathbf{s} + \mathbf{t} = \begin{pmatrix} 3 \\ 2 \end{pmatrix} + \begin{pmatrix} 1 \\ -4 \end{pmatrix} = \begin{pmatrix} 4 \\ -2 \end{pmatrix}$$

> You are adding the vectors **s** and **t.**

It is often easier to think of the diagram when you are adding vectors.

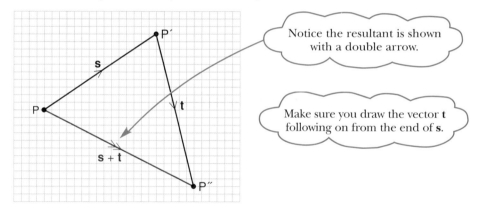

> Notice the resultant is shown with a double arrow.

> Make sure you draw the vector **t** following on from the end of **s**.

The vector **s** + **t** goes from the start of **s** to the end of **t**; it is called the **resultant** of **s** and **t**.

Is **t** + **s** the same as **s** + **t**?

Look at the diagram. People sometimes talk about the parallelogram rule for adding vectors. Why?

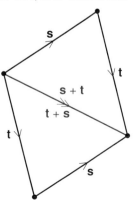

You can see from the diagram that

$$\mathbf{s} + \mathbf{t} = \mathbf{t} + \mathbf{s}$$

This is described by saying that vector addition is **commutative.**

The vector joining two points

 P is the point (3,4). Q is the point (5,8).

What is the vector $\overrightarrow{PQ}$?

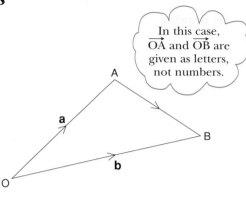

In this case, $\overrightarrow{OA}$ and $\overrightarrow{OB}$ are given as letters, not numbers.

Look at the triangle OAB in the diagram.

What is the vector $\overrightarrow{AB}$?

You can see from the diagram that

$$\overrightarrow{OA} + \overrightarrow{AB} = \overrightarrow{OB}$$
$$\overrightarrow{AB} = \overrightarrow{OB} - \overrightarrow{OA}$$

This can be written as $\overrightarrow{AB} = \mathbf{b} - \mathbf{a}$,
where $\mathbf{a}$ and $\mathbf{b}$ are the position vectors of A and B.

 What is the position vector of the mid-point of AB?

What about the point one quarter of the way from A to B?

You can use vectors even when the axes are not at right angles as in the next example.

Example

Find, in terms of $\mathbf{p}$ and $\mathbf{q}$, the vectors

a) $\overrightarrow{OU}$ **b)** $\overrightarrow{OV}$ **c)** $\overrightarrow{UV}$

shown in the diagram.

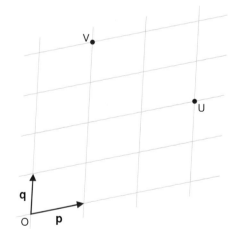

Solution

$$\text{a)} \quad \overrightarrow{OU} = 3\mathbf{p} + 2\mathbf{q}$$
$$\text{b)} \quad \overrightarrow{OV} = \mathbf{p} + 4\mathbf{q}$$
$$\text{c)} \quad \overrightarrow{UV} = \overrightarrow{OV} - \overrightarrow{OU}$$
$$= (\mathbf{p} + 4\mathbf{q}) - (3\mathbf{p} + 2\mathbf{q})$$
$$= -2\mathbf{p} + 2\mathbf{q}.$$

Example

$$\mathbf{p} = \begin{pmatrix} 1 \\ 1 \end{pmatrix}, \quad \mathbf{q} = \begin{pmatrix} 2 \\ 0 \end{pmatrix}, \quad \mathbf{r} = \begin{pmatrix} 0 \\ 1 \end{pmatrix}.$$

Find the magnitude and direction of $3\mathbf{p} + \mathbf{q} - 2\mathbf{r}$.

Solution

$$3\mathbf{p} + \mathbf{q} - 2\mathbf{r} = 3\begin{pmatrix} 1 \\ 1 \end{pmatrix} + \begin{pmatrix} 2 \\ 0 \end{pmatrix} - 2\begin{pmatrix} 0 \\ 1 \end{pmatrix}$$
$$= \begin{pmatrix} 3 \\ 3 \end{pmatrix} + \begin{pmatrix} 2 \\ 0 \end{pmatrix} + \begin{pmatrix} 0 \\ -2 \end{pmatrix}$$
$$= \begin{pmatrix} 5 \\ 1 \end{pmatrix}$$

Magnitude: $\sqrt{5^2 + 1^2} = \sqrt{26} = 5.1$ (2 significant figures)

Direction: $\tan \alpha = \dfrac{1}{5}$ $\alpha = 11°$ (nearest degree)

Exercise 10.2

1 Add these vectors:

a) $\begin{pmatrix} 2 \\ 3 \end{pmatrix}$, $\begin{pmatrix} 4 \\ -1 \end{pmatrix}$ and $\begin{pmatrix} 0 \\ 6 \end{pmatrix}$

b) $\begin{pmatrix} 1 \\ 1 \end{pmatrix}$, $\begin{pmatrix} 2 \\ 2 \end{pmatrix}$ and $\begin{pmatrix} -3 \\ -3 \end{pmatrix}$

c) $\begin{pmatrix} 4 \\ 1 \end{pmatrix}$, $\begin{pmatrix} 1 \\ 4 \end{pmatrix}$ and $\begin{pmatrix} 2 \\ 2 \end{pmatrix}$

d) $\begin{pmatrix} -1 \\ -3 \end{pmatrix}$, $\begin{pmatrix} -3 \\ -4 \end{pmatrix}$, $\begin{pmatrix} 2 \\ 1 \end{pmatrix}$ and $\begin{pmatrix} 0 \\ -6 \end{pmatrix}$

e) $6\mathbf{i} + 3\mathbf{j}$, $3\mathbf{i} - \mathbf{j}$ and $-8\mathbf{i} - \mathbf{j}$.

2 Given that $\mathbf{p} = \begin{pmatrix} 3 \\ 2 \end{pmatrix}$, $\mathbf{q} = \begin{pmatrix} -1 \\ 4 \end{pmatrix}$, and $\mathbf{r} = \begin{pmatrix} -6 \\ -2 \end{pmatrix}$, simplify:

a) $\mathbf{p} + \mathbf{q} + \mathbf{r}$

b) $2\mathbf{p} + 3\mathbf{q} + \mathbf{r}$

c) $2\mathbf{p} + \mathbf{q} - \mathbf{r}$

d) $-\mathbf{p} - \mathbf{q} - \mathbf{r}$

e) $3\mathbf{p} - 4\mathbf{q} - 2\mathbf{r}$.

3 Three vectors are defined as follows

$\mathbf{u} = \begin{pmatrix} 4 \\ 1 \end{pmatrix}$, $\mathbf{v} = \begin{pmatrix} -2 \\ -3 \end{pmatrix}$, $\mathbf{w} = \begin{pmatrix} 3 \\ 0 \end{pmatrix}$

For each of the following

(i) draw a diagram to illustrate it

(ii) give the answer in component form.

a) $\mathbf{u} + \mathbf{v}$

b) $\mathbf{u} + \mathbf{v} + \mathbf{w}$

c) $2\mathbf{v}$

d) $\mathbf{u} - \mathbf{v}$

4 The diagram shows three vectors, **p**, **q** and **r**.

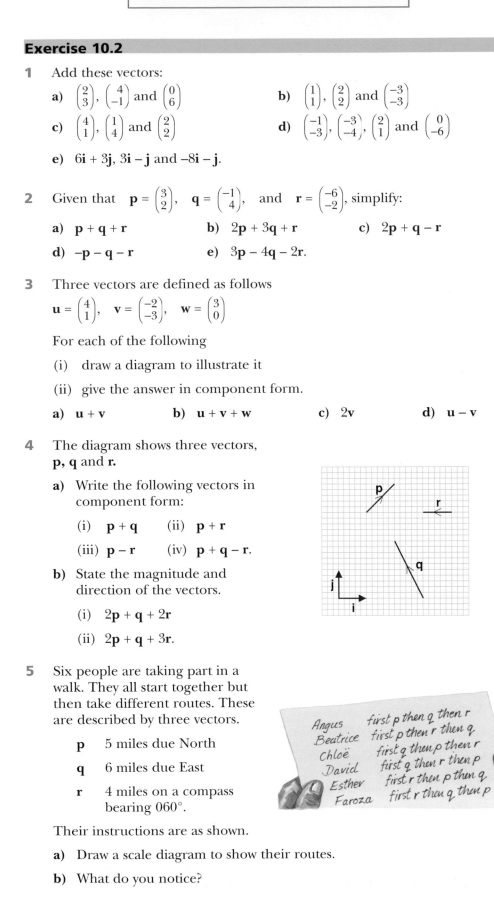

a) Write the following vectors in component form:

(i) $\mathbf{p} + \mathbf{q}$ (ii) $\mathbf{p} + \mathbf{r}$

(iii) $\mathbf{p} - \mathbf{r}$ (iv) $\mathbf{p} + \mathbf{q} - \mathbf{r}$.

b) State the magnitude and direction of the vectors.

(i) $2\mathbf{p} + \mathbf{q} + 2\mathbf{r}$

(ii) $2\mathbf{p} + \mathbf{q} + 3\mathbf{r}$.

5 Six people are taking part in a walk. They all start together but then take different routes. These are described by three vectors.

p   5 miles due North

q   6 miles due East

r   4 miles on a compass bearing 060°.

Their instructions are as shown.

Angus   first p then q then r
Beatrice   first p then r then q
Chloë   first q then p then r
David   first q then r then p
Esther   first r then p then q
Faroza   first r then q then p

a) Draw a scale diagram to show their routes.

b) What do you notice?

Exercise 10.2 *continued*

6 Vectors **l** and **m** are defined by $\mathbf{l} = \begin{pmatrix} 3 \\ 4 \end{pmatrix}$ and $\mathbf{m} = \begin{pmatrix} 4 \\ -3 \end{pmatrix}$.

  a) State the magnitudes and directions of **l** and **m**.

  b) Find the angle between **l** and **m**.

  c) Write, in component form, the vectors

   (i) $3\mathbf{l} + 4\mathbf{m}$ (ii) $4\mathbf{l} - 3\mathbf{m}$

  d) Use your answers to part **c)** to write the vectors

   (i) $\begin{pmatrix} 1 \\ 0 \end{pmatrix}$ (ii) $\begin{pmatrix} 0 \\ 1 \end{pmatrix}$

   in terms of **l** and **m**.

7 Vectors **p, q, r** and **s** are defined as follows

$$\mathbf{p} = 4\mathbf{i} + \mathbf{j}, \quad \mathbf{q} = \mathbf{i} + 5\mathbf{j}, \quad \mathbf{r} = -6\mathbf{i} - 2\mathbf{j}, \quad \mathbf{s} = \mathbf{i} - 4\mathbf{j}$$

  a) Draw a diagram showing $\mathbf{p} + \mathbf{q} + \mathbf{r} + \mathbf{s}$.

  b) What is the magnitude of $\mathbf{p} + \mathbf{q} + \mathbf{r} + \mathbf{s}$?

  c) Three vectors, **l**, **m** and **n** are such that $\mathbf{l} + \mathbf{m} + \mathbf{n} = \mathbf{0}$. What can you say about them?

8 Look at the diagram.

  a) Write, in terms of **p** and **q**, the vectors

   (i) $\overrightarrow{AB}$
   (ii) $\overrightarrow{DC}$

  b) What does this tell you about the quadrilateral ABCD?

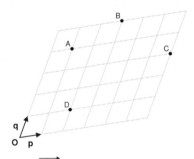

  c) Write, also in terms of **p** and **q**, the vector $\overrightarrow{OM}$ where M is the mid-point of CD.

  d) Describe the quadrilaterals ABMD and ABCM.

Investigation

The point A is $(-4, 4)$ and the point B is $(8, 4)$. The position vectors, $\overrightarrow{OA}$ and $\overrightarrow{OB}$, are denoted by **a** and **b.**

a) Using graph paper, draw a diagram showing the origin and the points A and B.

b) Mark on your diagram the point M, with position vector **m** given by
 $\mathbf{m} = \dfrac{1}{2}\mathbf{a} + \dfrac{1}{2}\mathbf{b}$.   What can you say about M?

c) Now mark the points L and N with position vectors
 $\mathbf{l} = \dfrac{3}{4}\mathbf{a} + \dfrac{1}{4}\mathbf{b}$ and $\mathbf{n} = \dfrac{1}{4}\mathbf{a} + \dfrac{3}{4}\mathbf{b}$.
 What can you say about the points L and N?

d) T is the point $(4, 4)$. Show that its position vector **t** can be written in the form $(1 - \alpha)\mathbf{a} + \alpha\mathbf{b}$ for a certain value of α which you are to find.

e) State a general rule for points on the line AB.

Using vectors in real-life problems

In many real life problems, vectors are given in magnitude–direction form. Sometimes it is easiest to use scale drawing.

Example

A boat is travelling at a speed of 12 km hr^{-1} through the water on a compass bearing of 060°. It is set by an ocean current of 4 km hr^{-1} in a direction 125°.

Find, using scale drawing, the speed and direction of the boat made good (i.e. over the sea bed).

Solution

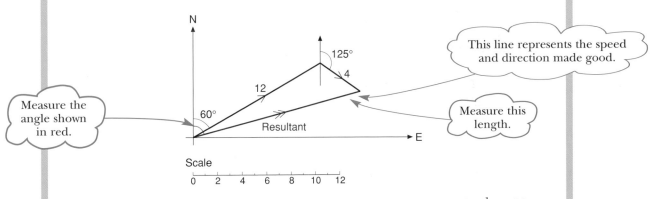

Measure the angle shown in red.

This line represents the speed and direction made good.

Measure this length.

Measuring the resultant gives the speed of the boat to be 14.2 km hr^{-1} and its direction 075°.

You can solve the same problem by calculation, and of course this gives a more accurate answer. This is how you would do it.

The velocities of the boat and the current have components

$$\begin{pmatrix} 12 \sin 60° \\ 12 \cos 60° \end{pmatrix} \quad \text{and} \quad \begin{pmatrix} 4 \sin 55° \\ 4 \cos 55° \end{pmatrix} \quad \begin{matrix} \text{East} \\ \\ \text{North} \end{matrix}$$

These are $\begin{pmatrix} 10.39 \\ 6.0 \end{pmatrix}$ and $\begin{pmatrix} 13.67 \\ 3.71 \end{pmatrix}$ (to 2 decimal places).

You find the resultant by adding these: $\begin{pmatrix} 13.67 \\ 3.71 \end{pmatrix}$

Magnitude : $\sqrt{\left(13.67^2 + 3.71^2\right)} = 14.16$

Direction : $\tan \alpha = \dfrac{3.71}{13.67} \Rightarrow \alpha = 15.2°$

Compass bearing is $090 - 15.2° = 074.8°$.

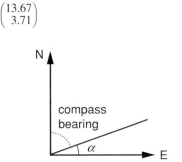

So, to reasonable accuracy, the boat is travelling at 14.2 km hr^{-1} on a bearing of 075°.

When an aircraft is blown by the wind, its direction and speed made good are called its **track** and **ground speed**.

Exercise 10.3

Use scale drawing for questions 1 to 5. You can check your answers by calculation.

1 A ship steers a course 140° at 12 knots.

It is set by a current of 2 knots at 030°.

What is its course and speed made good?

2 A jet aircraft flying at 550 knots on a course of 050° is caught in a cyclone blowing due South at 150 knots.

Find the aeroplane's track and ground speed.

3 A helicopter flies at 100 knots on a course of 085°.

The wind is blowing at 20 knots towards 135°.

Find the helicopter's track and ground speed.

4 A yacht is sailing on a course 105° at 5 knots.

It is being set by a current 2 knots flowing towards 350°.

Find the course and speed made good.

5 A racing pigeon flies at 60 km hr^{-1} heading in a direction 060°.

The wind is blowing at 20 km hr^{-1} towards 270°.

Find the bird's track and ground speed.

6 Peter, Queenie and Ros are pushing a car.

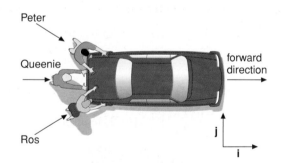

The forces they exert, in Newtons, are

Peter   205**i** – 40**j**,

Queenie 215**i**,

Ros   210**i** + 20**j**

a) Find the magnitudes of their forces. Who is pushing hardest?

b) Find the resultant of all three forces in

   (i) component form   (ii) magnitude–direction form.

c) What percentage of the resultant force is in the forward direction of the car?

Exercise 10.3 *continued*

7 A ship, the *Sea Spray*, leaves port at time $t = 0$ hours and sails with velocity $\begin{pmatrix} 12 \\ 4 \end{pmatrix}$ in kilometres per hour. Directions are $\begin{pmatrix} \text{East} \\ \text{North} \end{pmatrix}$.

   a) Taking the origin to be at the port, write down the position vectors of the *Sea Spray* after 1, 2 and 3 hours. Draw a graph to illustrate the ship's progress.

   Another ship, the *Mona L*, has position vector $\begin{pmatrix} 45 \\ -8 \end{pmatrix}$ when $t = 0$ and has velocity $\begin{pmatrix} -18 \\ 10 \end{pmatrix}$. The weather is foggy and neither ship's crew is using its radar so they cannot see each other.

   b) Show the progress of the *Mona L* on your graph paper, marking its position when $t = 0$, 1, 2 and 3.

   c) Do the ships collide, and if so when?

8 Throughout this problem the wind velocity is $\begin{pmatrix} -20 \\ 40 \end{pmatrix}$ km hr^{-1} in directions $\begin{pmatrix} \text{East} \\ \text{North} \end{pmatrix}$.

   a) Comment on this assumption.

   At noon a helicopter set off from Aberdeen, (sited at the origin $(0, 0)$) to fly the relief crew out to an oil rig at $(160, 280)$ km.

   The pilot flew with velocity $\begin{pmatrix} 100 \\ 100 \end{pmatrix}$ km hr^{-1} through the air.

   b) (i) On graph paper, draw a diagram showing Aberdeen, the oil rig, and the line representing one hour's flight.

   Add the wind vector to your diagram and mark the position of the helicopter after 1 hour.

   (ii) State the co-ordinates of this point and the fraction of the total distance travelled so far.

   (iii) Hence determine the time of arrival of the helicopter at the oil rig.

   On the return, the helicopter is to fly over a supply ship in order to pick up a sick crew member.

   The pilot flies for 1 hour with velocity $\begin{pmatrix} -60 \\ -120 \end{pmatrix}$ km hr^{-1} through the air.

   The helicopter is blown by the wind to the supply ship's position.

   c) Mark this leg of the journey on your diagram and give the co-ordinates of the supply ship.

   The pilot now sets a new course, and arrives in Aberdeen in 2 hours time.

   d) State the pilot's new velocity vector through the air.

   Does he fly faster on this final leg than he did on the way out to the oil rig?

Geometry with vectors

Sometimes using vectors can give you insight into geometrical problems, as in the next example.

Example

The diagram shows a regular hexagon ABCDEF with centre O.

$$\overrightarrow{AB} = \mathbf{p} \qquad \text{and} \qquad \overrightarrow{AF} = \mathbf{q}.$$

Find, in terms of $\mathbf{p}$ and $\mathbf{q}$

a) $\overrightarrow{BC}$ **b)** $\overrightarrow{AD}$.

c) State what your answers to parts **a)** and **b)** tell you about the lines BC and AD.

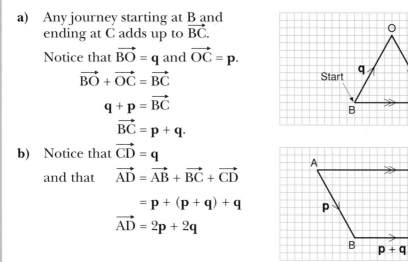

Solution

a) Any journey starting at B and ending at C adds up to $\overrightarrow{BC}$.

Notice that $\overrightarrow{BO} = \mathbf{q}$ and $\overrightarrow{OC} = \mathbf{p}$.

$$\overrightarrow{BO} + \overrightarrow{OC} = \overrightarrow{BC}$$

$$\mathbf{q} + \mathbf{p} = \overrightarrow{BC}$$

$$\overrightarrow{BC} = \mathbf{p} + \mathbf{q}.$$

b) Notice that $\overrightarrow{CD} = \mathbf{q}$

and that $\overrightarrow{AD} = \overrightarrow{AB} + \overrightarrow{BC} + \overrightarrow{CD}$

$$= \mathbf{p} + (\mathbf{p} + \mathbf{q}) + \mathbf{q}$$

$$\overrightarrow{AD} = 2\mathbf{p} + 2\mathbf{q}$$

c) You can see that $\overrightarrow{AD} = 2\overrightarrow{BC}$.

Both are $2\mathbf{p} + 2\mathbf{q}$.

This tells you two things:

- the length of AD is twice the length of BC;

- the direction of AD is the same as that of BC, i.e. AD and BC are parallel.

Exercise 10.4

1   In the diagram, OABC is a parallelogram.

O is the origin.

A is $(5, 0)$.

$\overrightarrow{OC}$ is $\begin{pmatrix} 3 \\ 4 \end{pmatrix}$.

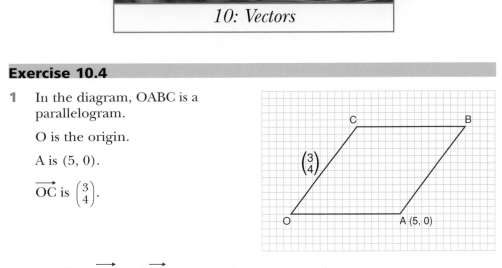

a)   Write $\overrightarrow{OA}$ and $\overrightarrow{AB}$ as vectors in component form.

b)   Write down the vector $\overrightarrow{OB}$ and the co-ordinates of point B.

c)   Find the lengths of OA and OC. What does this tell you about OABC?

2   A figure OABCDEFG is shown in the diagram.

a)   Write the following vectors in component form.

   (i) $\overrightarrow{AB}$ (ii) $\overrightarrow{DG}$

   (iii) $\overrightarrow{OC}$ (iv) $\overrightarrow{EF}$

What do your answers tell you about these four lines?

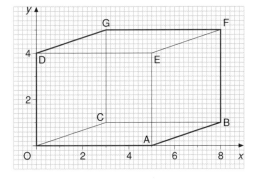

b)   Use vectors to show that DF is parallel to OB.

c)   Are the following statements true or false?

   (i) $\overrightarrow{OB} = \overrightarrow{OA} + \overrightarrow{AB}$

   (ii) $OB = OA + AB$

   (iii) $\overrightarrow{AB} = \overrightarrow{OB} - \overrightarrow{OA}$

   (iv) $\overrightarrow{DE} + \overrightarrow{EF} = \overrightarrow{OB}$

3   PQRS is a parallelogram. The diagonals PR and QS meet at M.

$\overrightarrow{PM} = \begin{pmatrix} 8 \\ 8 \end{pmatrix}$, $\overrightarrow{MQ} = \begin{pmatrix} 4 \\ -3 \end{pmatrix}$.

The co-ordinates of P are $(2, 1)$.

Find

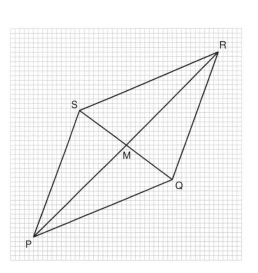

a)   the co-ordinates of Q, R and S

b)   the lengths of the sides of the parallelogram.

c)   Show that

   (i) $\overrightarrow{PM} = \frac{1}{2} \overrightarrow{PR}$

   (ii) $\overrightarrow{SM} = \frac{1}{2} \overrightarrow{SQ}$

Exercise 10.4 *continued*

4   EFGH is a quadrilateral.

$\overrightarrow{EF} = \begin{pmatrix} 3 \\ 8 \end{pmatrix}$, $\overrightarrow{FG} = \begin{pmatrix} -3 \\ -4 \end{pmatrix}$, $\overrightarrow{GH} = \begin{pmatrix} -3 \\ 4 \end{pmatrix}$.

a) Find $\overrightarrow{HE}$.

b) Draw EFGH.

Points J and K are such that $\overrightarrow{FJ} = 2\overrightarrow{FG}$ and $\overrightarrow{HK} = 2\overrightarrow{HG}$.

c) Add points J and K to your diagram and describe the figure JEKG.

5   ABCD is a square.

A is (2, 3), B is (6, 6) and $\overrightarrow{BC}$ is $\begin{pmatrix} -3 \\ 4 \end{pmatrix}$.

a) Find the co-ordinates of D.

b) Give the vectors $\overrightarrow{AC}$ and $\overrightarrow{BD}$ in component form.

c) Give the vectors $\overrightarrow{AC}$ and $\overrightarrow{BD}$ in magnitude–direction form.

d) What does your answer to part c) tell you about the lines AC and BD?

6   $\overrightarrow{OA}$ is $\begin{pmatrix} 1 \\ 2 \end{pmatrix}$ and $\overrightarrow{OB}$ is $\begin{pmatrix} -2 \\ 1 \end{pmatrix}$.

a) Draw a diagram, on graph paper, showing O, A and B. Measure the angle AOB.

b) Write $\overrightarrow{OA}$ and $\overrightarrow{OB}$ in magnitude–direction form. Use your answers to show that your measurement of angle AOB in part a) was correct.

c) Describe the relationship between the vectors $\mathbf{u} = \begin{pmatrix} 1 \\ 2 \end{pmatrix}$ and $\mathbf{v} = \begin{pmatrix} 6 \\ 12 \end{pmatrix}$.

d) Describe the relationship between the vectors $\mathbf{v} = \begin{pmatrix} 6 \\ 12 \end{pmatrix}$ and $\mathbf{w} = \begin{pmatrix} -2 \\ 1 \end{pmatrix}$.

e) Suggest a way of telling whether two vectors are at right angles, just by looking at their components. Test your idea on two vectors that you know to be perpendicular.

7   ABCDEFG is a regular hexagon.

$\overrightarrow{OA} = \mathbf{a}$, $\overrightarrow{OB} = \mathbf{b}$

a) Write down, in terms of **a** and **b**, the vectors

(i) $\overrightarrow{AB}$

(ii) $\overrightarrow{FC}$

b) Write down one geometrical fact about AB and FC which could be deduced from your answers to part a).

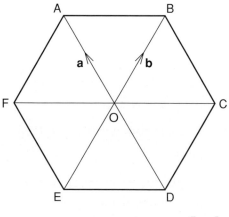

London

Exercise 10.4 *continued*

8 The diagram shows a triangle OAB, in which $\overrightarrow{OA} = \mathbf{a}$ and $\overrightarrow{OB} = \mathbf{b}$.

The points L and M are the mid-points of OA and OB.

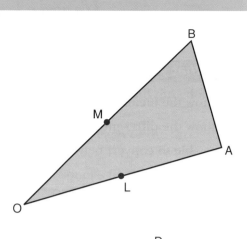

a) Write down the vector $\overrightarrow{AB}$ in terms of **a** and **b**.

b) Find the vector $\overrightarrow{LM}$.

c) Describe the relationship between LM and AB.

9 In the diagram, OPQR is a parallelogram.

A, B, C, D are the mid-points of the sides.

$\overrightarrow{OA} = \mathbf{a}$ $\overrightarrow{OB} = \mathbf{b}$

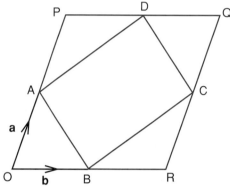

Find, in terms of **a** and **b**,

a) (i) $\overrightarrow{OP}$ (ii) $\overrightarrow{PQ}$

  (iii) $\overrightarrow{AB}$ (iv) $\overrightarrow{AD}$

  (v) $\overrightarrow{DC}$ (vi) $\overrightarrow{BC}$

b) What can you say about the shape ABCD?

10 The diagram shows a triangle UVW.

The points L, M and N are the mid-points of its sides.

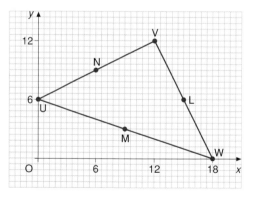

a) State the vector $\overrightarrow{UL}$, in component form.

b) The point P is on $\overrightarrow{UL}$, and $\overrightarrow{UP} = \frac{2}{3}\overrightarrow{UL}$.

  Find the co-ordinates of P.

c) The point Q is on $\overrightarrow{VM}$ and $\overrightarrow{VQ} = \frac{2}{3}\overrightarrow{VM}$.

  Find the co-ordinates of Q.

d) The point R is on WN and $\overrightarrow{WR} = \frac{2}{3}\overrightarrow{WN}$.

  Find the co-ordinates of R.

  What do you notice?

e) The position vectors $\overrightarrow{OU}$, $\overrightarrow{OV}$, $\overrightarrow{OW}$ and $\overrightarrow{OP}$ are denoted by **u, v, w** and **p**.

  Show that $\mathbf{p} = \frac{1}{3}(\mathbf{u} + \mathbf{v} + \mathbf{w})$.

f) Show that the result in part **e)** is true in general, not just for the particular points U, V and W in this question.

Mixed exercise 10.5 *continued*

7 In the diagram $\overrightarrow{OA} = \mathbf{a}$, $\overrightarrow{OB} = \mathbf{b}$, $\overrightarrow{OC} = 4\overrightarrow{OA}$ and $\overrightarrow{OD} = k\overrightarrow{OB}$.

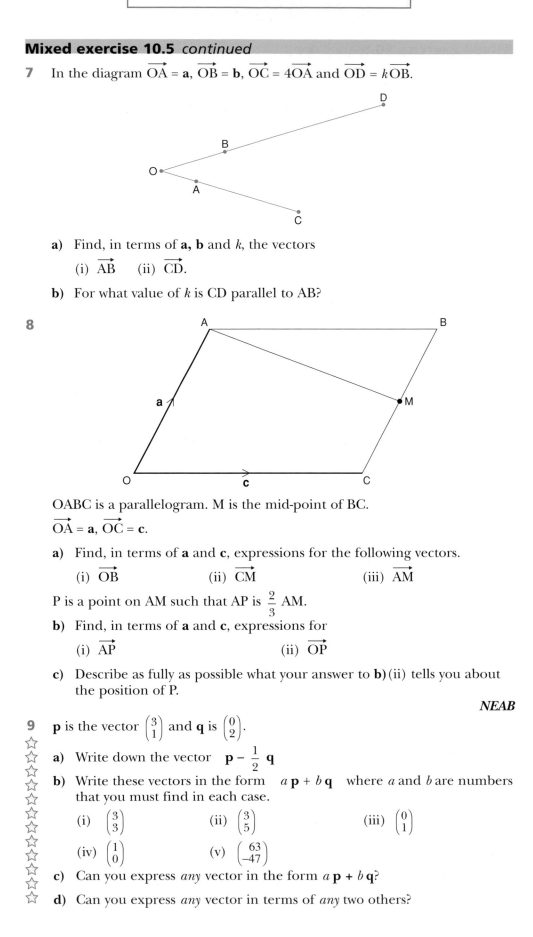

a) Find, in terms of **a, b** and k, the vectors

   (i) $\overrightarrow{AB}$ (ii) $\overrightarrow{CD}$.

b) For what value of k is CD parallel to AB?

8

OABC is a parallelogram. M is the mid-point of BC.

$\overrightarrow{OA} = \mathbf{a}$, $\overrightarrow{OC} = \mathbf{c}$.

a) Find, in terms of **a** and **c**, expressions for the following vectors.

   (i) $\overrightarrow{OB}$ (ii) $\overrightarrow{CM}$ (iii) $\overrightarrow{AM}$

P is a point on AM such that AP is $\dfrac{2}{3}$ AM.

b) Find, in terms of **a** and **c**, expressions for

   (i) $\overrightarrow{AP}$ (ii) $\overrightarrow{OP}$

c) Describe as fully as possible what your answer to **b)** (ii) tells you about the position of P.

NEAB

9 **p** is the vector $\begin{pmatrix} 3 \\ 1 \end{pmatrix}$ and **q** is $\begin{pmatrix} 0 \\ 2 \end{pmatrix}$.

a) Write down the vector $\mathbf{p} - \dfrac{1}{2}\,\mathbf{q}$

b) Write these vectors in the form $a\,\mathbf{p} + b\,\mathbf{q}$ where a and b are numbers that you must find in each case.

   (i) $\begin{pmatrix} 3 \\ 3 \end{pmatrix}$ (ii) $\begin{pmatrix} 3 \\ 5 \end{pmatrix}$ (iii) $\begin{pmatrix} 0 \\ 1 \end{pmatrix}$

   (iv) $\begin{pmatrix} 1 \\ 0 \end{pmatrix}$ (v) $\begin{pmatrix} 63 \\ -47 \end{pmatrix}$

c) Can you express *any* vector in the form $a\,\mathbf{p} + b\,\mathbf{q}$?

d) Can you express *any* vector in terms of *any* two others?

Chapter 11

Trigonometry 2

> **Before you start this chapter you should:**
>
> ★ be familiar with the work in Chapter 6.

The sine rule

So far, in trigonometry, you have worked only with right-angled triangles. To find x in this triangle, you would first have to divide it into two right-angled triangles, as shown in blue.

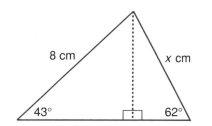

 Find x by dividing the triangle as shown. Start by finding the height of the triangle.

This is rather a long-winded method. However, you can generalise the method to find a rule.

In this triangle ABC, the side opposite angle A is labelled a, and the side opposite angle B is labelled b.

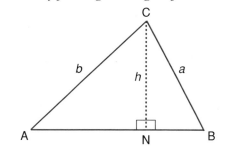

 Find an expression for h in terms of angle A and side b, using triangle ACN. Use this and triangle BCN to find an expression connecting angle A, angle B, side a and side b.

Here is the expression you should have found. (You may need to rearrange your answer to get the one shown below.)

$$\frac{a}{\sin A} = \frac{b}{\sin B}$$

Each side goes with the angle opposite it.

This is called the **sine rule**.

The rule can also be extended to include the angle C and its opposite side c.

$$\frac{a}{\sin A} = \frac{b}{\sin B} = \frac{c}{\sin C}$$

 Explain why the rule can be extended like this.

How would you write the sine rule for a triangle labelled XYZ?

Example

Use this rule to find x in the triangle at the top of the opposite page.

Solution

$$\frac{x}{\sin 43} = \frac{8}{\sin 62}$$

$$x = \frac{8}{\sin 62} \times \sin 43$$

$$x = 6.18 \quad \text{(in cm)}.$$

Finding an angle using the sine rule

You have used the sine rule to find the length of a side. You can also use the sine rule to find an angle.

To find an angle, it is easier to write the sine rule like this.

$$\frac{\sin A}{a} = \frac{\sin B}{b}$$

 Why is this the same as the other version of the sine rule?

Example

Find the angle x in this triangle.

Solution

$$\frac{\sin x}{7} = \frac{\sin 58}{8}$$

$$\sin x = \frac{\sin 58}{8} \times 7$$

$$x = 47.9° \quad \text{or} \quad x = 132.1°$$

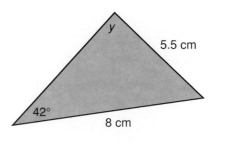

8 cm

x

58°

7 cm

 Why are there two possible values for x *?*

In fact, $x = 47.9°$ is the only possible correct answer.

 Why is it impossible for x *to be* 132.1° *?*

Sometimes both answers are possible, as in the next example.

Example

Find angle y in this triangle.

Solution

$$\frac{\sin y}{8} = \frac{\sin 42}{5.5}$$

$$\sin y = \frac{\sin 42}{5.5} \times 8$$

$$y = 76.7° \quad \text{or} \quad y = 103.3°$$

y

5.5 cm

42°

8 cm

 Why are both of these solutions possible?

 Note: Do not be influenced by what the diagram looks like. You can't assume that an angle is acute or obtuse just because it has been drawn that way.

Exercise 11.1

1 Use the sine rule to find *x* in each of these triangles.

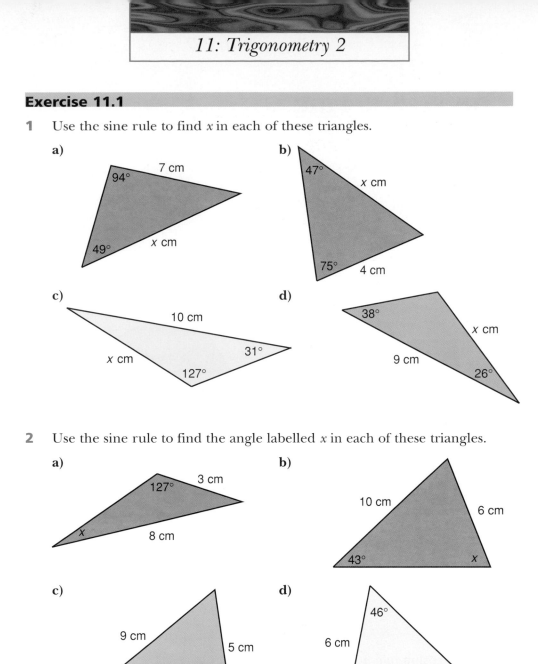

a)

7 cm
94°
49°
x cm

b)

47°
x cm
75°
4 cm

c)

10 cm
31°
x cm
127°

d)

38°
x cm
9 cm
26°

2 Use the sine rule to find the angle labelled *x* in each of these triangles.

a)

127°
3 cm
x
8 cm

b)

10 cm
6 cm
43°
x

c)

9 cm
5 cm
x
82°

d)

46°
6 cm
x
7 cm

3 Neil is on a countryside walk. He notices a windmill in the distance and finds that the bearing of the windmill is 142°. He then walks 3 km on a bearing of 053° and finds that the bearing of the windmill is now 206°.

a) Copy the diagram and fill in the known angles.

b) Find the distance of the windmill from each of the points where Neil took a bearing.

N
N
3 km

The cosine rule

Why can't you use the sine rule to find x in this triangle?

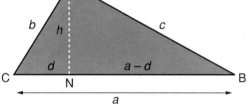

How could you find x by dividing the triangle into two right-angled triangles?

Again, you can find a rule by generalising the method.

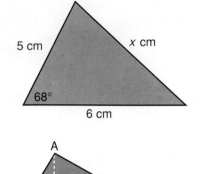

Pythagoras' theorem for triangle ANB:	$h^2 + (a - d)^2 = c^2$
Pythagoras' theorem for triangle ANC:	$h^2 + d^2 = b^2$
Subtract to eliminate h:	$(a - d)^2 - d^2 = c^2 - b^2$
Expand the brackets:	$a^2 - 2ad + d^2 - d^2 = c^2 - b^2$
Tidy up:	$a^2 - 2ad = c^2 - b^2$
Using triangle ACN:	$\cos C = \dfrac{d}{b}$
	$d = b \cos C$
Substitute in ①:	$a^2 - 2ab \cos C = c^2 - b^2$
	$a^2 + b^2 - 2ab \cos C = c^2$

This is the **cosine rule**. It is usually written like this.

$$c^2 = a^2 + b^2 - 2ab \cos C$$

The cosine rule can be used to find the third side of a triangle when you know the other two sides and the angle between them.

What happens to the cosine rule if C is 90°? Why?

Example

Use the cosine rule to find x in the triangle at the top of the page.

Solution

$$x^2 = 5^2 + 6^2 - 2 \times 5 \times 6 \cos 68°$$

$$x = 6.21 \text{ (in cm)}.$$

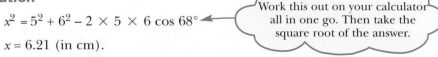

Work this out on your calculator all in one go. Then take the square root of the answer.

Work this out on your calculator and check that you get the same answer.

Using the cosine rule to find an angle

If you know all three sides of a triangle, you can use the cosine rule to find any of the angles.

It is easiest if you use a rearranged form of the cosine rule.

$$\cos C = \frac{a^2 + b^2 - c^2}{2ab}$$

> c is the side opposite the angle that you want to find.

? *Check that you can rearrange the other form of the cosine rule to get this one.*

Example

Find the angle C in this triangle.

Solution

$$\cos C = \frac{a^2 + b^2 - c^2}{2ab}$$

$$\cos C = \frac{6^2 + 7^2 - 8^2}{2 \times 6 \times 7}$$

> Work this out on your calculator and then use $\cos^{-1}$.

$$\cos C = \frac{21}{84}$$

$$C = 75.5°$$

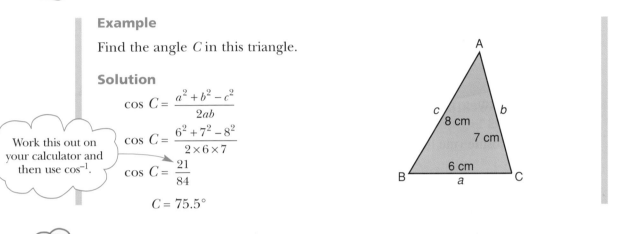

? *Check that you get the same answer on your calculator.*

? *Why is there only one possible answer, unlike when you use the sine rule to find an angle?*

For some situations, you need to use both the sine and cosine rules.

? *Explain how you would find x and y in these triangles.*

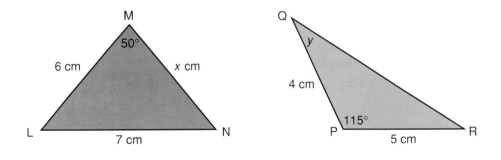

Exercise 11.3

1 Nicole walks 5 km on a bearing of 128°. She then walks a further 3 km on a bearing of 245°.

How far and on what bearing does she need to walk to get back to her starting point?

2 For the cuboid ABCDEFGH

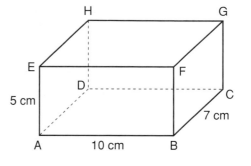

a) Find the lengths of these lines. Leave the square roots in your answers.

  (i) AC

  (ii) CH

  (iii) AH.

b) Find the angle ACH.

3 Three points P, Q and R in three dimensional space have co-ordinates (3, 1, –2), (5, –2, 1) and (–1, 0, 4) respectively.

Find the angle PQR.

4 A statue stands on a column.

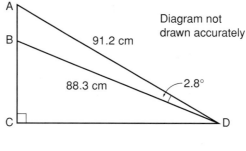

In the diagram AB represents the statue and BC represents the column.

Angle ACD = 90°.

Angle BDA = 2.8°.

AD = 91.2 m and BD = 88.3 m.

ABC is a vertical straight line.

a) Calculate the height, AB, of the statue. Give your answer, in metres, correct to 3 significant figures.

b) Calculate the height, BC, of the column. Give your answer, in metres, correct to 3 significant figures.

Edexcel

5 Find the angles A, B and C in this quadrilateral.

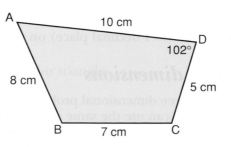

The area of a triangle

 How could you find the area of this triangle?

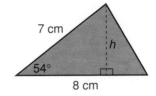

You cannot use directly the formula area = $\frac{1}{2}$ base × height, because you do not know the perpendicular height, h.

However, you can work out the height like this:

$$\sin 54° = \frac{h}{7}$$

$$\therefore h = 7 \sin 54°.$$

You can then find the area.

$$\text{Area} = \frac{1}{2} \times 8 \times 7 \sin 54°$$

$$= 22.7 \text{ cm}^2$$

You can generalise this method to find a formula for the area of a triangle.

 Write down an expression for h *in terms of* b *and angle* C.

Use this to write down an expression for the area of the triangle.

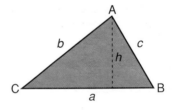

You should have found the following formula.

Area of a triangle = $\frac{1}{2}$ ab sin C.

Example

Use this formula to find the area of the triangle at the top of the page.

Solution

Area of triangle = $\frac{1}{2}$ × 7 × 8 × sin 54° = 22.7 cm^2

You can only use this formula for the area of a triangle if you know two sides and the angle between them.

 How could you find the area of these triangles?

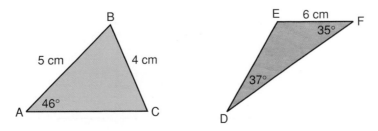

11: Trigonometry 2

Exercise 11.4

1 Find the area of each of these triangles.

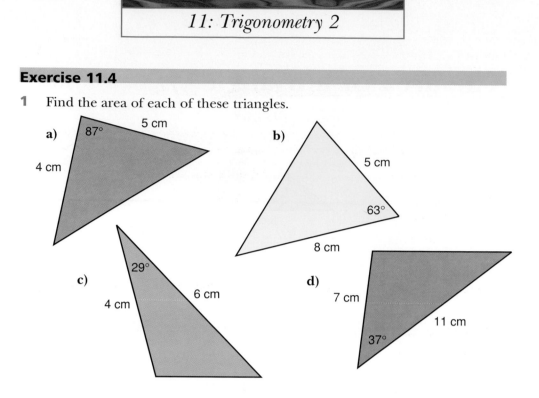

a) 5 cm, 87°, 4 cm

b) 5 cm, 63°, 8 cm

c) 29°, 6 cm, 4 cm

d) 7 cm, 11 cm, 37°

2 The diagram shows a field.

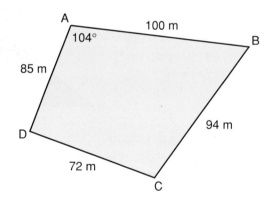

A   100 m   B
104°
85 m   94 m
D
72 m
C

a) Find the length of the diagonal BD.

b) Find the angle DCB.

c) Find the area of the field.

3 Each row of the table below gives some information about a triangle ABC.

For each row of the table, sketch the triangle ABC, fill in the given information and work out the rest of the information about the triangle.

Copy the table and complete it.

	$\angle A$	$\angle B$	$\angle C$	a	b	c	Area
a)	40°			6 cm	5 cm		
b)		58°				4 cm	15 cm^2
c)			74°	3 cm	7 cm		
d)					6 cm	8 cm	18 cm^2

Finishing off

Now that you have finished this chapter you should be able to:

★ use the sine and cosine rules to find sides and angles in triangles

★ use the sine and cosine rules to solve problems in two or three dimensions

★ find the area of a triangle.

Use the questions in the next exercise to check that you understand everything.

Mixed exercise 11.5

1 Find the values of a to d in the triangles below.

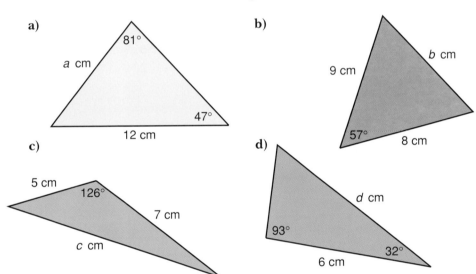

a) 81°, a cm, 47°, 12 cm

b) b cm, 9 cm, 57°, 8 cm

c) 5 cm, 126°, 7 cm, c cm

d) d cm, 93°, 32°, 6 cm

2 Find the angles marked with letters in the triangles below.

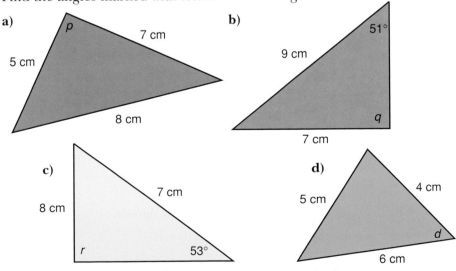

a) p, 7 cm, 5 cm, 8 cm

b) 51°, 9 cm, q, 7 cm

c) 7 cm, 8 cm, r, 53°

d) 4 cm, 5 cm, d, 6 cm

Mixed exercise 11.5 *continued*

3 Find the area of each of these triangles.

a)

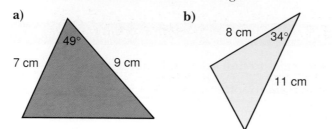

49°
7 cm   9 cm

b)

8 cm   34°
11 cm

4 The diagram shows a bicycle frame. AB is parallel to DC.

DC = DB = 38 cm.   AB = 56 cm.   Angle ABD = 52°.

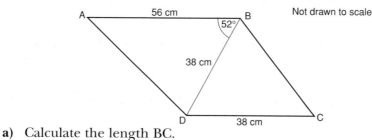

A   56 cm   B   Not drawn to scale
52°
38 cm
D   38 cm   C

a) Calculate the length BC.

b) Calculate the length AD.

NEAB

5 In the triangle ABC, AB = 6 cm, BC = 5 cm and angle BAC = 45°.

There are two possible triangles ABC that can be constructed with this information.

Calculate the **two** possible values of the angle BCA.

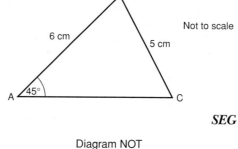

B   Not to scale
6 cm   5 cm
A 45°   C

SEG

6

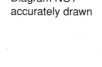

A   Diagram NOT accurately drawn
60°
x cm   5 cm
C   2x cm   B

In triangle ABC, AB = 5cm, AC = x cm, BD = 2x cm and angle BAC = 60°.

a) Show that $3x^2 + 5x - 25 = 0$

b) Solve the equation $3x^2 + 5x - 25 = 0$

Give your answers correct to 3 significant figures.

D is the point on AC such that angle ADB = 104°.

c) Calculate the length of BD.

Edexcel

Chapter 12

Polar co-ordinates

Before you start this chapter you should be able to:

★ use cartesian (*x*, *y*) co-ordinates

★ use simple trigonometry in right-angled triangles

★ use the sine and cosine rules

★ understand and perform transformations using cartesian co-ordinates.

Use the questions in this exercise to check that you remember these topics.

Review exercise 12.1

1 A ladder 3 m long is leaning against a wall. The ladder makes an angle of 58° with the horizontal ground.

    a) Find the height of the top of the ladder.

    b) Find the distance from the foot of the ladder to the wall.

2 Avonford's market place is in the shape of a square ABCD. There is a clock tower at A. The clock is 36.4 m above the ground and its angle of elevation from C is 20°.

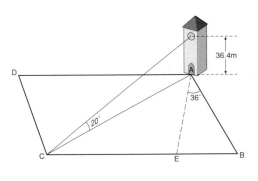

    a) Calculate the length of the diagonal AC.

    b) Calculate the length of the side of the square.

The entrance to the Town Hall is at E such that angle BAE = 36°.

    c) Calculate the length of AE, and so find the angle of elevation of the clock from E.

3 Look at the diagram.

    a) Write down a single transformation that maps shape F onto shape A.

    b) Write down a single transformation that maps shape F onto shape B.

    c) Write down a single transformation that maps shape A onto shape B.

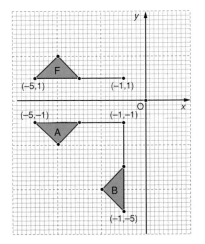

149

Review exercise 12.1 *continued*

4   Copy the diagram on squared paper or graph paper.

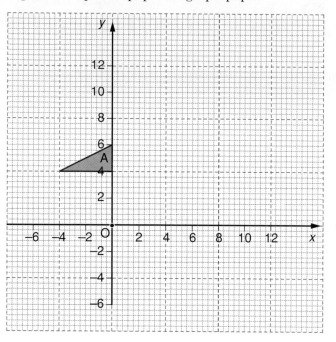

a)   Rotate triangle A through 90° anticlockwise about O. Label this triangle B.

b)   Enlarge triangle A by a scale factor of $\frac{5}{2}$ with centre of enlargement (−4, 2). Label this triangle C.

c)   Draw the translation $\begin{pmatrix} 7 \\ -6 \end{pmatrix}$ of triangle A, and label this triangle D.

5   a)   On a sheet of squared paper or graph paper, put an origin at the bottom left, and draw parallelogram ABCD with A at (6, 9), B at (6, 15), C at (8, 17) and D at (8, 11).

b)   Enlarge ABCD using centre of enlargement (10, 15) and scale factor 2.

c)   (i)   Calculate the area of ABCD.

(ii)   Calculate the area of the enlarged parallelogram.

(iii)   Write the ratio of these areas in its lowest form.

The polar system

After an accident on board a fishing trawler, the captain radioed for help. He gave the trawler's position as *30 kilometres east of Newcastle.*

In mathematics, when a position is described using a distance and a direction, it is said to be in **polar co-ordinates**. The distance is measured from the **pole** and the angle is measured anticlockwise from the **initial line** as shown below.

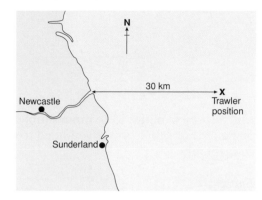

Any point P can be identified using cartesian co-ordinates in the form (x, y), or using polar co-ordinates in the form (r, θ).

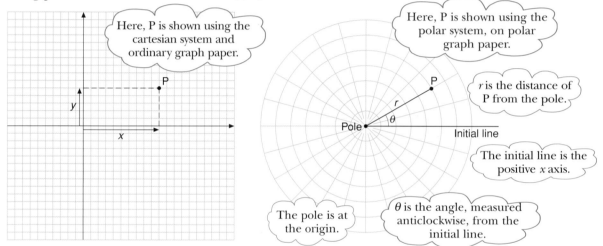

Here, P is shown using the cartesian system and ordinary graph paper.

Here, P is shown using the polar system, on polar graph paper.

r is the distance of P from the pole.

The initial line is the positive *x* axis.

The pole is at the origin.

θ is the angle, measured anticlockwise, from the initial line.

You can convert the co-ordinates of any point from one form to the other.

This is the point $(0, 1)$ in cartesian co-ordinates. It is the point $(1, 90)$ in polar co-ordinates.

 What are the polar co-ordinates of the points A and B in this diagram?

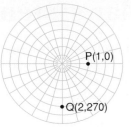

What are the cartesian co-ordinates of the points P and Q in this diagram?

P(1,0)

•Q(2,270)

The above examples were quite simple, because the points were all on the *x* or *y* axis. For other points you need to use trigonometry to convert the co-ordinates.

Example

a) Convert the polar co-ordinates of point A (100, 120°) to cartesian form.

b) Convert the cartesian co-ordinates of point B(−3, −4) to polar form.

Solution

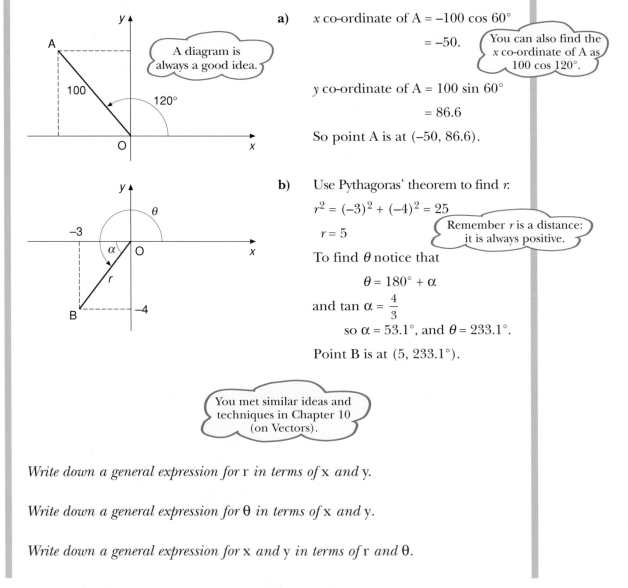

a) *x* co-ordinate of A = −100 cos 60°

= −50.

You can also find the x co-ordinate of A as 100 cos 120°.

A diagram is always a good idea.

y co-ordinate of A = 100 sin 60°

= 86.6

So point A is at (−50, 86.6).

b) Use Pythagoras' theorem to find *r*:

$$r^2 = (-3)^2 + (-4)^2 = 25$$

$$r = 5$$

Remember r is a distance: it is always positive.

To find θ notice that

$$\theta = 180° + \alpha$$

and $\tan \alpha = \dfrac{4}{3}$

so $\alpha = 53.1°$, and $\theta = 233.1°$.

Point B is at (5, 233.1°).

You met similar ideas and techniques in Chapter 10 (on Vectors).

Write down a general expression for r *in terms of* x *and* y.

Write down a general expression for θ *in terms of* x *and* y.

Write down a general expression for x *and* y *in terms of* r *and* θ.

Exercise 12.2

1 Find the cartesian co-ordinates of P in each of these.

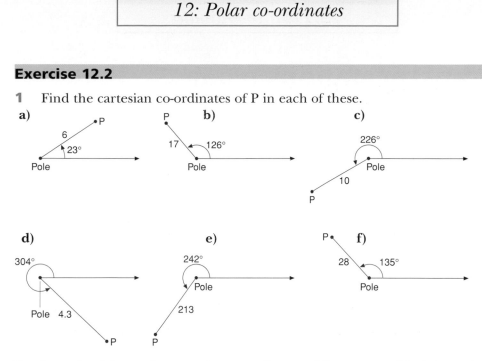

2 In each of these, the cartesian co-ordinates of P are given. Find the polar co-ordinates of P.

a) (5, 12)

b) (−8, 15)

c) (−9, −40)

d) (11, −60)

e) (−20, 21)

f) (−16, −63)

3 A set of kitchen scales has a circular dial as shown. The pointer has length 9 cm.

With the centre of the dial as the pole, express the position of the tip of the pointer in polar co-ordinates when the reading is:

a) 2 kg

b) 1 kg

c) 8 kg

d) 5 kg.

4 **a)** Through what angle does the hour hand of a clock pass

(i) in one hour?   (ii) in 10 minutes?

A clock has a hour hand 3 cm long and a minute hand 5 cm long.

b) Find the polar co-ordinates of the tip of each hand when the clock shows

(i)   3 o'clock   (ii) 5 o'clock
(iii) 6.30 p.m.   (iv) 7.40 p.m.

Transformations using polar co-ordinates

You have already met transformations using cartesian co-ordinates. Some transformations are much easier to handle if you use the polar system.

Example

In the diagram, P_1 is the reflection of point P in the line OA.

Find the polar co-ordinates of the point P_1.

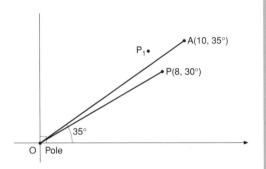

Solution

Line OP_1 is a reflection of line OP in line OA, so

$OP_1 = OP = 8$ units

and, $\angle P_1OA = \angle POA = 5°$.

So P_1 is the point $(8, 40°)$.

 Sketch a copy of the diagram above and show on it the point $B(10, 90°)$.

Add the points Q and Q_1, which are reflections of P and P_1 in the line OB.

What rotation about O would map P onto Q_1?

 The diagrams below show shapes that have been enlarged by a scale factor of 2, with the pole as centre of enlargement.

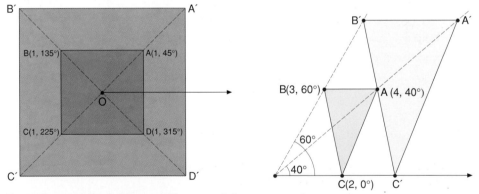

In each case, find the co-ordinates of the new vertices.

What rule can you identify about the effect on polar co-ordinates of an enlargement centred on the pole?

Check your rule on some other shapes.

Exercise 12.3

1

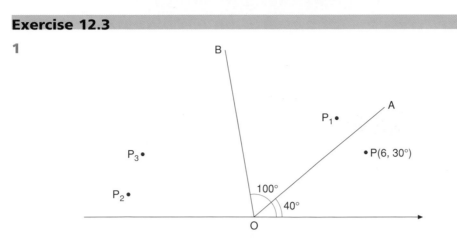

a) The point P has co-ordinates $(6, 30°)$, and P_1 is the reflection of P in OA. Find the co-ordinates of P_1.

b) The point P_2 is the reflection of the point P in the line OB. Find the polar co-ordinates of P_2.

c) The point P_3 is the reflection of the point P_1 in the line OB. Find the polar co-ordinates of P_3.

d) What rotation about O will map P onto P_3?

2 On polar graph paper, draw the triangle A $(3, 0°)$, B $(4, 0°)$, C $(5, 30°)$.

a) Rotate triangle ABC through $45°$ anticlockwise and write down the co-ordinates of the resulting triangle's vertices, A', B' and C'.

b) Reflect $A'B'C'$ in the line $\theta = 90°$ to obtain a triangle $A''B''C''$. Write down the co-ordinates of the points A'', B'' and C''.

c) Reflect $A''B''C''$ in the line $\theta = 200°$ to obtain a triangle A''', B''', C'''. Write down the co-ordinates of the points A''', B''' and C'''.

d) What rotation will map $A'''B'''C'''$ onto ABC?

3 The points A $(2, 10°)$, B $(2, 30°)$, C $(4, 20°)$ form a triangle. The triangle is enlarged by scale factor 3 and then rotated through $50°$ anticlockwise.

Give the final position of the points in polar co-ordinates.

4 Find the mirror line when $(5, 10°)$ maps to $(5, 110°)$, $(3, 20°)$ maps to $(3, 100°)$ and $(1, 40°)$ maps to $(1, 80°)$.

5 Zoe performs an enlargement followed by a rotation on the points $(2, 10°)$, $(4, 70°)$ and $(6, 100°)$.

The points become $(5, 40°)$, $(10, 100°)$ and $(15, 130°)$ respectively.

a) State the scale factor of the enlargement.

b) State the angle of rotation.

Radar screens – an application of polar co-ordinates

Radar screens make use of polar co-ordinates. The pole is at the radar installation. A lighted vector sweeps the screen as the radar system sweeps the surrounding area. Ships and other objects show up on the screen as lighted 'blips' recording their distance and direction.

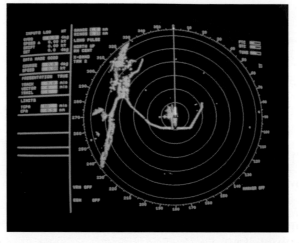

Example

A computer-controlled lightship is fitted with radar. When the *Beatrice* strikes a rock at (50, 74°) and sends out a distress call, the lightship immediately detects that the *Adelaide* is also nearby, at (70, 90°), travelling due South.

The lightship calls the *Adelaide* and gives a distance, *d* kilometres, and a course to steer, so that the crew of the *Adelaide* can assist that of the *Beatrice*.

What is the value of *d*, and what is the bearing?

Solution

The distance, *d*, is given by the cosine rule:

$$d^2 = 70^2 + 50^2 - 2 \times 50 \times 70 \times \cos 16°$$

$$= 671.2$$

So *d* = 25.9 km.

The *Adelaide* must travel approximately 26 km to reach the *Beatrice*.

The angle α is given by the sine rule:

$$\sin \alpha = \frac{50 \times \sin 16°}{26} = 0.5300$$

$$\text{so } \alpha = 32°.$$

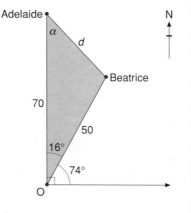

The *Adelaide's* course (or bearing) should be 180 – α, i.e. 148°.

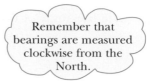

Remember that bearings are measured clockwise from the North.

Exercise 12.4

1 Find the distance between the pairs of ships shown on the following radar screens.

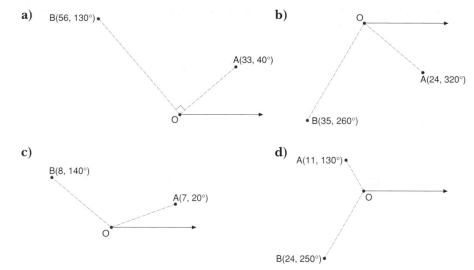

2 A rubber dinghy carrying two children has been blown out to sea by the wind.

An anchored lightship sees them at position (9600, 110°) on the radar screen. The units are metres.

The lightship calls the *Enid* which is at position (8500, 50°) and requests her to travel on a bearing of 280° to intercept the dinghy which is being blown on a bearing of 160°.

a) Find the distance between the dinghy and the *Enid* at this moment.

b) Draw a clear diagram, showing the lightship, the dinghy, the *Enid* and the interception point. (Look carefully at the angles.)

c) State the polar co-ordinates of the interception point.

d) Calculate the distance that the dinghy will travel to the interception point.

3 A lightship noted the positions of the following ships at 8 a.m. and again at 11 a.m.

For each ship, find the distance and direction of travel. (The screen is orientated with the initial line pointing to the East.)

	8 a.m.		11 a.m.	
	distance	angle	distance	angle
a) *Bright Buoy*	81	100	50	172
b) *Hope*	5	20	8	80
c) *Happy Days*	10	30	5	88
d) *Astra*	34	190	40	316

Finishing off

Now that you have finished this chapter you should be able to:

★ use the conventions for writing polar co-ordinates

★ use polar co-ordinates in solving problems.

Use the questions in the next exercise to check that you understand everything.

Mixed exercise 12.5

1 For each of these pairs of polar co-ordinates, draw a diagram and convert to cartesian form.

    a) $(100, 63°)$ **b)** $(12, 164°)$ **c)** $(20, 267°)$ **d)** $(50, 282°)$

2 For each of these pairs of cartesian co-ordinates, draw a diagram and convert to polar form.

    a) $(10, 6)$ **b)** $(11, –2)$ **c)** $(–4, –9)$ **d)** $(–1, 3)$

3 At mountain tops you sometimes find diagrams like the one below, giving distances and directions to other peaks. This allows you to identify the peaks that you can see around you.

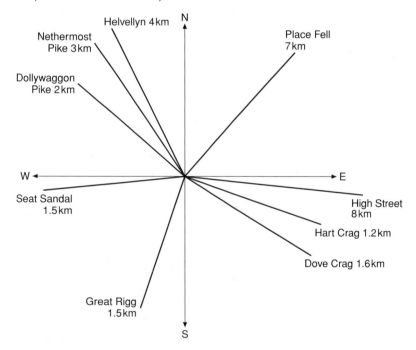

Choose three peaks on the diagram, and for each one measure the angle from due East and give its polar co-ordinates.

Mixed exercise 12.5 continued

4 A car speedometer reads kph as shown.

The pointer on the dial is 6 cm long and is pointing to 30 kph at the moment. The dial reads from 0 to 150 kph.

Find the polar co-ordinates of the tip of the points when the speedometer reading is

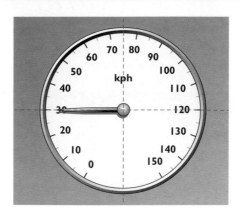

a) 0 kph   **b)** 30 kph
c) 75 kph   **d)** 120 kph.

5 On polar graph paper draw the triangle ABC with vertices A (6, 0°), B (9, 30°) and C (5, 60°).

a) Rotate triangle ABC through 90° anticlockwise and state the co-ordinates of new triangle A′B′C′.

b) Reflect A′B′C′ in the line θ = 180° and state the co-ordinates of the new triangle A″B″C″.

c) Reflect A″B″C″ in the line θ = 270° and state the co-ordinates of the new triangle A‴B‴C‴.

d) What rotation will map A‴B‴C‴ onto ABC?

6 The points A (4, 0°), B (8, 20°) and C (12, 40°) form a triangle.

The triangle ABC is enlarged by scale factor 2.5 and then rotated through 90° anticlockwise.

Give the final position of the vertices, using polar co-ordinates.

7 Find the mirror line when (6, 30°) maps to (6, 150°), (10, 50°) maps to (10, 130°) and (2, 70°) maps to (2, 110°).

8 Under an enlargement followed by a rotation, the point (2, 10°) maps to (7, 60°), the point (6, 30°) maps to (21, 80°), and the point (10, 70°) maps to (35, 120°).

a) State the scale factor of the enlargement.

b) State the angle of rotation.

9

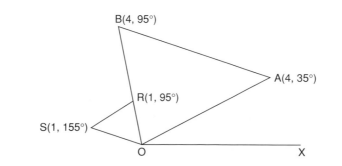

Prove that the triangles SOB and ROA in the diagram are congruent.

Chapter 13

Review: Arithmetic

This chapter revises work on:

★ the basic arithmetic in which you need to be confident.

Review exercise 13.1

1   A water butt has a capacity of 50 gallons. Approximately how many litres does it contain when it is three quarters full?

2   Amy sees a jacket in a French store. It is priced at 975 francs.

There are 9.63 francs to a pound.

Find the approximate cost of the jacket in pounds.

Show clearly what approximations you have made.

3   **a)** Write as the product of prime factors (i) 60 and (ii) 135.

b) What is the highest common factor of 60 and 135?

c) What is the lowest common multiple of 60 and 135?

4   Work out

a) $-5 + 4$ **b)** $-2 - 3$ **c)** $(-4) \times (+9)$ **d)** $(-42) \div (+6)$

e) $\dfrac{-21}{-3}$ **f)** $\dfrac{(+15) \times (-6)}{(+10)}$ **g)** $(-1)^4$ **h)** $\dfrac{(+48)}{(-8)} - \dfrac{(-36)}{(+9)}$

5   Work out

a) $(3 + 4) \times 5$ **b)** $3 + (4 \times 5)$

c) $3 + 4 \times 5$ **d)** $6 - 9 + 4$

e) $6 - (9 + 4)$ **f)** $3 + (6 \div 3) - 1$

g) $[6 \times (5 - 2)] + 4$ **h)** $(6 \div 2)^2 + (18 \div 3)$

6   Work out

a) $1\frac{1}{4} + 2\frac{3}{16}$ **b)** $5\frac{2}{5} - 1\frac{1}{2}$ **c)** $9\frac{3}{8} - 7\frac{2}{3}$ **d)** $15\frac{3}{4} + 11\frac{5}{6}$

e) $4\frac{2}{3} \times 1\frac{6}{7}$ **f)** $5\frac{5}{8} \times 4\frac{1}{2}$ **g)** $3\frac{5}{8} \div 2$ **h)** $8\frac{1}{4} \div 1\frac{3}{8}$

7   Work out

a) $1.85 + 2.7$ **b)** $5 - 0.63$ **c)** 3.3×4.1 **d)** 2.3×0.05

e) 6.2^2 **f)** $5.8 \div 0.2$ **g)** $0.03 \div 1.2$ **h)** $0.6 \div 0.006$

8   In each of these, arrange the numbers in order of size, smallest first.

a) $\frac{1}{9}$, 0.1, 0.9, $\frac{1}{11}$, 0.09   **b)** 0.67, $\frac{17}{25}$, 0.667, $\frac{2}{3}$, 0.6666

Review exercise 13.1 *continued*

9 Kim is carrying out a survey on people's eating habits. From the questionnaires returned to her she produces this chart to show people's favourite type of food when they eat out.

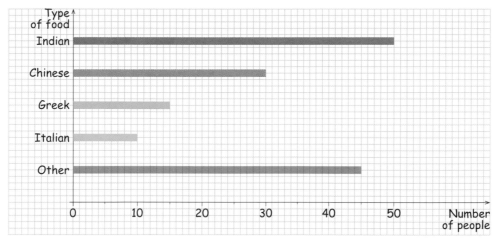

a) What percentage of these favour (i) Chinese? (ii) Indian?

b) Which type of food is favoured by 10% of Kim's respondents?

c) Kim sent out 600 questionnaires. She expected a 30% return. How many questionnaires short of this target is she?

10 A holiday costs £379 this year. The same holiday next year costs 5% more. Toby gets a 5% discount when he buys a holiday for next year. How much does he pay for the holiday?

11 Write each ratio in a common unit and then express it in its simplest form.

a) 4 cm:80 mm

b) $1\frac{1}{2}$ hours:36 minutes

c) 3 kg:875 g

d) 5 cm:1 km

e) 70 cl:0.5 l

f) 1.2 m:450 mm.

12 a) Share £630 in the ratio 3:4.

b) Share £2450 in the ratio 5:3:2.

13 Mahmood and Calum share a bonus in the ratio 4:7. Calum gets £33 more than Mahmood. How much is the bonus?

14

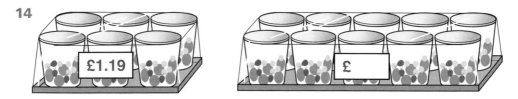

What is the highest price that can be written on the ten pack price tag so that the ten pack is better value than the six pack?

15 Musicmakers Limited puts one sixth of its profits into improving its premises. The remainder is shared by Jack and Ruth, the owners, in the ratio 5:4.

Jack gets £27 500. What is the total profit?

Percentage calculations

Reminder

- A 15% increase can be calculated by multiplying by 1.15

    $100\% + 15\% = 115\%$ and $\dfrac{115}{100} = 1.15$.

- Similarly, an 8% decrease can be calculated by multiplying by 0.92.

Review exercise 13.2

1 In a sale a dress costs £32.40.

The original price has been reduced by 10%.

What was the original price?

NEAB

2 A tourist buys a stereo which costs £155.10, including VAT at 17.5%.

Tourists do not have to pay VAT.

How much does the tourist pay?

MEI

3 A large car manufacturer makes an agreement about its employees' wage increases in the next three years.

a) One employee's wages rise by exactly 4% in each of the next three years. He is currently being paid £10 625 per year.

How much will he be paid per year after three years?

b) A second employee's wages will rise by exactly 4% next year.

Next year he will be paid £13 468.

How much is he currently being paid per year?

MEI

4 £500 is invested for 2 years at 6% per annum compound interest.

a) Work out the total interest earned over two years.

£250 is invested for 3 years at 7% per annum compound interest.

b) By what single number must £250 be multiplied to obtain the total amount at the end of the 3 years?

London

5 a) Paula invests £2000 in a bank which pays interest at 5.3% per year compound interest. The interest is added to the account at the end of each complete year.

How much will her investment be worth after four complete years?

b) Paula invests £1000 in another bank. The investment will be worth £2000 after 10 years.

What rate of compound interest is this?

MEI

Review exercise 13.2 *continued*

6 In a sale a pair of trainers costs £25.
This is a saving of 20%.

What was the original price of the shoes?

NEAB

7 **a)** The Inland Revenue expects
a further 1.5 million to return
their forms by the end of
the month.

What percentage of taxpayers
are expected **not** to have
returned their forms by then?

THE DAILY MOON

No. 6,251   MONDAY 3 July 2000   75p

Forms sent out to 8 million taxpayers

Only 3.3 million
have returned
forms so far !!

b) A newspaper surveyed 1000 taxpayers chosen at random.

Only 48% had studied the form, of whom 45% said they understood it.

How many of those surveyed said they understood the form?

c) In the survey, 41% said they would pay an accountant to complete the
form for them.

The average charge by accountants is £60 per form.

If the survey is representative, how much would accountants receive in
total from the 8 million people who originally received the form?

MEI

8 When a ball is dropped onto a
floor, it bounces and then rises.
This is shown in the diagram.

The ball rises to 80% of
the height from which it
was dropped.

It was dropped from a height
of 3 metres.

a) Calculate the height of the
rise after the first bounce.

The ball bounces a
second time.

It rises to 80% of the height of
the first rise.

b) Calculate the height of the
second rise.

c) The ball carries on bouncing in this way.

Each time it rises to 80% of the last rise.

For how many bounces does it rise to a height greater than 1 metre?

NEAB

Accuracy

Reminder

- When a length l is given in metres as $l = 23$, you know that

    $$22.5 \leq l < 23.5.$$

- When an area A m^2 is given as 23 m by 14 m, you know that

    $$22.5 \times 13.5 \leq A < 23.5 \times 14.5.$$

Review exercise 13.3

1 Sections of a railway line are measured to the nearest metre as either 200 m or 80 m.

What are the upper and lower bounds on the total length of 15 sections, consisting of eight 200 m sections and seven 80 m sections?

SEG

2 A full jar of coffee weighs 750 g. The empty jar weighs 545 g. Both weights are accurate to the nearest 5 g.

Calculate the maximum and minimum possible values of the weight of the coffee in the jar.

MEG

3 Mr Jones weighs his case on his bathroom scales which weigh to the nearest kilogram.

He finds that his case weighs 20 kg.

a) What are the greatest and least weights of the case?

On the way to the airport he removes his sweater from the case.

At the airport the scales give the weight of his case as 19.4 kg to the nearest tenth of a kilogram.

b) What is the heaviest weight that the sweater could be?

NEAB

4 $x = 40$, correct to the nearest 10. $y = 60$, correct to the nearest 10.

a) (i) Write down the lower bound of x.

(ii) Write down the upper bound of y.

b) Calculate the greatest possible value of xy.

c) Calculate the least possible value of $\dfrac{x}{y}$.

Give your answer correct to 3 significant figures.

d) Calculate the greatest possible value of $\dfrac{x+10}{x}$.

Give your answer correct to 3 significant figures.

London

5 On the scales in Ali's book shop the weight of a book correct to 2 decimal places is 0.62 kg.

    a) Write down

        (i)   the lower bound of the weight of the book;

        (ii) the upper bound of the weight of the book.

    Ali needs to work out the weight of 50 copies of the book. He uses his value for the weight of one book.

    b) Calculate

        (i)   the lower bound of the weight of 50 books;

        (ii) the upper bound of the weight of 50 books.

    c) Calculate the greatest possible error that could occur in calculating the weight of 50 copies of the book.

    d) Write down the greatest possible error that could occur in calculating the weight of 500 copies of the book.

London

6 Cleo used a pair of scales to measure, in kilograms, the weight of a brick. The scales were accurate to the nearest 100 g.

    She read the scales as accurately as she could and wrote down the weight as 1.437 kg. Anthony said that this was not a sensible weight to write down. Explain why Anthony was correct.

London

7 The formula
$$x = \frac{10}{a - b}$$
is used to calculate a value of x from measured values of a and b.

    Louise measures a as 5.1 and b as 3.4.

    What should Louise quote as the maximum possible true value of x?

MEI

8 **a)** A roll of dress material measures 23 metres, correct to the nearest metre. A shopkeeper cuts material of length 6 m 40 cm, correct to the nearest 10 cm, from the roll. What is the maximum possible length of material left on the roll?

    b) Salma is doing an environmental science project about a park in her town. She uses a local map with a scale of 1:20 000 to estimate the distance from her home to the park and to estimate the area of the park.

        (i)   Salma measures the map distance from her home to the park gate as 16.3 cm, correct to the nearest mm. Calculate, in kilometres, the minimum possible distance from Salma's home to the park gate.

        (ii) The area representing the park on the map is 7 cm^2, correct to the nearest cm^2. Find the maximum possible area of the park in km^2.

MEG

Finishing off

> **Now that you have finished this chapter you should:**
>
> ★ feel confident in your arithmetic.

Use the questions in the next exercise to check that you understand everything.

Mixed exercise 13.4

1   Write down the value of x, y and z.

a)

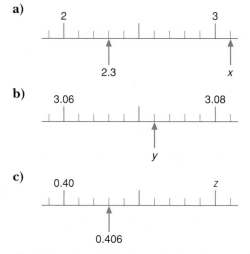

b)

c)

d)   Write the following decimals in order, smallest first.

   0.0016,   0.000 985,   0.01,   0.002

SMP

2   A farm has an area of 324 hectares of land.

   $\dfrac{1}{6}$ of the land is woodland and $\dfrac{5}{18}$ is pasture.

   The rest of the land is arable.

   a)   What fraction of the land is arable?

   b)   Calculate the area of arable land.

NEAB

3   A walking club hires a coach for a journey of 210 miles.

   The coach company charges 90p per mile plus £38.

   49 walkers travel on the coach.

   Each walker is charged £5 for the journey.

   Without using a calculator, do a rough calculation to check whether the charge is about right.

   Show all the approximations you make.

MEI

Mixed exercise 13.4 *continued*

4 **a)** Express the following numbers as the products of their prime factors.

    (i) 72   (ii) 80

    b) Two cars go around a race track. The first car takes 1 minute 12 seconds to complete a circuit and the other takes 1 minute 20 seconds.

        They start together on the starting line.

        Find the length of time, in minutes, before they are together again.

                                                     SEG

5 There are 12 inches in 1 foot.

    There are 3 feet in a yard.

    There are 2.54 centimetres in 1 inch.

    Express 1 metre in yards. Give your answer correct to 3 decimal places.

                                                       London

6 On Liftoff flights the fare from London to New York is £310.

    From March 31st the fares will be increased by 13%.

    A discount of 4.5% will be offered on night flights.

    How much will a ticket for a night flight from London to New York cost after March 31st?

                                                       SMP

7 In this question you MUST use your calculator and you MAY write down any stage of your calculation.

        Evaluate $\quad \dfrac{(23.4+35.6) \times 5.7}{200.3 \times (16.2-8.15)}$

                                                       London

8 **a)** Karen and Carl divided a packet of 48 biscuits in the ratio 1:2.

        How many biscuits did Carl receive?

    b) Sam ate $\frac{2}{3}$ of the sweets in a bag. Tom ate $\frac{1}{4}$ of the **remaining** sweets.

        (i) What fraction of the **original** number of sweets did Tom eat?

        (ii) There were 9 sweets left after Sam and Tom had eaten their sweets. How many sweets were originally in the bag?

                                                     MEG

9 Lee wants to find the area of a rectangular field. He uses a measuring wheel to measure the length and width of the field.

    Unfortunately this wheel is only accurate to within 10%.

    a) Work out the maximum possible overestimate in the calculated area of the field.

    b) Work out the maximum possible underestimate in the calculated area of the field.

                                                       MEG

Mixed exercise 13.4 *continued*

10 A lake is 320 metres wide. On a map, the lake is shown as 8 millimetres wide.

What area would be shown on the map for a marsh with area 12 square kilometres?

MEI

11 **a)** Find the percentage change when £1640 is increased to £1845.

   b) In 1995 Mr and Mrs Mann paid £160.48 for their house insurance. The cost of insurance has risen by 2.5% each year.

   How much should they pay in 1998?

MEG

12 The number 1998 can be written as $2 \times 3^n \times p$, where n is a whole number and p is a prime number.

   i) Work out the values of n and p.

   ii) Using your answers to part i), or otherwise, work out the factor of 1998 which is between 100 and 200.

London

13 Le Goff deliver 50 boxes to Paris.

They charge 990 French francs to deliver each box.

£1 = 8.85 French francs.

Work out Le Goff's charge, in £, for delivering the 50 boxes.

Give your answer correct to the nearest £.

London

14 There are 14 pounds in a stone.

There are 2.2 pounds in a kilogram.

A man weighs 13 stone 6 pounds.

Work out his weight in kilograms.

Give your answer to the nearest kilogram.

London

15 **a)** A parcel is weighed on digital scales which record weight correct to the nearest one pound. The scales record 12 pounds. What is the least possible weight of the parcel?

   b) **(i)** Convert 12.35 pounds to kilograms, taking 1 kg to be 2.2 pounds. Write down all the figures shown on your calculator display.

   (ii) Write down your answer to part **b)**(i) correct to the nearest kilogram.

   c) A second parcel is weighed on the digital scales and its weight is also recorded as 12 pounds. When the scales are set to record weights in kilograms, correct to the nearest kilogram, the weights shown for the parcels are not the same.

   Suggest a possible reason for this.

MEG

Mixed exercise 13.4 *continued*

16

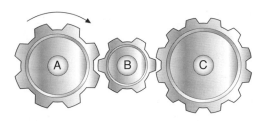

The diagram shows three intersecting cog wheels.

Wheel A has 8 cogs.

Wheel B has 6 cogs.

Wheel C has 12 cogs.

a) Wheel A turns clockwise. In which direction does wheel B turn?

b) Wheel A makes 3 complete revolutions.

    (i)   How many complete revolutions does wheel B make?

    (ii) How many complete revolutions does wheel C make?

MEG

17 The formula $f = \dfrac{uv}{u+v}$ is used in the study of light.

a) Calculate f when $u = 14.9$ and $v = -10.2$.

    Give your answer correct to 3 significant figures.

b) By rounding the values of u and v in part **a)** to 2 significant figures, check whether your answer to **a)** is reasonable.

    Show your working.

MEG

18 The diagram shows an 'off road vehicle' and a scale model of the same vehicle.

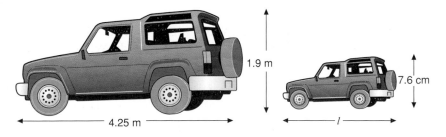

a) Calculate the length, l, of the model.

b) The area of the spare wheel cover in the model is 7.1 cm^2.

    Calculate the area of the spare wheel cover on the actual vehicle.

    Give your answer in square centimetres.

SMP

Chapter 14

Review: Equations and formulae

> **This chapter revises work on:**
>
> ★ inequalities
>
> ★ simultaneous linear equations
>
> ★ quadratic equations
>
> ★ finding a formula.

Inequalities

Inequalities can be solved in the same way as equations, except that if you multiply or divide both sides by a negative number, you must reverse the inequality sign.

Explain why this is the case.

Example

Solve the inequality $2x - 5 > 5x + 4$.

Solution

Two possible ways of solving the inequality are shown below.

$$2x - 5 > 5x + 4$$
$$-3x - 5 > 4$$
$$-3x > 9$$
$$x < 9 \div (-3)$$
$$x < -3$$

> The inequality sign is reversed when dividing by −3.

$$2x - 5 > 5x + 4$$
$$-5 > 3x + 4$$
$$-9 > 3x$$
$$-3 > x$$
$$x < -3$$

> In this case the x terms are collected on the right to avoid getting a negative x term.

> Notice that the inequality sign has been reversed.

Quadratic inequalities

Example

Solve the inequality $2x^2 + 1 \geq 9$.

Solution

$$2x^2 + 1 \geq 9$$
$$2x^2 \geq 8$$
$$x^2 \geq 4$$
$$x \leq -2 \quad \text{or} \quad x \geq 2$$

This graph illustrates the solution to the inequality.

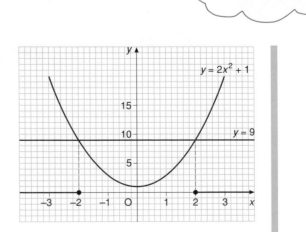

Review exercise 14.1

1 Solve these inequalities.

a) $3x + 4 > 13$

b) $1 - 4x \le 9$

c) $x^2 < 16$

d) $4x - 1 \ge x + 11$

e) $3 - 2x > 1 - 5x$

f) $2x^2 - 3 > 5$

g) $4(2x - 1) \le 3(6 - x)$

h) $(x - 4)(x + 2) < (x - 1)(x - 3)$

i) $\dfrac{2x}{3} \ge \dfrac{x + 2}{4}$

j) $\dfrac{3x - 1}{4} \le \dfrac{3 - 2x}{5}$

2 **a)** Solve the inequality $2x - 3 < 4 - 3x$.

b) Draw the graphs of $y = 2x - 3$ and $y = 4 - 3x$ on the same set of axes.

c) Use your graphs to verify the solution that you found in **a)**.

3 Richard has a choice of three different gas suppliers. Company A has a £5 quarterly standing charge plus 50p per unit used. Company B has a £12 quarterly standing charge plus 48p per unit used. Company C has no standing charge and charges 52p per unit used.

a) Which would be the cheapest supplier if Richard used very little gas?

b) Which would be the cheapest supplier if Richard used a lot of gas?

c) Richard uses n units of gas per quarter. For what values of n should Richard use company A?

4 Sam makes a triangle out of three straws.

The straws have lengths x, $4x$ and $(x + 5)$.

The longest straw has length $4x$.

Sam puts the longest straw on the table.

He places the other two straws as shown in the diagram.

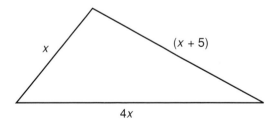

a) Explain why

$$x + (x + 5) > 4x.$$

b) Solve the inequality

$$x + x + 5 > 4x.$$

NEAB

Simultaneous equations

Example 1

Solve the simultaneous equations

$$2p + q = 7 \qquad ①$$
$$4p + 3q = 15 \qquad ②$$

Solution

$$
\begin{array}{ll}
① \times 3 & 6p + 3q = 21 \\
② & 4p + 3q = 15 \\
\text{Subtract} & 2p \quad\;\; = 6 \\
& \qquad p = 3 \\
\text{Substitute into ①:} & 6 + q = 7 \\
& \qquad q = 1
\end{array}
$$

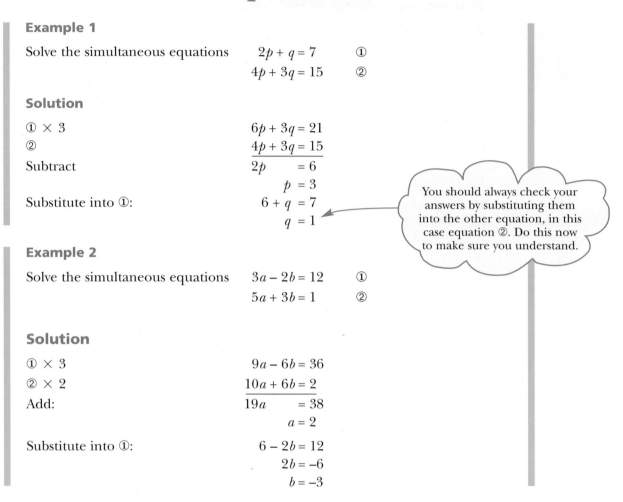

> You should always check your answers by substituting them into the other equation, in this case equation ②. Do this now to make sure you understand.

Example 2

Solve the simultaneous equations

$$3a - 2b = 12 \qquad ①$$
$$5a + 3b = 1 \qquad ②$$

Solution

$$
\begin{array}{ll}
① \times 3 & 9a - 6b = 36 \\
② \times 2 & 10a + 6b = 2 \\
\text{Add:} & 19a \qquad = 38 \\
& \qquad a = 2 \\
\text{Substitute into ①:} & 6 - 2b = 12 \\
& \qquad 2b = -6 \\
& \qquad b = -3
\end{array}
$$

? *Why were the equations subtracted in Example 1 but added in Example 2?*

The method used in Examples 1 and 2 is called **elimination**.

Example 3 shows the method of **substitution**.

Example 3

Solve the simultaneous equations

$$5x - 2y = 5 \qquad ①$$
$$y = 2x - 1 \qquad ②$$

Solution

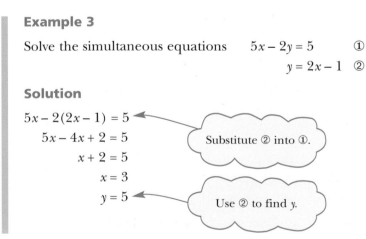

$$
\begin{aligned}
5x - 2(2x - 1) &= 5 \\
5x - 4x + 2 &= 5 \\
x + 2 &= 5 \\
x &= 3 \\
y &= 5
\end{aligned}
$$

> Substitute ② into ①.

> Use ② to find *y*.

? *Why was the method of substitution easier to use than the method of elimination in Example 3?*

Review exercise 14.2

1 Solve these pairs of simultaneous equations.

a) $2x + y = 7$
$3x - y = 3$

b) $3a + 2b = 8$
$2a - b = 10$

c) $4p + q = 11$
$5p + 3q = 12$

d) $3c - 4d = 5$
$7c - 2d = -3$

e) $3g + 2h = 13$
$4g - 3h = -11$

f) $2x - 3y = -2$
$y = 3x - 4$

g) $5w - 2z = -16$
$3w - 5z = -21$

h) $3p + 4q = 2$
$2p + 9q = -5$

i) $s = 3t - 1$
$2s = 7t - 4$

j) $a = 2b + 7$
$b = 3a - 11.$

2 Find the point of intersection of each of these pairs of graphs.

a) $y = 4x + 1$ and $y = 10 - 2x$

b) $y = 3x - 2$ and $2x + 3y = 16$

c) $3x - y = 10$ and $2y + x = 1.$

3 Julie buys 3 bars of chocolate and 5 packets of crisps for £2.59.

Simon buys 2 bars of chocolate and 3 packets of crisps for £1.64.

Find the cost of a bar of chocolate and the cost of a packet of crisps.

4 A graph has equation

$y = x^2 + ax + b.$

The graph goes through the
points with co-ordinates $(1, -2)$
and $(-2, -5)$.

Find the values of a and b.

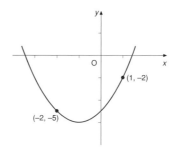

5 The cost, W pounds, of a chest of drawers may be calculated using the formula

$W = k + md$

k and m are constants and d is the number of drawers.

The cost of a chest of drawers with 4 drawers is £117.

The cost of a chest of drawers with 6 drawers is £149.

a) Use the information to write down two equations in k and m.

b) Solve the equations to find the value of m.

Edexcel

Quadratic expressions and equations

Factorising quadratic expressions

Example

Factorise

a) $ab + 2a - 3b - 6$ 　　　　**b)** $x^2 - 5x + 4$ 　　　　**c)** $2y^2 + y - 3$

Solution

a) Start by factorising in pairs.

$$ab + 2a - 3b - 6 = a(b + 2) - 3(b + 2)$$

$$= (a - 3)(b + 2)$$

> $b + 2$ is a common factor.

b) You need to split up the middle term before factorising in pairs. To do this, find two numbers which multiply to give the last term, 4, and add to give the coefficient of the middle term, −5.

These numbers are −4 and −1.

$$x^2 - 5x + 4 = x^2 - 4x - x + 4$$

$$= x(x - 4) - (x - 4)$$

$$= (x - 1)(x - 4)$$

> In a simple example like this, you may be able to go straight to the answer, but you should check by multiplying out.

c) In this example the coefficient of the squared term is not 1, so you have to use a slightly different method to find how to split up the middle term.

First multiply the last term by the coefficient of the first term to get −6. Now you need to find two numbers which multiply to give −6 and add to give the coefficient of the middle term, 1.

These numbers are −2 and 3.

$$2y^2 + y - 3 = 2y^2 - 2y + 3y - 3$$

$$= 2y(y - 1) + 3(y - 1)$$

$$= (2y + 3)(y - 1)$$

Solving quadratic equations

Some quadratic equations can be solved by factorising.

Example

Solve these equations

a) $x^2 + 2x - 8 = 0$ 　　　　**b)** $x^2 - 6x + 9 = 0$ 　　　　**c)** $12x^2 + 14x + 4 = 0$

Solution

a) 　$x^2 + 2x - 8 = 0$

　$(x + 4)(x - 2) = 0$

　$x = -4$ or 2

> Either $x + 4 = 0$
> or $x - 2 = 0$.

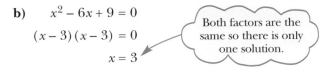

b) $x^2 - 6x + 9 = 0$

$(x - 3)(x - 3) = 0$

> Both factors are the same so there is only one solution.

$x = 3$

c) First take out the common factor 2.

$12x^2 + 14x + 4 = 0$

$2(6x^2 + 7x + 2) = 0$

$2(2x + 1)(3x + 2) = 0$

$x = -\dfrac{1}{2}$ or $-\dfrac{2}{3}$

> Make sure you can see why these are the solutions.

Using the quadratic formula

Some quadratic equations cannot be solved by factorising because their solutions are not rational. Instead, you can use the quadratic formula.

The solutions of the equation $ax^2 + bx + c = 0$ are given by

$$x = \frac{-b \pm \sqrt{(b^2 - 4ac)}}{2a}.$$

> This is the quadratic formula.

Some quadratic equations do not have solutions at all. Part **b** of the example below shows what happens when you try to use the quadratic formula on an equation with no solutions.

Example

Solve these equations, where possible.

a) $2x^2 + 3x - 6 = 0$ **b)** $3x^2 - x + 4 = 0$

Solution

a) $a = 2$, $b = 3$ and $c = -6$, so

$$x = \frac{-3 \pm \sqrt{3^2 - 4 \times 2 \times -6}}{2 \times 2}$$

$$= \frac{-3 \pm \sqrt{9 + 48}}{4}$$

$$x = \frac{-3 + \sqrt{57}}{4} \quad \text{or} \quad \frac{-3 - \sqrt{57}}{4}$$

$$x = 1.137 \quad \text{or} \quad -2.637$$

$y = 2x^2 + 3x - 6$

> These are the roots. They are either side of the line of symmetry.

b) $a = 3$, $b = -1$ and $c = 4$, so

$$x = \frac{1 \pm \sqrt{1^2 - 4 \times 3 \times 4}}{2 \times 3}$$

$$x = \frac{1 \pm \sqrt{1 - 48}}{6}$$

$$x = \frac{1 \pm \sqrt{-47}}{6}$$

$y = 3x^2 - x + 4$

> There are no roots as the graph does not cut the x-axis.

It is not possible to find the square root of a negative number, so there are no solutions.

 What does the value of $\sqrt{b^2 - 4ac}$ tell you about the solutions of the equation?

Review exercise 14.3

1 Factorise these quadratic expressions.

a) $x^2 + 7x + 10$

b) $x^2 - 5x + 6$

c) $x^2 + 3x - 4$

d) $x^2 - 9$

e) $2x^2 + 11x + 5$

f) $3x^2 + 4x - 4$

g) $4x^2 - 13x + 3$

h) $6x^2 + 5x - 6$

i) $6x^2 + 7x - 10$

j) $4x^2 - 4x + 1$

k) $8x^2 - 26x + 15$

l) $12x^2 + 20x + 3$

2 Solve these quadratic equations by factorising.

a) $x^2 - 7x + 12 = 0$

b) $x^2 - 4x - 12 = 0$

c) $2x^2 + 7x - 4 = 0$

d) $x^2 - 2x + 1 = 0$

e) $3x^2 - 11x - 4 = 0$

f) $x^2 - 9 = 0$

g) $4x^2 - 8x - 5 = 0$

h) $10x^2 + 9x - 9 = 0$

i) $4x^2 - 20x + 25 = 0$

j) $8x^2 + 3x - 5 = 0$

k) $12x^2 - 11x - 15 = 0$

l) $12x^2 + 13x - 22 = 0$

3 Solve these quadratic equations, if possible, by using the quadratic formula.

a) $x^2 + 2x - 2 = 0$

b) $x^2 - 3x + 1 = 0$

c) $2x^2 + 5x + 1 = 0$

d) $3x^2 - x + 2 = 0$

e) $2x^2 - 2x - 5 = 0$

f) $4x^2 + x - 4 = 0$

g) $-x^2 + 3x + 3 = 0$

h) $3x^2 + 4x + 6 = 0$

i) $-2x^2 + 5x - 1 = 0$

j) $5x^2 + 3x - 4 = 0$

k) $4x^2 - x - 2 = 0$

l) $-3x^2 + 3x + 1 = 0$

4 Rearrange these equations into the form $ax^2 + bx + c = 0$ and solve them by any appropriate method.

a) $x^2 + 3x = 1$

b) $2 - 3x^2 = 5x$

c) $(x - 3)(x + 1) = 4$

d) $(2x - 1)^2 = x + 3$

e) $x + \dfrac{3x}{x+2} = 2$

f) $\dfrac{4}{x} - \dfrac{1}{x^2} = 2$

g) $\dfrac{1}{x} + \dfrac{2}{x-1} = 3$

h) $\dfrac{2x-1}{x+3} = \dfrac{x+1}{3x+2}$

5 The perimeter of a rectangle is 20 cm and its area is 22 cm^2. Find the length and width of the rectangle.

6 Tom is travelling to visit some friends. There are two possible routes. The motorway route is 200 km and the 'A' road route is 180 km.

Tom uses the motorway on the way there and the 'A' roads on the way back. He finds that his average speed is 20 km/h more on the motorway route, and that it takes him 30 minutes less than the 'A' road route.

What was Tom's average speed on the motorway route?

Finding a formula

Linear sequences

In a linear sequence, the step from one number to the next is the same each time.

Example

Find the nth term of the sequence 2, 5, 8, 11, 14 ...

Solution

The numbers go up in threes, so the formula for the nth term involves multiplying by 3.

$$n\text{th term} = 3n - 1$$

> If you cannot see this straight away, think of each term as the first term + a number of 3s. Work out how many 3s you add on for the first term, the second term, etc. How many for the nth term? You can now write an expression for the nth term, that simplifies to $3n - 1$.

Quadratic sequences

In a quadratic sequence, the second differences are equal. You may be able to find the rule by comparing the sequence with the sequence of square numbers, or by finding a pattern in the factors of each term, as shown in the examples below.

Example

Find the nth term in each of the following sequences.

a) 2, 5, 10, 17, 26 ...

b) 3, 8, 15, 24, 35 ...

Solution

a) 2   5   10   17   26
    3   5   7   9
      2   2   2

> first differences
>
> second differences

All the second differences are the same, so the sequence must be quadratic.

Each term is one more than the equivalent term of the sequence of square numbers, 1, 4, 9, 16, 25..., so

$$n\text{th term} = n^2 + 1$$

b) 3   8   15   24   35
    5   7   9   11
      2   2   2

Again, the difference table shows that the sequence is quadratic.

The sequence can be written as

$$1 \times 3, \quad 2 \times 4, \quad 3 \times 5, \quad 4 \times 6, \quad 5 \times 7...$$

This pattern can be generalised to give the nth term.

$$n\text{th term} = n(n + 2)$$

In the examples above, the rule that has been found is the most obvious rule. However, there may be other correct formulae.

Find as many rules as you can for a sequence beginning 1, 2 ...

Review exercise 14.4 *continued*

7   This pattern is called a Mystic
    Rose. Lines are drawn from each
    dot to every other dot.

    This Mystic Rose has 6 dots and
    15 lines.

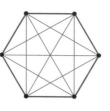

   a) Find the number of lines in
       a Mystic Rose with

       (i) 2 dots   (ii) 3 dots   (iii) 4 dots

   b) Find a formula for the number of lines in a Mystic Rose with n dots.

   c) A Mystic Rose has 210 lines. How many dots does it have?

8   Here is a number pattern that describes the arrangement of counters.

   a) Copy and complete the patterns for the 3rd, 4th, 10th and nth row.

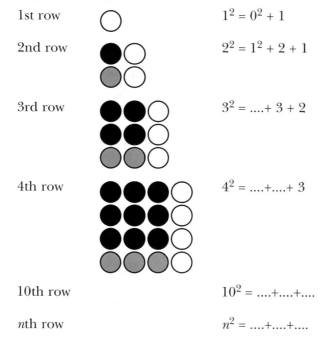

   1st row $1^2 = 0^2 + 1$

   2nd row $2^2 = 1^2 + 2 + 1$

   3rd row $3^2 = ...+ 3 + 2$

   4th row $4^2 = ...+....+ 3$

   10th row $10^2 = ...+....+....$

   nth row $n^2 = ...+....+....$

   b) Show that the right hand side of the nth row simplifies to n^2.

                                                              Edexcel

9

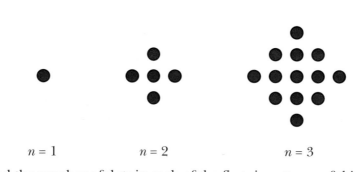

       $n = 1$ $n = 2$ $n = 3$

   a) Find the number of dots in each of the first six patterns of this sequence.

   b) Find a formula for the number of dots in the nth pattern of the sequence.

Finishing off

Now that you have finished this chapter you should be able to:

★ find a formula for a linear, quadratic or exponential sequence

★ solve linear equations and inequalities

★ solve simultaneous linear equations

★ solve quadratic equations by factorisation or the formula.

Use the questions in the next exercise to check that you understand everything.

Mixed exercise 14.5

1 Solve these equations.

  a) $2x + 5 = 4 - 3x$ **b)** $10 - x = 3 - 4x$

  c) $\dfrac{2x+1}{3} = \dfrac{x-3}{2}$ **d)** $\dfrac{2x+1}{x-4} = \dfrac{4x}{2x-3}$

  e) $\dfrac{3x-2}{6} + \dfrac{x+1}{4} = 3$ **f)** $\dfrac{4}{x} - \dfrac{3}{2x} = 2$

  g) $\dfrac{x+1}{6x} + \dfrac{2x-1}{9x} = 1$ **h)** $\dfrac{2x+1}{x-1} - \dfrac{x+1}{x+3} = 1$

2 Solve these inequalities.

  a) $3x - 2 > 5 - x$ **b)** $2x + 5 \le 4x - 7$

  c) $x^2 - 2 \ge 7$ **d)** $2(1 - 2x) < 3(x + 4)$

  e) $\dfrac{x-3}{2} < \dfrac{2-x}{3}$ **f)** $3x^2 + 2 < x^2 + 4$

  g) $\dfrac{3x+1}{4} < \dfrac{2x-1}{5}$ **h)** $(x - 2)(x + 3) \ge x(x - 4)$

  i) $\dfrac{x+1}{2} + \dfrac{2x-1}{3} \le 4$ **j)** $\dfrac{3x-2}{2} - \dfrac{1-x}{4} \le 1$

3 Solve these pairs of simultaneous equations.

  a) $2a + 3b = 9$ **b)** $3x - 4y = 8$
    $5a + b = 16$ $4x + 2y = 7$

  c) $5p + 2q = -9$ **d)** $4c - 3d = 4$
    $3p - 5q = 7$ $3c - 5d = 14$

  e) $4x - 3y = 4$ **f)** $3s - 7t = 5$
    $y = 3x + 2$ $5s - 2t = 18$

  g) $3p = 2q - 3$ **h)** $a = 2b - 5$
    $2p = 12 - q$ $b = 3a + 10$

Mixed exercise 14.5 *continued*

4   Solve these quadratic equations, where possible.

   a) $x^2 + 2x - 15 = 0$

   b) $2x^2 - 7x + 6 = 0$

   c) $x^2 + 3x - 5 = 0$

   d) $3x^2 - x + 1 = 0$

   e) $2x^2 + 5x = 2$

   f) $6 + x - x^2 = 0$

   g) $\dfrac{x+2}{2x+1} = \dfrac{x-2}{x+1}$

   h) $\dfrac{1}{x} - \dfrac{3}{x+1} = 2$

   i) $\dfrac{3x-2}{x+1} + \dfrac{2x-1}{x-2} = 1$

   j) $\dfrac{2x+1}{4x} + \dfrac{1+x}{2x^2} = 1$

5   Find a formula for the nth term of each of these sequences.

   a) 4, 7, 10, 13, 16 ...

   b) 5, 8, 13, 20, 29 ...

   c) 6, 18, 54, 162 ...

   d) 2.5, 3, 3.5, 4, 4.5 ...

   e) 3, 12, 27, 48, 75 ...

   f) 3, 15, 75, 375...

   g) 3, 1, −1, −3, −5 ...

   h) 4, 8, 16, 32, 64 ...

6   A company makes compact discs (CDs).

   The total cost, P pounds, of making n compact discs is given by the formula

   $$P = a + bn$$

   where a and b are constants.

   The cost of making 1000 compact discs is £58 000.

   The cost of making 2000 compact discs is £64 000.

   a) Calculate the values of a and b.

   The company sells the compact discs at £10 each.

   The company does not want to make a loss.

   b) Work out the minimum number of compact discs the company must sell.

   Edexcel

7   Fred cycled from home to his friend's house and back again.

   The distance from Fred's home to his friend's house is 20 km.

   On his way from home to his friend's house, Fred cycled at x km per hour. On the way back, Fred's speed had decreased by 2 km per hour.

   It took Fred 4 hours altogether to cycle to his friend's house and back.

   a) Write down an equation for x.

   b) Show that the equation can be written as

   $$x^2 - 12x + 10 = 0.$$

   c) Solve the equation in part **b)**. Give your answers correct to 1 decimal place.

   Only one of the answers in part **c)** can be Fred's speed.

   d) Explain why.

   Edexcel

Mixed exercise 14.5 *continued*

8   Here is a sequence:

$$2, \quad 5, \quad 8, \quad 11, \quad 14, \ldots$$

1st term $= 2 + 3 \times 0 = 2$

2nd term $= 2 + 3 \times 1 = 5$

3rd term $= 2 + 3 \times 2 = 8$

4th term $= 2 + 3 \times 3 = 11$

5th term $= 2 + 3 \times 4 = 14$

a)   Copy and complete the following:

    (i)   50th term =

    (ii) nth term =

Here is another sequence:

$$3, \quad 7, \quad 11, \quad 15, \quad 19, \ldots$$

b)   (i)   Find the 50th term.

    (ii)   Find the nth term.

MEG

9   Rods can be fixed together using bolts.

The diagrams show rods fixed together to form a pattern of hexagons in a row.

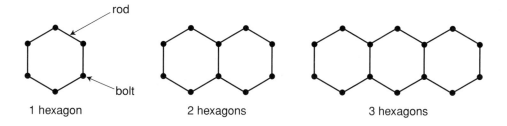

1 hexagon   2 hexagons   3 hexagons

The table shows the number of bolts needed when hexagons are joined in a row.

Number of hexagons	1	2	3	4	5	6	7
Number of bolts	6	10	14	18	22	26	30

Write down an expression, in terms of n, for the number of bolts needed to form a pattern of n hexagons in a row.

Edexcel

Mixed exercise 14.5 *continued*

10 a)

While examining ways of packaging pipes, John produced the sequence in Table 1.

Table 1

Position		1st term		2nd term		3rd term		4th term		5th term		6th term
Sequence		1		7		19		37		61		91
1st differences			6		12							
2nd differences				6								

(i) Copy and complete Table 1 to show the first and second differences.

(ii) Find the next two terms in the sequence, assuming the pattern continues.

b) The formula for the nth term of a sequence is $an^2 + bn + c$, where a, b, and c are constants.

Table 2

Position	1st term		2nd term		3rd term
Sequence	$a + b + c$		$4a + 2b + c$		
1st differences		$3a + b$			
2nd differences					

(i) Explain why the 3rd term is $9a + 3b + c$.

(ii) Copy and complete Table 2 to show the first three terms of the sequence, and the first and second differences.

c) The formula for the nth term of the sequence in Table 1 is

$an^2 + bn + c$.

By comparing Table 1 and Table 2 find a, b, and c.

MEI

Mixed exercise 14.5 *continued*

11 The expression $\dfrac{n(n+1)}{2}$

is the nth term in the sequence of triangular numbers

1,   3,   6,   10, ...

a) Write down an expression, in terms of n, for the nth term of the sequence

10,   30,   60,   100, ...

b) The sum of the nth term and the $(n-1)$th term of the sequence of triangular numbers is a square number.

Use an algebraic method to show this.

Edexcel

Investigation

Look at the following pattern.

$$(1\tfrac{1}{2})^2 = 2\tfrac{1}{4}$$

$$(2\tfrac{1}{2})^2 = 6\tfrac{1}{4}$$

$$(3\tfrac{1}{2})^2 = \ldots$$

Investigate how this pattern continues.

Find an expression for the square of $(n + \tfrac{1}{2})$.

Prove this using algebra.

Chapter 15

Review: Area and volume

This chapter revises work on:

★ perimeter and area of plane shapes

★ length of an arc and area of a sector

★ volume and surface area of solid shapes

★ the effect of enlargement on area and volume

★ dimensions of a formula.

Perimeter and area of plane shapes

You will find the formulae you need for the area of a triangle, a parallelogram, a trapezium and a circle, and for the circumference of a circle, on the *Information* page at the front of this book.

Sectors of circles

In a circle with radius r, the length of an arc subtended by an angle θ is given by the formula

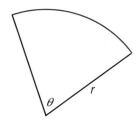

$$\textbf{arc length} = \frac{\pi r \theta}{180}$$

The area of a sector with an angle θ is given by the formula

$$\textbf{area of sector} = \frac{\pi r^2 \theta}{360}$$

 Explain why these formulae are true.

The effect of enlargement on area

If a shape is enlarged by a scale factor of x, the area is multiplied by a factor of x^2.

 Explain why this rule is true.
This diagram may help.

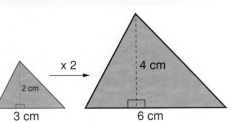

186

Review exercise 15.1

1 Find the perimeters and areas of each of these shapes.

(You will have to use Pythagoras' theorem to find some of the side lengths.)

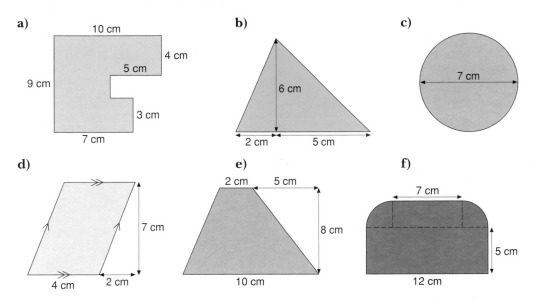

a)
10 cm
4 cm
5 cm
9 cm
3 cm
7 cm

b)
6 cm
2 cm   5 cm

c)
7 cm

d)
7 cm
4 cm   2 cm

e)
2 cm   5 cm
8 cm
10 cm

f)
7 cm
5 cm
12 cm

2 Find the perimeter and area of each of these sectors of circles.

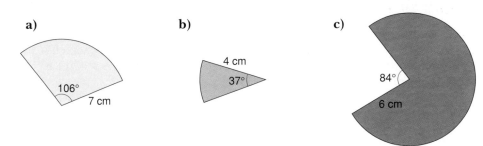

a)
106°
7 cm

b)
4 cm
37°

c)
84°
6 cm

3 In each of these, the two shapes are similar.

Find the area of the second shape of each pair.

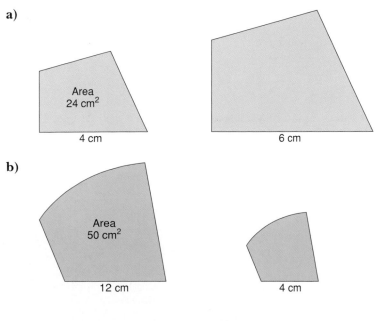

a)
Area
24 cm²
4 cm
6 cm

b)
Area
50 cm²
12 cm
4 cm

Review exercise 15.1 *continued*

4 A pizza has a radius 15 cm.
A cut 20 cm long is made
across the pizza, as shown
in the diagram.

Find the area of the smaller
segment of the pizza.

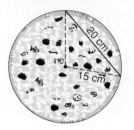

5 The diagram below shows the target region for a school javelin throwing
competition.

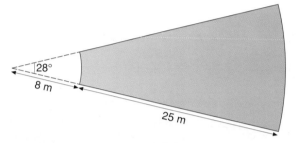

a) Find the area of the target region.

b) A white line is to be painted round the perimeter of the target region.
What is its length?

6 A picture framer sells glass for frames at a price proportional to the
area of glass needed. A customer wants glass for two frames, which are
similar shapes. The prices of the two pieces of glass are £8.40 and £5.20.
The larger frame is 15 cm long.

How long is the smaller frame?

7

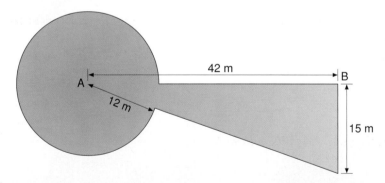

The diagram shows a plan of a water-hazard on a new golf course. The hazard
is bounded by the arc of a circle centre A and part of a right-angled triangle
ABC. The radius of the circle is 12 metres, AB = 42 m, BC = 15 m.

Calculate the surface area of the water.

MEI

8 Three circles with radii 2 cm, 4 cm
☆ and 6 cm touch each other as shown
☆ in the diagram.
☆
☆ Find the area coloured blue.

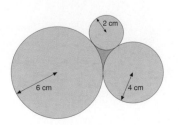

Volume and surface area of solid shapes

You will find the formulae you need for volumes and surface areas of solid shapes on the *Information* page at the front of the book.

 Explain why the formulae for the volume of a cuboid, a prism and a cylinder are true.

 Explain how the formulae for the area of the curved surface of a cylinder and a cone are derived.

The effect of enlargement on volume

**If a solid shape is enlarged by a scale factor of *x*,
the volume is multiplied by a factor of x^3.**

 Explain why this rule is true.

Dimensions of formulae

You have met a large number of formulae for perimeters, areas and volumes. You can tell whether a particular formula is for length, area or volume by considering the number of dimensions in the formula.

The number of dimensions in a formula is the number of measurements of length that are multiplied together in the formula. (Numbers, like 2 or π, do not count as dimensions.)

Formulae for lengths have one dimension, for area have two and for volume have three.

Examples

$$lwh$$

This formula has three dimensions, *l*, *w* and *h*. It is a formula for volume.

 What solid shape has this volume?

$$4\pi r^2$$

This formula has two dimensions as r^2 means $r \times r$. It is a formula for area.

 This is actually a surface area. What solid shape has this surface area?

$$2(l + h)$$

This formula has one dimension. The *l* and the *h* have been added together so they count as one dimension. It is a formula for length.

 What shape has this perimeter?

Review exercise 15.2

1 Find the volume of each of these solid shapes.

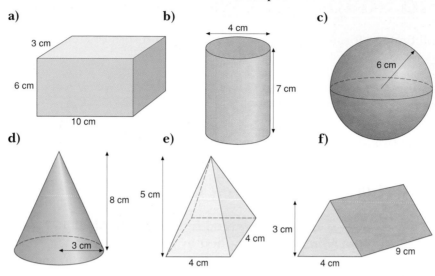

a)

3 cm

6 cm

10 cm

b)

4 cm

7 cm

c)

6 cm

d)

8 cm

3 cm

e)

5 cm

4 cm

4 cm

f)

3 cm

4 cm

9 cm

2 Find the surface area of each of the solids in Question 1.

3 In each of these, the two solid shapes are similar.

Find the volume of the second shape in each pair.

a)

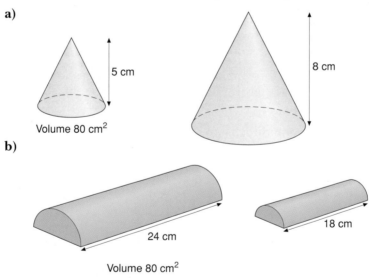

5 cm

Volume 80 cm²

8 cm

b)

24 cm

Volume 80 cm²

18 cm

4 Draw a table with four columns, headed 'Length', 'Area', 'Volume' and 'None of these'. Check the dimensions of each formula below, then write it in the appropriate column.

a) $\frac{4}{3}\pi p^3$

b) $\pi p(p + r)$

c) $\frac{1}{3} p^2 q$

d) $p + q + r$

e) $pq^2 r$

f) πpq^2

g) πp^2

h) $\frac{1}{2} pq$

i) $\frac{1}{3}\pi p^2 q$

j) $2\pi q(p + q)$

k) $2\pi p$

l) $pq + pr^2$

m) pqr

n) $4\pi p^2$

o) $2(pq + qr + pr)$

Review exercise 15.2 *continued*

5   Beside each of your formulae in **4** above, indicate to which of these shapes it applies. For example, the formula in **4a)** is the volume of a sphere, so you put 'E' beside it.

Try to do this without reference to the *Information* page.

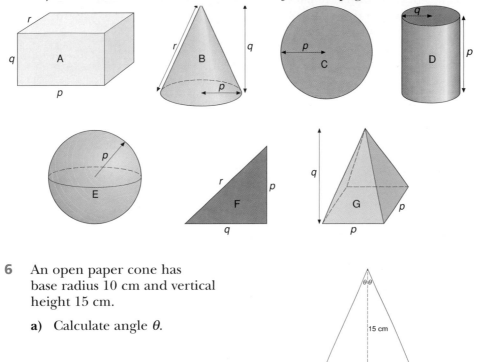

6   An open paper cone has base radius 10 cm and vertical height 15 cm.

   a)   Calculate angle *θ*.

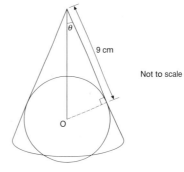

The cone is sitting over a ball and the base of the cone is below the centre, O, of the ball.

The distance from the vertex of the cone to the point of contact between the cone and the ball is 9 cm.

   b)   Calculate the volume of the ball.

Not to scale

SEG

7   A child's plastic bucket is in the shape of the frustrum of a cone (the shape left over when the top is sliced off). The diagram shows its dimensions.

   a)   Find the volume of sand that the bucket can hold.

   b)   Find the area of plastic needed to make the bucket.

Review exercise 15.2 *continued*

8 Jelly beans are sold in tubes which are cylinders of radius 3 cm and height 12 cm.

    a) Calculate the volume of one of the tubes.

Tubes of jelly beans are packed into a carton in the shape of a cuboid measuring 60 cm by 30 cm by 12 cm.

    b) (i) How many tubes may be packed into a carton?

        (ii) Find the volume of empty space in a carton filled with tubes of jelly beans.

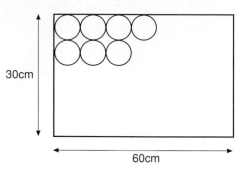

MEG

9 A water tank on a new estate is being planned. The favoured design is a cone, with internal dimensions as shown.

    a) Calculate the total volume of water the tank can hold.

    b) Calculate the surface area of the inside of the tank, ignoring any lid.

The tank will be made of concrete and its external dimensions are shown on the second diagram.

A cubic metre of water weighs 1.0 tonne. A cubic metre of concrete weighs 2.4 tonnes.

    c) Calculate how much the tank and water will weigh when the tank is full.

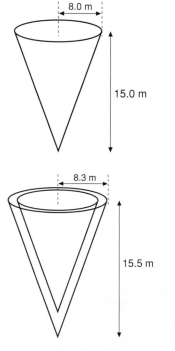

MEI

10 A popcorn carton is made in the shape of an inverted (upside down) truncated pyramid (a pyramid with its top cut off).

The base of the carton is a square of side 8 cm and the top is a square of side 12 cm. The height of the carton is 20 cm.

    a) Find the volume of the carton.

    b) Find the area of card needed to make the carton.

Finishing off

Now that you have completed this chapter you should be able to:

★ find perimeters and areas of shapes including rectangles, triangles, parallelograms, trapezia and circles;

★ find the length of an arc and the area of a sector;

★ find volumes and surface areas of solid shapes including cuboids, prisms, cylinders, cones, spheres and pyramids;

★ distinguish between formulae for length, area and volume by using dimensions;

★ work out the effect of enlargement on areas and volumes.

Use the questions in the next exercise to check that you understand everything.

Mixed exercise 15.3

1 Find the area and perimeter of each of the shapes below.

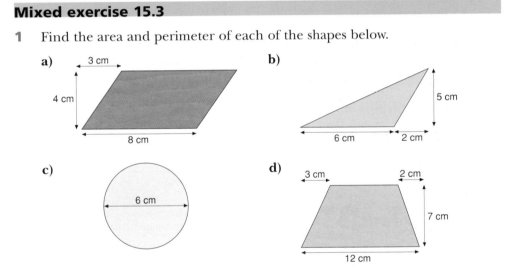

2 Find the volume and surface area of each of the solid shapes shown below.

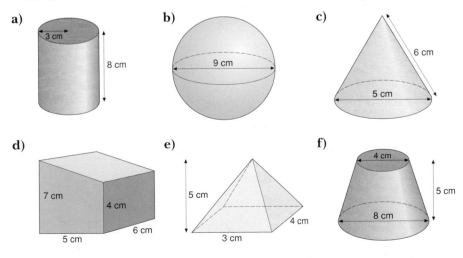

Mixed exercise 15.3 *continued*

3 For each of the formulae below, use dimensions to say whether the
formula is for a length, an area, a volume or none of these.

   a) $2ab$ **b)** $\pi a^2 b$ **c)** $2\pi(a+b)$

   d) $a^2 b + ab$ **e)** $ab(a+2b)$ **f)** $\dfrac{1}{2}\pi b^2$

4 A piece of cheese is in the shape
of a prism. The cross-section of
the prism is a sector of a circle
with radius 12 cm. The height of
the piece of cheese is 4 cm.

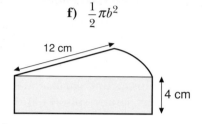

   a) The volume of the cheese is 150 cm³. What is the angle of the sector?

   b) The piece of cheese is to be covered with a rind. What will be the area
   of the rind?

5 Tins of baked beans are sold in three different sizes: small, medium and
large, each similar in shape. The heights of the tins are 8 cm, 12 cm
and 15 cm.

   a) The smallest tin contains 200 g of baked beans. What weight of baked
   beans do the other two tins contain?

   b) The label on the smallest tin has an area of 150 cm². What are the areas
   of the labels on the other two tins?

6 A horizontal pipe with length 5 m
and radius 50 cm contains water
to a depth of 30 cm. Find the
volume of water in the pipe.

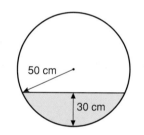

7 The diagram shows the area used for a shot putt competition. It consists of
two parts:

   a circle of radius 1 m from where the shot is thrown;

   a sector of angle 30° and radius 26 m which overlaps with the throwing
   circle as shown.

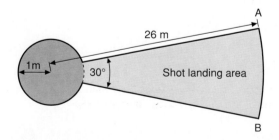

   a) The throwing circle is made of concrete to a depth of 5 cm.

   Calculate the volume of the concrete, stating your units.

   b) Calculate the shaded area into which the shot can land.

SEG

Mixed exercise 15.3 *continued*

8 A cafe sells cups of soft drinks in three sizes: standard (250 ml), large (400 ml) and extra-large (500 ml). The three sizes of cup are all similar shapes. The standard size cup is 10 cm tall and the area of its base is 30 cm². Find the heights and the areas of the bases of the other two sizes.

9

Chips are sold in containers shaped as a cone.

The cone is made from a sector of a circle with radius 20 cm and angle 120°.

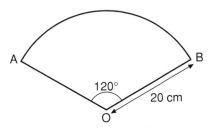

a) Calculate the length of the arc AB shown in the above diagram.

The line OA is joined to the line OB to form the cone.

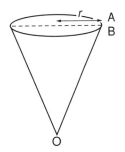

b) Calculate the radius, *r*, of the cone.

The cone holds 64 chips.

A similar smaller cone is made using a sector of a circle with radius 15 cm and an angle of 120°.

c) Calculate the number of chips which the smaller cone will hold. Assume all the chips are the same size and shape.

MEG

Mixed exercise 15.3 *continued*

10 The diagram represents the cross-section of a road tunnel.

The width of the road is 7 m and the side walls are 3.5 m high.

The roof is an arc of a circle centre O.

Calculate the area of the cross-section of the tunnel.

(Remember to state the units in your answer.)

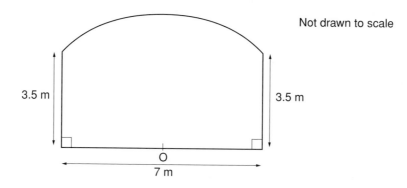

Not drawn to scale

3.5 m   3.5 m

O

7 m

NEAB

11 A pendant made in the shape of a letter C is made from part of a circle, as shown in the diagram. The radius of the outer edge is 2 cm and the radius of the inner edge is 1.5 cm. The pendant is 2 mm thick.

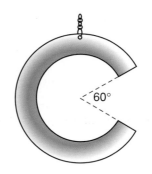

60°

a) Find the volume of the pendant.

b) Find the surface area of the pendant.

12 A supermarket is running a special promotion during which some of its products are sold with "20% extra free".

a) A tub of ice-cream in the promotion is similar in shape to the original tub. By what percentage have the dimensions of the tub increased?

b) A cylindrical tin of biscuits in the promotion is the same height as the original tin. By what percentage has the diameter of the tin increased?

Chapter 16

Review: Geometry

This chapter revises work on:

★ angles at a point, parallel lines, angle properties of triangles and polygons

★ locus

★ properties of quadrilaterals and circles

★ transformations.

Angles

Angles at a point

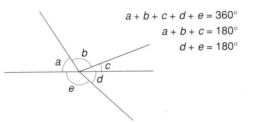

Two angles which add up to 180° are said to be **supplementary**.

The sum of the angles formed by lines meeting at a point is 360°.

The sum of the angles on a straight line is 180°.

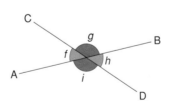

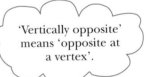

'Vertically opposite' means 'opposite at a vertex'.

When two lines cross, the **vertically opposite** angles they form are equal.

This is because

$f = 180° - g$ (straight line AB)

$h = 180° - g$ (straight line CD)

and therefore

$f = h$

and similarly

$g = i.$

Parallel lines

The angles formed by a line crossing two parallel lines can be paired in various ways:

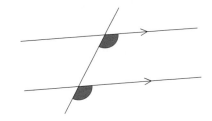

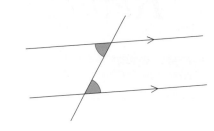

These are corresponding angles. They are equal.

These are alternate angles. They are equal.

Write down all the pairs of equal angles in this figure. For each pair, say whether the angles are corresponding, alternate, vertically opposite, or none of these.

What can you say about all the other pairs of angles?

The converse results are also true: if a pair of corresponding angles (for example x and y) or alternate angles (x and z) are equal then the lines AB and CD are parallel.

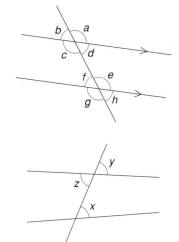

The angles of a triangle

The diagram shows triangle ABC with side BC extended to D. The line CE is drawn parallel to BA.

Then $a = e$ (alternate angles)

and $b = f$ (corresponding angles).

Therefore $\angle ACD = e + f = a + b$.

Each exterior angle of a triangle is equal to the sum of the two interior opposite angles.

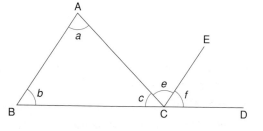

Also $a + b + c = e + f + c = 180°$ (straight angle).

The sum of the interior angles of a triangle is 180°.

Draw any triangle and mark all six exterior angles. What is the sum of these angles?

The angles of a polygon

A diagonal of any quadrilateral divides the quadrilateral into two triangles, so the angle sum of a quadrilateral is $2 \times 180° = 360°$.

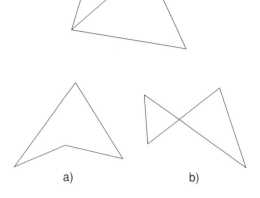

 Is this still true for
a) a re-entrant quadrilateral (an arrow head),

b) a crossed quadrilateral?

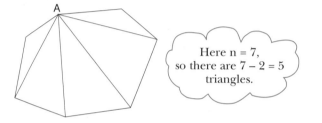

a)   b)

A convex polygon with n sides is divided into $(n-2)$ triangles by all the diagonals through a particular vertex A. Each side of the polygon except the two meeting at A is the side opposite A in one of these triangles. Therefore:

the sum of the interior angles of an n-sided polygon is $180(n-2)°$.

Here n = 7, so there are $7 - 2 = 5$ triangles.

 How can you modify this argument to deal with a re-entrant polygon?

If one exterior angle is drawn at each vertex (in the same sense round the polygon) then the sum of the interior and exterior angles at each vertex is 180°, and the sum of all the interior and exterior angles is $180n°$. Since the interior angles contribute $180(n-2)°$, the exterior angles must make up the remaining $2 \times 180°$. Therefore:

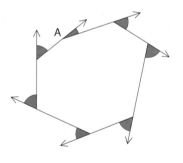

the sum of the exterior angles of any polygon is 360°.

You can also see this by imagining that you walk once round the polygon. At each corner you turn through the exterior angle, and altogether you turn through 360°.

A polygon is **regular** if a) all its sides are equal and b) all its angles are equal.

 Are these conditions independent (i.e. can there be a polygon for which a) is true and b) false, or for which a) is false and b) true)?
Does your answer depend on the value of n?

If a regular polygon has n sides then each exterior angle is $\frac{360°}{n}$ and each interior angle is $180° - \frac{360°}{n}$.

Review exercise 16.1

1 Find the angles marked
with letters.

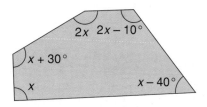

2 Find x in this pentagon.

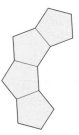

3 A heptagon (seven sides) has angles 100°, 132°, 135°, 158° and three
equal angles. What size is each of the equal angles?

4 Each interior angle of a regular polygon with n sides is a whole multiple of 5°.
List all the possible values of n.

5 a) (i) Calculate each interior angle of a regular pentagon.

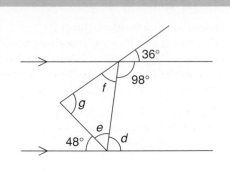

   (ii) If regular pentagons are placed together as indicated in the
         diagram will they eventually form a closed ring? If so, how many
         pentagons will be used?

b) Investigate the same idea using
   (i) regular hexagons and
   (ii) regular heptagons.

6 It is known that the plans of some Elizabethan theatres were regular
polygons, but scholars do not have firm evidence for the number of sides.

Archaeologists excavated part of the corner of such a theatre. The angle
between adjacent sides was difficult to measure, but was definitely
between 163° and 166°.

What possible numbers of sides does this give?

(Note: the new Shakespeare's Globe Theatre at Bankside in London
has 24 sides.)

Locus

A *locus* (plural *loci*) is the set of points which satisfy a given condition or set of conditions. Every point of the locus must satisfy all the conditions, and every point which satisfies all the conditions must be included in the locus. Here all loci are in two dimensions.

- The locus of points a fixed distance *r* from a fixed point C is the circle with radius *r* and centre C.

- The locus of points whose distance from C is less than *r* is the interior of this circle.

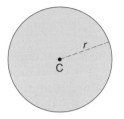

- The locus of points a fixed distance from an infinite straight line is a pair of lines parallel to the given line.

- If the given line is finite then the red line is the locus.

- The locus of points equidistant from two fixed points is the perpendicular bisector of the line joining these points.

- The locus of points equidistant from two non-parallel lines is the pair of bisectors of the angle formed by these lines.

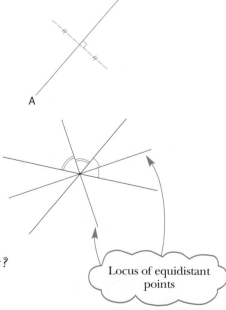

 What is the angle between the two angle bisectors?

Locus of equidistant points

Review exercise 16.2

1 Draw triangle ABC with AB = 4 cm, AC = 7 cm and ∠BAC = 58°.

    a) Draw the locus of points equidistant from AB and AC (or these lines extended).

    b) Draw the locus of points equidistant from B and C.

    Mark on your diagram the two points P, Q which are equidistant from B and C and also equidistant from AB and AC. Measure the distance PQ.

2 When the Walton family go down to the beach they sit in an area where they are at least 20 m away from the car park, not more than 30 m from the café door, and more than 5 m from the high tide mark. On a scale drawing, shade the area within which they sit.

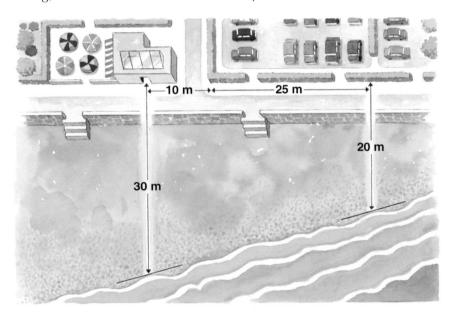

3 There are three secondary schools in Heretown. Toplea School is 7 miles from Yoosterby High and 9 miles from Frankly Comprehensive. Yoosterby and Frankly are 12 miles apart, and the railway station is halfway along the straight road joining them.

    Gill and Len want to move house. They want Toplea to be the nearest secondary school and Len would like to be within 3 miles of the station. Show on a scale drawing the locus of points in an ideal position for the new house.

4 Two parties, A and B, set off from a base camp on an exploratory survey travelling at the same speed, A on a bearing of 048° and B on a bearing of 136°. A vehicle carrying supplies sets off from the camp at the same time as A and B.

    a) Draw an accurate diagram showing the route the supply vehicle should follow if it is always equal distances from A and B.

    The supply vehicle is to keep as near to A and B as possible.

    b) Should the supply vehicle travel faster or slower than A?

    c) Find the ratio of the supply vehicle's speed to A's speed.
       (Give your answer in the form *k*: 1.)

Properties of particular shapes

Quadrilaterals

The family of quadrilaterals can be arranged in a scheme which progresses from the most general to the most specific. At each stage something extra is added to the definition, and therefore the quadrilateral gains additional properties, while of course keeping all the properties which have come before. So, for example, the diagonals of a square bisect each other (because a square is a parallelogram), bisect its angles (because it is a rhombus) and are equal (because it is a rectangle).

For each shape, definitions are given on the left; other properties on the right. Definitions and properties accumulate as shown by the connecting arrows.

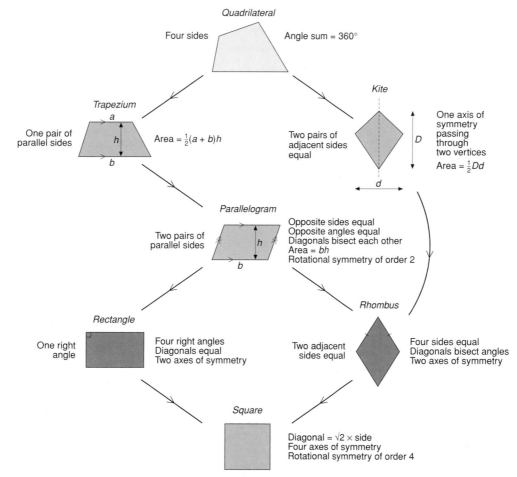

 Use congruent triangles to prove some of these properties.

A significant general result (such as 'If a quadrilateral is a parallelogram then its opposite sides are equal') is called a **theorem**. This can be turned around to give the **converse** ('If a quadrilateral has opposite sides equal then it is a parallelogram'). This converse is true, but the converse of a true theorem can be false.

 The theorem 'If a quadrilateral is a rectangle then its diagonals are equal' is true, but the converse 'If a quadrilateral has equal diagonals then it is a rectangle' is false. How would you draw a diagram to demonstrate this?

Circles

Every diameter of a circle is an axis of symmetry, and any rotation about the centre will map a circle to itself. These properties follow immediately from this symmetry:

- The perpendicular bisector of any chord is a diameter of the circle.

 Explain how to find, by construction, the centre of a given circular arc.

Explain how to construct a circle through the vertices of a given triangle.

- The tangent at a point of a circle is perpendicular to the radius through that point.

Proof

In the diagram, T is any point on a circle with centre C and the line PT is perpendicular to the radius CT.

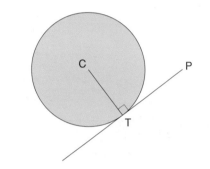

The figure is symmetrical about CT, so if PT went through any other point Q on the circle it would also go through Q_1, the reflection of Q in CT.

This is impossible since the three points P, Q, Q_1 do not lie on a straight line.

Therefore PT meets the circle only at T, and so PT is the tangent at T.

- The two tangents drawn from a point to a circle are equal in length.

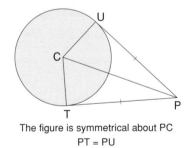

The figure is symmetrical about PC
PT = PU

Other circle properties come from this key theorem.

- The angle at the centre is twice the angle at the circumference standing on the same arc, i.e. $\angle AOB = 2 \times \angle ACB$.

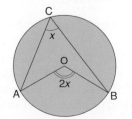

Prove the above statement. (Start by drawing the radius CO, which divides AOBC into two isosceles triangles.)

Note that this key theorem applies for all positions of C, even though the diagrams look very different:

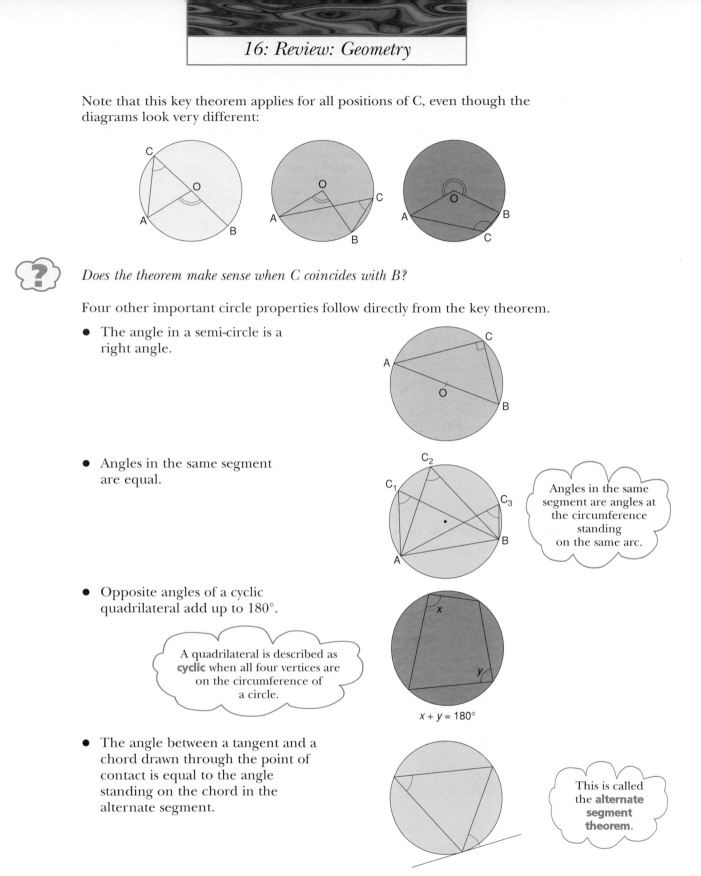

Does the theorem make sense when C coincides with B?

Four other important circle properties follow directly from the key theorem.

- The angle in a semi-circle is a right angle.

- Angles in the same segment are equal.

  Angles in the same segment are angles at the circumference standing on the same arc.

- Opposite angles of a cyclic quadrilateral add up to 180°.

  A quadrilateral is described as **cyclic** when all four vertices are on the circumference of a circle.

  $x + y = 180°$

- The angle between a tangent and a chord drawn through the point of contact is equal to the angle standing on the chord in the alternate segment.

  This is called the **alternate segment theorem**.

Prove these four properties.

Review exercise 16.3

1 ABCD is a parallelogram and M is the mid-point of AB. If P is any point on CD and BQ is drawn parallel to MP to meet CD (produced if necessary) at Q, prove that PQ = $\frac{1}{2}$ DC.

2 Prove that a cyclic parallelogram is a rectangle.

3 The diagram shows a square cut on the slant from squared paper.

Prove that XY = PQ.

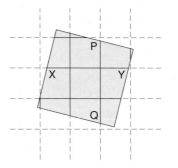

4 ABCD is a parallelogram in which AB = 2AD and M is the mid-point of AB. Prove that ∠CMD is a right angle.

5 Prove that the four angle bisectors of a parallelogram form a rectangle whose diagonals are parallel to the sides of the parallelogram.

6 In each part **a)** to **f)** find the size of the angles marked with letters, stating the geometrical properties you have used to find your answers.

a)

b)

c)

d)

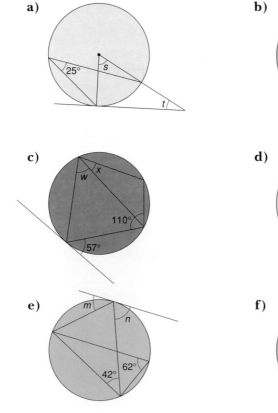

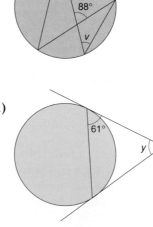

e)

f)

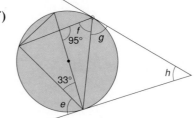

Review exercise 16.3 *continued*

7 P is any point on the circle passing through the vertices of a rectangle ABCD. Prove that

   a) $PA^2 + PC^2 = PB^2 + PD^2$

   b) the angles APD and ACD are either equal or supplementary.

8 Prove that the circles which have two sides of a triangle as diameters meet again on the third side.

9 PQRS is a cyclic quadrilateral.

   The bisector of $\angle P$ meets the circle again at H. Prove that HR is the external bisector of $\angle QRS$.

10 The diagram shows a circle touching the sides of a triangle.

   Prove that AT = AS = half the perimeter of triangle ABC.

   Explain how you could construct the centre of this circle if the triangle ABC is given.

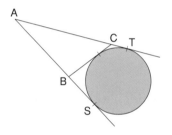

11 TP is the tangent at a point T of a circle.

   Chords TA, TB, TC are drawn so that $\angle PTA = \angle ATB = \angle BTC = x°$, where $x < 60$.

   a) Find expressions in terms of x for $\angle ABT$ and $\angle BCT$.

   b) Prove that AB is parallel to TC.

   c) Prove that CA bisects $\angle TCB$.

Transformations

A transformation **T** is a process which maps a geometrical object P (a point, a line, a shape or a region) onto an image Q.

The notation used for this is **T**(P) = Q. ← Read '**T** of P equals Q'.

A point A which is not moved by the transformation is called an **invariant** point; for an invariant point **T**(A) = A.

The transformation which leaves everything where it is, i.e. for which every point is invariant, is called the **identity** transformation.

Reflection

To describe a reflection you need to state a single line, called the **axis of reflection** or **mirror line**. Then each point A maps to the point A_1 such that the axis of reflection is the perpendicular bisector of AA_1.

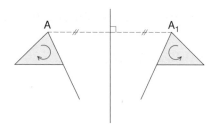

The image is congruent to the object, but its sense or 'handedness' is reversed (e.g. when a drawing of a right hand is reflected the image looks like a left hand). The object and image together make a figure which has the axis of reflection as an axis of symmetry.

If you are given an object and its image after reflection you can construct the axis of reflection by joining any point to its image and drawing the perpendicular bisector of this line.

Rotation

To describe a rotation you need to state the **centre of rotation**, and the **angle and sense** (clockwise or anticlockwise) of rotation.

The object and image are congruent, and the angle between any straight line in the object and the corresponding line in the image equals the angle of rotation.

If you are given an object and its image after rotation you can find the centre of rotation by choosing two points, A, B, of the object and their images A_1, B_1. The centre is where the perpendicular bisectors of AA_1 and BB_1 intersect.

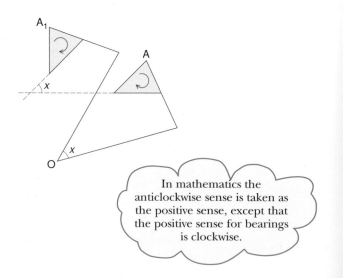

In mathematics the anticlockwise sense is taken as the positive sense, except that the positive sense for bearings is clockwise.

 What is the connection with the construction for finding the centre of a given circular arc?

Translation

To describe a translation you need to
state the **translation vector** which
describes how any one point A maps
to its image A_1. Then for any other
point B and its image B_1 the lines AA_1
and BB_1 are equal and parallel.

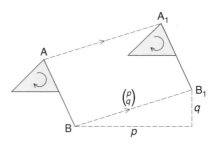

Every point is shifted the same distance
in the same direction, so the object
and image are congruent, and any
straight line in the object is parallel to
the corresponding line in the image.

If the object and image are drawn on a co-ordinate grid then the translation
vector can be given as a column vector $\begin{pmatrix} p \\ q \end{pmatrix}$, in which p is the shift in the x
direction and q is the shift in the y direction.

Enlargement

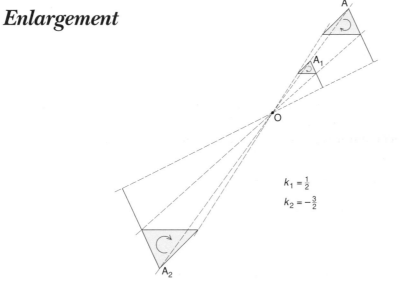

$k_1 = \frac{1}{2}$

$k_2 = -\frac{3}{2}$

To describe an enlargement you need to state the **centre of enlargement** and
the **scale factor**. If the centre is O and the scale factor is k then the point A
maps to the point A_1 on the line OA such that $OA_1 = k \times OA$.

If k is positive then A_1 is on the same side of O as A, but if k is negative then O
is between A and A_1.

The object and image are similar, but if $-1 < k < 1$ then the image is smaller
than the object (though the transformation is still called an enlargement).

If you are given an object and its image after enlargement you can find the
centre by using two object points, A and B, and their images A_1 and B_1.

The straight lines AA_1 and BB_1 (produced if necessary) meet at the centre O,
and the scale factor equals $\dfrac{OA_1}{OA}$ (negative if O is between A and A_1).

The identity transformation can be thought of as an enlargement with scale factor 1.
Can you describe the identity transformation of
a) a reflection
b) a rotation
c) a translation?

Combining transformations

The image produced by one transformation **T** can be used as the object of a second transformation **U**. If **T**, mapping P to Q, is followed by **U**, mapping Q to R, then Q = **T**(P) and R = **U**(Q). Therefore R = **U**(**T**(P)), which is usually simplified to R = **UT**(P).

> Read 'R equals **U** of **T** of P'.

The combined transformation of **T** followed by **U** is called **UT**. Notice that the first transformation is written on the **right** closest to the point P.

*Suppose that **T** is translation $\begin{pmatrix} 2 \\ 3 \end{pmatrix}$, **U** is a half turn about the origin, and P is the point (1, 4).*

*Find the co-ordinates of **UT**(P) and **TU**(P).*

Does the order of combining these transformations matter?

Review exercise 16.4

1 This diagram shows part of a border pattern.

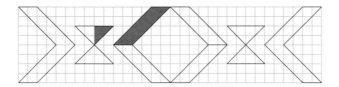

    a) Copy the diagram.

    b) Using the section shaded red as object, describe transformations that would create the rest of the pattern section drawn here.

    c) On your copy, colour or shade differently sections of the pattern that can be used to produce the border

        (i)   using only rotations,

        (ii) using only translations.

2 Draw triangle ABC with vertices (1, 4), (4, 2) and (6, 3). Using this as the object in each case, draw the image after

    a) reflection in $y = x$ and label it $A_1B_1C_1$

    b) enlargement centre (1, 2), scale factor −2 and label it $A_2B_2C_2$

    c) rotation through 90° anticlockwise about (0, 2) and label it $A_3B_3C_3$

    d) translation $\begin{pmatrix} -9 \\ 3 \end{pmatrix}$ and label it $A_4B_4C_4$.

    e) Describe the transformation which maps $A_2B_2C_2$ onto $A_4B_4C_4$.

Review exercise 16.4 *continued*

3 The triangle T has vertices (2, 2), (3, 5), (6, 2).

Three transformations are defined:

M is reflection in $y = x$,

N is reflection in $y = -x$,

E is enlargement with centre O and scale factor 2.

a) On the same diagram draw
   (i)   **T**
   (ii) **M**(T)
   (iii) **EM**(T)
   (iv) **NEM**(T).

b) Describe the single transformation which is the same as the compound transformation **NEM**.

4 Draw on squared paper a scalene quadrilateral Q (so that Q has no two sides equal).

Add to your diagram the images of Q after half-turns about the mid-points of each of the sides of Q.

Then draw the images of these images after half-turns about the mid-points of *their* sides, and so on.

Hence prove that every quadrilateral will tessellate. You must give reasons why the quadrilaterals fit together exactly.

Draw another example to see whether the same applies to a re-entrant quadrilateral (an arrow head).

Finally, look at the pattern formed by the mid-points you have used, and comment.

5 The diagram shows two successive reflections in two parallel mirror lines.

The object P is reflected to P_1 in mirror line m_1, and then P_1 is reflected to P_2 in mirror line m_2. The distance between m_1 and m_2 is x.

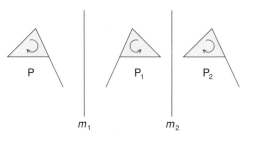

a) Give a full description of the single transformation which maps P to P_2.

b) Investigate what happens when the original object is

   (i) between m_1 and m_2,   (ii) to the right of m_2.

c) Investigate what happens if the order of the reflections is reversed.

d) Investigate two successive reflections in two non-parallel mirror lines.

Finishing off

Now that you have finished this chapter you should be able to:

★ use the properties of angles at a point, angles formed by parallel lines, and angles connected with triangles and other polygons

★ use loci

★ use the properties of special quadrilaterals

★ use the angle and tangent properties of circles

★ use reflection, rotation, translation and enlargement, and be able to combine these transformations.

Use the questions in the next exercise to check that you understand everything.

Mixed exercise 16.5

1 ABCDEF is a regular hexagon.

  a) Show how you can calculate that angle ABC is 120°.

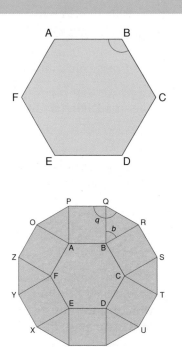

Squares are placed on each side of the hexagon.

The polygon OPQRSTUVWXYZ is formed by joining the outer corners of the squares, as shown in the diagram.

  b) (i) Calculate the size of angle QBR (*b* in the diagram). Show your method clearly.

   (ii) Calculate the size of angle PQR (*q* in the diagram).

  c) (i) What type of triangle is QBR?

   (ii) Explain why the sides of the polygon O P Q R S T U V W X YZ are all equal.

NEAB

2   The diagram shows parts of three regular polygons which meet at vertex X. One of these polygons is a square and a second is a regular hexagon.

How many sides does the third regular polygon have?

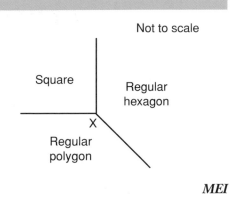

Not to scale

Square

Regular hexagon

X

Regular polygon

MEI

3   Draw a scale diagram with scale 1 cm to 1 km showing the positions of two oil rigs, A and B, which are 7 km apart with B on bearing 210° from A.

Ships are asked to keep out of the region less than 2 km from oil rig B.

a) Shade that part of the diagram which represents the region less than 2 km from B.

A boat sails so that it is always the same distance from A as it is from B.

b) On the diagram draw the route taken by the boat.

The 7 km distance has been rounded to the nearest kilometre.

c) (i)   Write down the minimum distance it could be.

(ii) Write down the maximum distance it could be.

London

4   The diagram represents a rectangular car park. There is a light at the corner at A. The light shines on the car park up to a distance of 30 metres from A.

Copy the diagram to a scale of 1 cm to 10 m.

a) Shade part of your diagram which represents the region of the car park lit by the light.

A guard patrols the car park.

He comes in through a door at corner B.

He then walks across the car park, keeping the same distance from the walls AB and BC.

The guard stops 5 metres from wall DC. He then walks to a door in wall AD. He keeps exactly 5 metres from wall DC.

b) On your diagram, draw the path that the guard takes.

London

A   B

40 m

D   60 m   C

Mixed exercise 16.5 *continued*

5

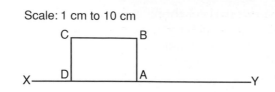

Scale: 1 cm to 10 cm

The diagram represents a box which is to be moved across a floor XY.

AD = 30 cm and AB = 20 cm.

First the box is rotated about the point A so that BC becomes vertical. Then the box is rotated about the new position of the point B so that CD becomes vertical.

a) Make a scale drawing of the diagram above (scale 1 cm to 10 cm) and draw on it the locus of the point C.

b) Calculate the maximum height of C above the floor. Give your answer correct to one decimal place.

(A measurement from the scale drawing is unacceptable.)

London

6 A, B, C, D and E are points on the circumference of a circle centre O. ∠BDC is 32°.

Write down the values of

a) ∠CAB,

b) ∠COB,

c) ∠DCB,

d) ∠DEC.

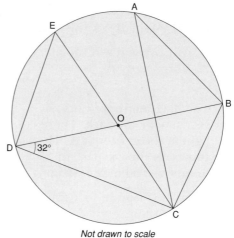

Not drawn to scale

NEAB

Mixed exercise 16.5 *continued*

7 In the diagram, the circle through A, B, C, D and E has centre O, which lies on AC. AT is the tangent to the circle at A.

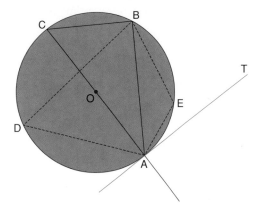

a) Explain why angles TAC and ABC are right angles.

b) If angle TAB = 58°, find the following angles, in each case giving a reason for your answer:

(i)   BAC

(ii) ACB

(iii) ADB

(iv) AEB.

MEI

8 The diagram shows a circle centre O.

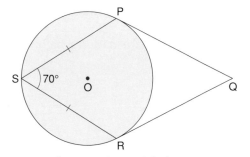

diagram not accurately drawn

PQ and QR are tangents to the circle at P and R respectively.

S is a point on the circle.

∠PSR = 70°

PS = SR.

a) (i)   Calculate the size of ∠PQR.

(ii) State the reason for your answer.

b) (i)   Calculate the size of ∠SPO.

(ii) Explain why PQRS cannot be a cyclic quadrilateral.

London

Mixed exercise 16.5 *continued*

9   A triangle ABC has vertices A(4,3), B(5,1), C(1,1).

     a)   On a copy of the diagram, draw an enlargement of triangle ABC by scale factor 3 from the centre of enlargement E(4,2).

        Label the enlarged triangle $A_1B_1C_1$.

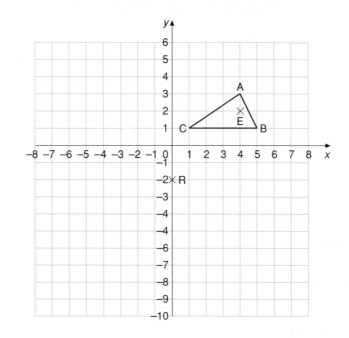

     b)   Draw the image of the triangle $A_1B_1C_1$ after it has been rotated through 180° about the point R(0,−2).

        Label the new triangle $A_2B_2C_2$.

     c)   Describe fully the *single* transformation which would map $A_2B_2C_2$ back on to triangle ABC.

NEAB

10   The diagram shows a trapezium labelled Q.

    Three transformations are defined:

    M is a reflection in the *x* axis.

    T is a translation with vector $\begin{pmatrix} 2 \\ 4 \end{pmatrix}$.

    D is a reflection in the line *y = x*.

    a)   On a copy of the diagram draw and label:

       (i)   **M(Q)**

       (ii)   **TM(Q)**

       (iii) **DTM(Q)**.

    b)   Describe the *single* transformation which maps Q onto **DTM(Q)**.

SEG

Review: Statistics

Using statistics

Statistics is widely used in real life to help people investigate situations and make the best decisions based on the available information.

This process can be broken down into stages:

- Decide what questions you need to answer
- Collect the relevant data
- Analyse your data. (Suitable ways of displaying data may help.)
- Use your findings to answer the questions.

Much of the work in this chapter fits into the last two stages.

Reminder

When designing questionnaires your questions should be relevant, simple, have definite answers if possible (as opposed to being open questions) and be unbiased. It is advisable to carry out a **pilot survey** first.

Data can be **categorical** (e.g. favourite subject or career choice) or **numerical** (e.g. age or number of students in a class). Numerical data can be **continuous** (e.g. age) or **discrete** (e.g. number of students in a class).

The data display should show the data in a fair and not misleading way.

- In pictograms the icons should all be the same size.

- In bar charts and vertical line charts you should use the broken line symbol (⌇) when the vertical axis (representing frequency) does not start at zero.

- When using pie charts to compare data sets of different sizes you must remember that the area of each pie chart, and not the radius, is proportional to the total amount that it represents.

Review exercise 17.1

1 In a survey to investigate people's newspaper reading habits, the following two questions are asked:

   a) 'Do you agree that this town's daily paper is a complete waste of money?'

   b) 'If you take a newspaper, state which one and whether you take it daily or only at weekends and if not, how you normally keep up with political news – radio? television?'

   Explain, in each case, why the question is unsatisfactory and give a better question, or series of questions, to replace it.

   MEI

2 The following data are collected for a group of students. State whether they are categorical or numerical. If they are numerical say also whether they are continuous or discrete.

   a) the height of each student

   b) the place of birth of each student

   c) the distance, in km, that each student travels to school each day

   d) the year in which each student was born.

3 Sleepwell are a company selling beds. They own four stores in a large city. This dual bar chart shows the number of beds sold by each store in the first quarter (January to March) of the current year and the same period of the previous year.

   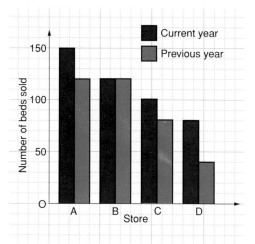

   a) Draw up a table showing the number of beds sold at each store in the first quarter of each year.

   b) For each year draw a pictogram to represent the data.

   c) Comment on your results and discuss the advantages and disadvantages of each method of representing the data.

4 This vertical line chart shows the number of 'A' level passes achieved by Year 13 students at Avonford High School last year.

   What percentage of these students obtained

   a) no 'A' level passes

   b) two or more 'A' level passes?

   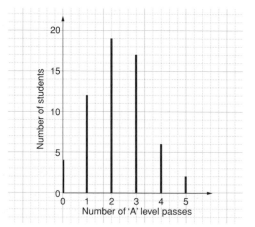

Sampling

When you collect data you almost always have to take a sample from the population. You use the sample to make judgements about the whole population so it is important that the sample is chosen in a way that makes it representative of the population.

Rebecca wants to find out the reactions of villagers to proposals for a road by-pass. There are 400 people in the village and Rebecca decides to take a 10% sample.

One method of obtaining this sample is to interview the first 40 people who use the village shop on Monday morning. Do you think this is a good approach or not?

Simple random sampling

Rebecca wants to obtain a **random sample**. In a simple random sample one villager is as likely to be chosen as any other.

Rebecca has a list of names of the 400 villagers. She is going to write their names on separate pieces of paper, put them in a hat, and draw out 40 pieces of paper. She decides that this method, although correct, will be rather tedious so she opts to use random number tables like the one shown here.

Table of random numbers
28 96 41 30 50 26 47 38 33 00 92 47 51 19 82 14 53 74 27 93
06 35 76 09 22 41 58 92 03 05 66 72 84 13 99 34 62 39 04 60
57 63 10 29 44 72 84 60 93 24 18 03 88 30 11 32 86 57 32 58
64 00 49 81 35 19 05 29 14 84 03 48 76 20 13 77 28 53 20 94

On her list, Rebecca numbers the villagers from 1 to 400, using using 001 for 1 etc., and uses the table of random numbers in the following way.

Rebecca starts on the top row of the table and takes three digits at a time. When the number formed does not correspond to a villager she discards it and goes on to the next. She also ignores any number which repeats. Here is her sample.

289	641	305	026	473	833	009
No.289	Ignore	No.305	No.26	Ignore	Ignore	No.9

Stratified sampling

In the village 100 people live south of the river and 300 people live north of the river. Rather than take 40 people at random from the whole village Rebecca might decide to take a **stratified sample**. She obtains this by taking 10 villagers at random from the south of the river and 30 at random from the north of the river. This ensures that the sample, like the population, consists of one quarter from the south and three quarters from the north.

A stratified sample is likely to be more representative of the population than a simple random sample but may be more difficult to organise.

Review exercise 17.2

1 Using the table of random numbers on page 221, and beginning at the start of the second line, choose 10 numbers in the following ranges.

    a) 1–999   **b)** 1–5378.

2 My random number calculator gives these numbers:

    0.529 0.174 0.023 0.953 0.815 0.772 0.739 0.263 0.110 0.894

    Show how these numbers may be used to simulate the following

    a) the choice of a sample of students numbered 1 to 1000

    b) the throwing of a fair, 12-faced die giving the scores from 1 to 12

    c) the choice of a card from an ordinary pack of 52 playing cards.

3 In a school there are 420 pupils in the lower school, 310 pupils in the middle school, and 130 pupils in the upper school.

    a) How many pupils from each part of the school should be included in a stratified random sample of size 100?

    b) Explain briefly, in what circumstances a stratified random sample might be taken rather than a simple random sample.

                                                               SEG

4 Sam was making a survey of pupils in his school.

    He wanted to find out their opinions on noise pollution by motor bikes.

    The size of each year group in the school is shown below.

Year group	Boys	Girls	Total
8	85	65	150
9	72	75	147
10	74	78	152
11	77	72	149
6th form	93	107	200
			798

Sam took a sample of 80 pupils.

    a) Explain whether or not he should have sampled equal numbers of boys and girls in year 8.

    b) Calculate the number of pupils he should have sampled in year 8.

                                                              London

Review exercise 17.2 *continued*

5   Fiona, Raiza and Simon conduct a survey on the way pupils travel to their school. To do this they each decide to take a 10% sample. The school has 800 pupils.

   a) Give one advantage and one disadvantage of using a sample to obtain the data.

   b) Fiona decides to go outside the school gate at 8.45 a.m. and ask the first 80 pupils who arrive.

   Give one reason why this is not a good way to obtain the sample.

   c) Raiza decides to take a simple random sample of 10% of the pupils.

   Describe a way in which Raiza might select her random sample.

   d) Simon decides to take a stratified random sample.

   Give one advantage this may have over a simple random sample and suggest possible strata.

   MEG

6   The CANTOR company has been employed by a newspaper to conduct an opinion poll just before a general election. They decide to pick a sample of 1200 people.

   Two methods are suggested for choosing the sample.

   (i)   CANTOR has a computer tape, listing the electoral register for the whole country. From this, the computer will select 1200 names at random, who will then be interviewed by CANTOR's staff.

   (ii) Interviewers will be sent to a factory in Leeds, a building society office in Edinburgh, a housing estate in London and a village in Devon, and 300 people will be interviewed in each.

   a) Explain briefly **one** advantage and **one** disadvantage of each method.

   b) Suggest a method for selecting the sample which is better than either (i) or (ii).

   MEI

7   Mee Ling thinks that pupils who come to school by bus are more likely to be late than those who do not travel by bus.

   In order to test whether or not this is true, she carries out a survey on 100 pupils, from years 7 and 8, for 5 consecutive Tuesdays.

   The results are shown in the table.

Method of travel	Number of student-days	Number of lates
Bus	150	40
Cycle	50	10
Car	100	22
Walk	200	25
Total	500	97

   a) Do the results suggest that Mee Ling is correct?
   Show the working on which you base your answer.

   b) Suggest three ways in which Mee Ling could have improved her survey.

   MEG

Scatter diagrams

Matthew is investigating whether the price of second-hand Cruiseround cars depends on the recorded mileage. He plots his data on the scatter diagram below.

There seems to be a definite trend so Matthew draw a **line of best fit**.

This line is drawn by eye but, if drawn accurately, it will pass through the mean point. In this case, the mean of the mileages is 39 400 miles and the mean of the prices is £4400. The mean point is (39 400, 4400).

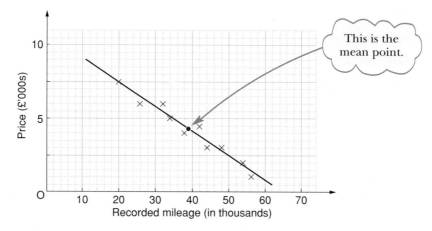

The line of best fit can be used to estimate an unknown value.

Matthew's sister has a Cruiseround car with 30 000 recorded miles and wants a guide as to what price to sell it for. Matthew looks at the line of best fit and finds that a mileage of 30 000 corresponds to a price of about £5800.

Matthew's friend, Sacha, plans to spend about £3500 buying a Cruiseround car. What recorded mileage is it likely to have? Matthew looks at the line of best fit and finds that a price of £3500 corresponds to a recorded mileage of around 44 000 miles.

How much would you expect to pay for a Cruiseround car with 70 000 recorded miles?

In the diagram above the points lie close to a straight line with negative slope; there is strong negative linear correlation.

Here are some other examples of linear correlation.

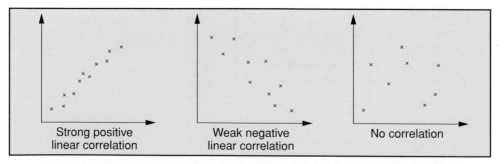

Although there may be strong correlation between two quantities it does not follow that one causes the other. It may be that some third factor is responsible.

Review exercise 17.3

1   The table below shows the number of hours of sunshine and the maximum temperature in 10 British towns on one day.

Maximum temperature (°C)	12	13	14	14	15	16	17	19	20	21
Number of hours of sunshine	9.8	11.8	10.2	12.4	13.2	11.8	13.7	15.4	15.2	16.9

a)   Plot these data on a scatter diagram.

b)   Draw a line of best fit on the scatter diagram.

c)   Use your line of best fit to estimate

(i)   the number of hours of sunshine when the maximum temperature was 18 °C,

(ii) the maximum temperature when the number of hours of sunshine recorded in the day was 12 hours.

London (adapted)

2   A research team visits a remote island. As part of a conservation exercise, the weight and length of each of 10 birds of one particular species are taken. These are recorded in the table below.

Length (cm)	11	14	20	21	30	32	37	37	40	42
Weight (g)	275	275	700	600	800	1000	700	850	1050	1150

a)   Plot these data on a scatter diagram.

b)   Describe the correlation between the weight and the length of the birds.

c)   On your scatter diagram draw a line of best fit for these data.

d)   Another bird of the same species, of length 26 cm, is caught. Use your line drawn in part c) to find an estimate of its weight.

e)   Calculate the gradient of your line of best fit drawn in part c).

MEG (adapted)

3   Eight children took examinations in English and French. Their marks are shown in the table.

	Afzal	Brenda	Colin	Debbie	Elin	Farokh	Glen	Helen
English	42	34	49	53	55	59	66	33
French	38	53	47	55	49	59	68	35

a)   Plot these data on a scatter diagram.

b)   On the scatter diagram, draw the line of best fit.

c)   One child said: 'I am OK at French but hopeless at English'. Which child might have said this?

d)   Ingrid scores 15 in the English examination.
State, with a reason, whether it would be sensible to predict her French mark using the line of best fit.

MEI (adapted)

Histograms

Natasha is a recruitment officer. She gives all job applicants a written test to assess their basic number skills. This table shows how long they spent doing the test.

Time t minutes	$0 < t \leq 2$	$2 < t \leq 3$	$3 < t \leq 4$	$4 < t \leq 5$	$5 < t \leq 8$
No. of applicants	4	6	8	5	3

Natasha is going to represent these data on a histogram. She is aware that the class intervals do not all have the same width. The heights of the bars of the histogram must take this into account if the display is to give the right impression.

She calculates the height of each bar by working out $\dfrac{\text{Frequency}}{\text{Class width}}$

This is called the **frequency density** and in this case it is frequency per minute.

Class	Class width (in minutes)	Frequency	Frequency density $= \dfrac{\text{Frequency}}{\text{Class width}}$
$0 < t \leq 2$	2	4	2
$2 < t \leq 3$	1	6	6
$3 < t \leq 4$	1	8	8
$4 < t \leq 5$	1	5	5
$5 < t \leq 8$	3	3	1

Natasha can now draw this histogram.

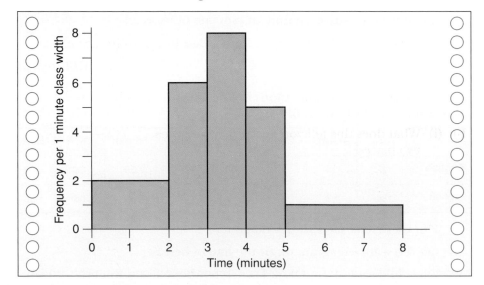

Remember, when drawing a histogram, that:

- it is used to display continuous data

- the area of the bar represents the class frequency

- there are no gaps between bars unless there is an empty class.

Review exercise 17.4

1 Shoppers in a supermarket on Christmas Eve were asked how far they had travelled to shop. Their replies were recorded and grouped as below.

Draw a histogram to display these data.

Distance (miles)	0 –	2 –	3 –	4 –	5 –	10 –
Number of shoppers	64	26	22	28	60	0

MEI (adapted)

2 Beth is investigating the age of cars. She does a survey of the cars in a supermarket car park one Monday morning.

Her results are shown in the table.

a) Draw a histogram to illustrate the results of Beth's survey.

Glyn did a similar survey of the cars in a motorway service station car park one Monday lunchtime.

Here is a sketch of his histogram.

Age of cars, A years	Number of cars
$0 < A \leq 1$	14
$1 < A \leq 2$	17
$2 < A \leq 4$	26
$4 < A \leq 6$	22
$6 < A \leq 9$	30
$9 < A \leq 12$	27
$12 < A \leq 15$	12
$15 < A \leq 20$	1
$A > 20$	0

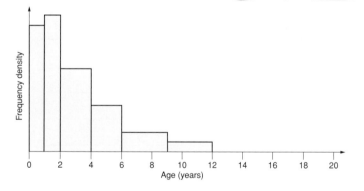

b) **(i)** What does this tell you about the ages of cars surveyed in the two places?

(ii) Give a possible reason for the difference in the shapes of the histograms.

NEAB (adapted)

3 A sample was taken of the telephone calls to a school switchboard. The lengths of the telephone calls are recorded, in minutes, in this table.

Time in minutes (t)	$0 < t \leq 1$	$1 < t \leq 3$	$3 < t \leq 5$	$5 < t \leq 10$	$10 < t \leq 20$
Number of calls	12	32	19	20	15

Draw a histogram to show this information.

MEG (adapted)

Review exercise 17.4 *continued*

4   Leon recorded the lengths, in minutes, of the films shown on television in one week. His results are shown in the histogram.

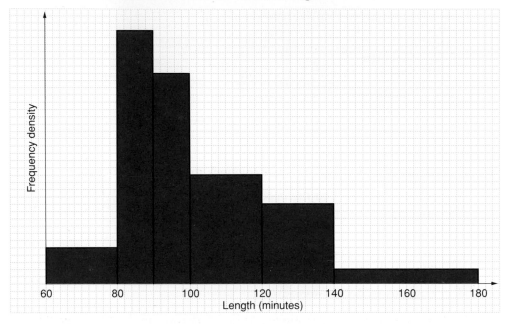

Twenty films had lengths from 60 minutes, up to, but not including, 80 minutes.

a)   Copy the table and use the information in the histogram to complete it.

Length (minutes)	Frequency
60 up to but not including 80	20
80 up to but not including 90	
90 up to but not including 100	
100 up to but not including 120	
120 up to but not including 140	
140 up to but not including 180	

Leon also recorded the lengths, in minutes, of all the films shown on television in the following week. His results are given in the table below.

Length (minutes)	Frequency	Frequency density
60 up to but not including 90	72	48
90 up to but not including 140	x	
140 up to but not including 180	y	

b)   Copy and complete the table giving your answers in terms of x and y.

London (adapted)

Finishing off

> **Now that you have finished this chapter you should be able to:**
>
> ★ explain how to obtain a simple random sample
>
> ★ explain how to obtain a stratified sample
>
> ★ draw and use a line of best fit on a scatter diagram
>
> ★ draw and interpret a histogram for continuous data with varying class widths.

Use the questions in the next exercise to check that you understand everything.

Mixed exercise 17.5

1 Paul helps in his school library.

He notices that some pupils who go into the library do not borrow books. Paul knows those pupils are using books, magazines, careers information, the CD-ROM or the photocopier.

Paul decides to use a questionnaire to find out how pupils at the school use the library. Here is part of Paul's questionnaire.

> ### School Library Questionnaire
> **1. Please tick the box to show which year you are in.**
>
> ☐ Year 7   ☐ Year 8   ☐ Year 9   ☐ Year 10   ☐ Year 11

a) Write down another question Paul could ask in his questionnaire.

Make sure you include a section for the pupil's response.

b) Paul gives the pupils a questionnaire when he stamps their books.

Is this a suitable way to give out the questionnaires?

Give a reason for your answer.

c) At Paul's school their are 200 pupils in each of years 7 to 11. There are approximately equal numbers of girls and boys. Describe how Paul could select a 10% stratified sample which is representative of all the pupils at the school.

NEAB (adapted)

Mixed exercise 17.5 *continued*

2   A bus company attempted to estimate the number of people who travel on local buses in a certain town. They telephoned 100 people in the town one evening and asked: 'Have you travelled by bus in the last week?'

Nineteen people said 'Yes'. The bus company concluded that 19% of the town's population travel on local buses.

Give three criticisms of this method of estimation.

MEG

3   The table shows the total number of unemployed, and the total number of criminal offences, for seven regions of England in 1993.

Region	Unemployed (thousands)	Criminal offences (ten thousands)
North	170	40
Yorkshire & Humberside	240	66
East Midlands	180	47
East Anglia	80	17
South West	210	45
West Midlands	280	56
North West	320	72

Source: Regional Trends 30

a)   Plot a scatter graph of these data.

b)   Draw a line of 'best fit' on the scatter diagram.

c)   Use your line to estimate the total number of criminal offences in a region with 130 thousand unemployed in 1993.

In the south east of England, 920 thousand people were unemployed in 1993.

d)   Give **one** reason why it would not be sensible to extend your line on the scatter graph and use it to estimate the total number of criminal offences for the south east of England.

SEG (adapted)

4   A doctor's patients are divided by age into groups as shown in the table below.

Age *(x)* in years	$0 \leq x < 5$	$5 \leq x < 15$	$15 \leq x < 25$	$25 \leq x < 45$	$45 \leq x < 75$
Number of patients	14	41	59	70	16

a)   Draw a histogram to represent this distribution.

b)   The doctor wishes to choose a stratified random sample of 40 patients.

Explain, with any appropriate calculations, how this can be done.

MEG (adapted)

Chapter 1: Variation

Exercise 1.1

1. a) 2 cm   b) 800 g
2. a) 1.8   b) 2.83 seconds
3. a) 0.0625   b) 2.9   c) 72.8% increase
4.

x	5	9	15
y	6	18	36

5. a) 69 kg   b) 1.72 m (1 m 72 cm)
6. a) $t \propto d$ because $t = 2d$
   b) (i) $d = 3$ should have given $t = 4.5$
      (ii) 1.3 (1 d.p.)
7. a) B   b) C   c) A
8. a) 25   b) 1.44

Exercise 1.2

1. a) $y = \dfrac{1000}{x^2}$ b) 250   c) 10
2. a) 500   b) 3 minutes 20 seconds
   c) Ask your teacher to check your answer
3. a) 2 m from centre   b) 27.8 kg
   c) Ben needs to be $3\frac{1}{3}$ m from the centre and the seesaw only extends 3 m.
4. a) Ask your teacher to check your answer
   b)

r (cm)	2.0	2.5	3.0
h (cm)	10.0	6.5	4.4

5. a)

Station	Wavelength (m)	Frequency (kHz)
Talk radio	1089	275
Radio 4	1515	198
Radio 5	693	433
Virgin	1215	247

   b) Ask your teacher to check your answer
6. a) $F = \dfrac{2.5}{d^2}$ b) 0.1   c) 100
7. a) 75   b) 9   c) Division by 4
   d) $0 < x < 81$

Mixed exercise 1.3

1. a) P is directly proportional to d or P varies directly with d
   b) $P = kd$ where k is the constant of proportionality
   c) No. $P = 0.45d$ for the first three data pairs but not for the fourth.

2. a) $P = \dfrac{327\,600}{V}$
   b) (i) 168   (ii) 650
3. a) $m = 40d^2$ b) 640   c) 125%
4. a) $N = \dfrac{320}{L^2}$ b) 889
5. a) 54.7 (3 s.f.)   b) 3.25 (3 s.f.)
6. a) graph (iv)   b) graph (ii)
   c) graph (v)
7. a) 31 250   b) 7812   c) $d = \sqrt{\dfrac{k}{N}}$ d) 3.95 cm
8. $T = \dfrac{1}{5}\sqrt{L}$

Chapter 2: Indices, rationals and irrationals

Review exercise 2.1

1. a) 81   b) $\dfrac{1}{2}$ c) 1   d) 5
   e) 8   f) $\dfrac{1}{36}$ g) 4   h) $\dfrac{1}{10}$
   i) $\dfrac{1}{125}$ j) 9   k) 32   l) $\dfrac{1}{125}$
2. a) 6^6 b) 5^8 c) 3^3 d) 2^6
   e) $7^{\frac{3}{2}}$ f) $2^{\frac{5}{2}}$ g) $3^{\frac{5}{2}}$ h) $4^{\frac{2}{3}}$
3. a) 3   b) $\dfrac{3}{2}$ c) 2   d) 4
4. 0.873
5. $x, \sqrt{x}, x^0, x^{-1}, \dfrac{1}{x^2}$
6. a) 3.11×10^{11} b) 4.53×10^{-8}
   c) 3.72×10^8 d) 9×10^9
   e) 1.56×10^{-4} f) 5×10^8
   g) 8×10^{10} h) 4×10^{11}
7. 7.5×10^4
8. a) (i) 4.524×10^{-6} mm^2 (ii) 1.214×10^{-2} mm
   b) 25 000
9. a) £3.604×10^{10} b) £1070

Exercise 2.2

1. a) $3\sqrt{2}$ b) $2\sqrt{15}$ c) $4\sqrt{3}$ d) $3\sqrt{7}$
   e) $3\sqrt{6}$ f) $7\sqrt{2}$ g) $8\sqrt{2}$ h) $5\sqrt{3}$
   i) $10\sqrt{2}$ j) $7\sqrt{6}$ k) $6\sqrt{5}$ l) $13\sqrt{2}$
2. a) $\sqrt{12}$ b) $\sqrt{63}$ c) $\sqrt{50}$ d) $\sqrt{80}$
   e) $\sqrt{108}$ f) $\sqrt{490}$ g) $\sqrt{24}$ h) $\sqrt{135}$

3 a) $3 + 7\sqrt{3}$ b) $2\sqrt{2} - 1$

c) $-\sqrt{5}$ d) $3\sqrt{6} + 5$

e) 4 f) $5\sqrt{3} - \sqrt{2} - 2$

g) $8\sqrt{3} - \sqrt{2}$ h) $\sqrt{5} - 6\sqrt{3}$

i) $5\sqrt{2}$ j) $\sqrt{3}$

4 a) $4\sqrt{5} + 15$ b) $7 + 3\sqrt{3}$

c) $51 + 32\sqrt{2}$ d) $32 + 3\sqrt{6}$

e) $17 - \sqrt{5}$ f) $46 - 19\sqrt{2}$

g) $23\sqrt{7} - 60$ h) $22 - \sqrt{3}$

i) $23 + 11\sqrt{5}$ j) $-3 - 5\sqrt{3}$

5 a) $\sqrt{5}$ b) $\sqrt{10}$ c) $\sqrt{2}$ d) $\dfrac{\sqrt{2}}{7}$

e) $\sqrt{6}$ f) $8\sqrt{5}$ g) $4 - \sqrt{3}$ h) $2\sqrt{3} - 2$

6 a) 23 b) 529 c) 23^n

7 a) $a = 10, b = 3$ ($a = 11, b = 24; \ldots$)

b) an infinite number

Exercise 2.3

1 a) $\dfrac{2}{9}$ b) $\dfrac{6}{11}$ c) $1\dfrac{8}{99}$ d) $\dfrac{77}{90}$

e) $2\dfrac{217}{495}$ f) $\dfrac{17}{150}$ g) $\dfrac{107}{111}$ h) $\dfrac{1}{7}$

2 a) irrational   b) rational
c) rational   d) irrational
e) rational   f) irrational
g) irrational   h) rational
i) irrational   j) rational
k) irrational   l) rational

3 a) 3.5 is one possibility   b) 3.24 is one possibility

4 a) 20 is one possibility   b) 6 is one possibility

5 a) $\sqrt{2} + 2\sqrt{2} = 3\sqrt{2}$ is one possibility

b) $\sqrt{2} + (3 - \sqrt{2})$ is one possibility

6 a) rational, it is $\dfrac{2}{3}$

b) (i) $\dfrac{39}{50}$ is one possibility

(ii) $\sqrt[3]{2}$ is one possibility

(iii) $\dfrac{1}{\sqrt{2}}$ is one possibility

7 a) $a = \pi, b = 7 - \pi$ is one possibility

b) $c = \sqrt{2}, d = \sqrt{8}$ is one possibility

8 $\sqrt[3]{80}$ is one possibility

Mixed exercise 2.4

1 36 seconds

2 -3

3 a) $\dfrac{3}{2}$ b) $\dfrac{9}{2}$

4 a) $-2 + 3\sqrt{3}$ b) $29 + 9\sqrt{3}$

c) $37 + 20\sqrt{3}$

5 a) $\dfrac{3}{11}$

b) (i) $\dfrac{3}{4}$ (ii) $6\dfrac{3}{4}$ c) $3\sqrt{3}$

6 a) 17.64 is one possibility

b) $c = \sqrt{3}, d = \sqrt{12}$ is one possibility

7 a) $q = \sqrt{8}, r = \sqrt{2}$ is one possibility

b) 15.625 is one possibility

8 a) $72^{\frac{1}{2}}, 18^{\frac{1}{2}}$

b) (i) 24 cm

(ii) irrational; $\sqrt{18}$ is irrational

9 a) A rational number can be written in the form $p\big/q$ where p and q are integers

b) Ask your teacher to check your answer

c) $\sqrt[3]{2}$ is one possibility

Chapter 3: Manipulating expressions

Review exercise 3.1

1 a) $3x + 6y$ b) $15p - 10q$
c) $8r + 12s - 4t$ d) $xy + xz$
e) $a^2 - ab$ f) $6cd - 9ce$
g) $2p^2 + 4pq - 6pr$ h) $6a^2b - 9ab^2 + 12abc$

2 a) $2(2a + 3b)$ b) $p(q - r)$
c) $x(x - 2y)$ d) $s(2r + s - 1)$
e) $3c(d + 2c + 3)$ f) $ab(2a - 3b)$
g) $4pqr(p + 2q)$ h) $3x^2y^2(3x - 4)$
i) $5pq(1 - 2p)$ j) $5fg(2f - 3h + 5g)$

3 a) $xy - 2x + 3y - 6$ b) $a^2 + 5a + 4$
c) $p^2 - 3p - 10$ d) $x^2 - 8x + 16$
e) $a^2 - 7a + 12$ f) $z^2 - 9$
g) $2pq - 6p + q - 3$ h) $2x^2 - x - 6$
i) $6a^2 + 11a + 4$ j) $12c^2 + 11c - 15$

4 a) $4a + 9$ **b)** $10pq + 4p - 12q$
  c) $-3x - 1$ **d)** $5y^2 + 5$

5 a) $\dfrac{11}{15}$ **b)** $\dfrac{7}{12}$ **c)** $\dfrac{31}{24}$ **d)** $\dfrac{11}{35}$

  e) $\dfrac{23}{18}$ **f)** $\dfrac{13}{24}$ **g)** $\dfrac{4}{7}$ **h)** $\dfrac{1}{3}$

  i) $\dfrac{5}{6}$ **j)** $\dfrac{20}{9}$ **k)** $\dfrac{7}{15}$ **l)** $\dfrac{16}{21}$

6 a) $x = 3.5$ **b)** $x = 15$
  c) $x = -1.75$ **d)** $x = -5$
  e) $x = 5$ **f)** $x = -3$

  g) $x = 1.4$ **h)** $x = \dfrac{14}{3}$

  i) $x = \dfrac{1}{4}$ **j)** $x = -7$

  k) $x = 2.2$ **l)** $x = 1.25$

  m) $x = \dfrac{3}{11}$ **n)** $x = -\dfrac{8}{13}$

Exercise 3.2

1 a) $\dfrac{1}{3}$ **b)** $\dfrac{1}{y}$ **c)** $\dfrac{a}{2}$

  d) $\dfrac{2p}{3q}$ **e)** $\dfrac{s+2}{t}$ **f)** cannot be simplified

  g) $\dfrac{g-3}{2g}$ **h)** $\dfrac{4}{2-y}$ **i)** $\dfrac{2y-1}{3z}$

2 a) $\dfrac{1}{x-1}$ **b)** cannot be simplified

  c) $\dfrac{p}{p-2}$ **d)** $\dfrac{c+3}{2c-1}$ **e)** $\dfrac{2}{t}$

  f) cannot be simplified

3 a) $\dfrac{8}{15}$ **b)** $\dfrac{2}{3}$ **c)** $\dfrac{5}{2}$

  d) $\dfrac{21}{10}$ **e)** $\dfrac{x^2}{3}$ **f)** $\dfrac{3a^2}{2b^2}$

  g) $\dfrac{3y}{4}$ **h)** $\dfrac{3cd}{8}$ **i)** $\dfrac{2p(q+1)}{q}$

4 a) $\dfrac{z+1}{2}$ **b)** $\dfrac{t}{4s^2}$ **c)** $\dfrac{4a(b+1)}{3b}$

  d) $\dfrac{3}{2}$ **e)** $\dfrac{x}{8y}$ **f)** $\dfrac{b^2}{a^2}$

5 a) $\dfrac{a^3}{9}$ **b)** $\dfrac{2500a}{9\pi b}$ **c)** 29

Exercise 3.3

1 a) $\dfrac{11}{12}$ **b)** $\dfrac{7}{15}$ **c)** $\dfrac{31}{35}$

  d) $\dfrac{11x}{15}$ **e)** $\dfrac{13y}{28}$ **f)** $\dfrac{5a}{4}$

  g) $\dfrac{2c+5}{12}$ **h)** $\dfrac{15p-11}{24}$ **i)** $\dfrac{6y-5x}{5}$

2 a) $\dfrac{7}{2a}$ **b)** $\dfrac{4z+3}{z^2}$ **c)** $\dfrac{b-2a}{ab}$

  d) $\dfrac{p+3}{p(p+1)}$ **e)** $\dfrac{6x-6}{(x+1)(x-2)}$ **f)** $\dfrac{y^2-5y}{y^2-1}$

g) $\dfrac{a^2-5a+1}{(a+2)(2a+1)}$ **h)** $\dfrac{pq+11p+2q+2}{(q-1)(q+3)}$

i) $\dfrac{8wz-w^2}{(w+z)(z-2w)}$ **j)** $\dfrac{-4a-2}{a(a^2-1)}$

3 a) $\dfrac{2x^2+x-2}{(x+1)(x+2)}$ **b)** $x = -1.2$

4 a) $\dfrac{x-2}{x(x-1)}$ **b)** $x = 3$

5 a) $\dfrac{1}{x(x+2)}$ **b)** $\dfrac{1}{(a+1)(a-1)(2a+1)}$

Exercise 3.4

1 a) $x = \dfrac{z-y}{w}$ **b)** $x = s - t$

  c) $x = a(b+c)$ **d)** $x = \dfrac{y}{z}$

  e) $x = p - qr$ **f)** $x = s - \dfrac{r}{t}$

  g) $x = \sqrt{bc - a}$ **h)** $x = \dfrac{e^2+d}{c}$

  i) $x = q(p-r)^2$ **j)** $x = \sqrt{\dfrac{f}{g}} + h$

  k) $x = \left(\dfrac{w}{z} - y\right)^2$ **l)** $x = \sqrt{\dfrac{b}{a-c}}$

2 a) $x = \dfrac{d-b}{a-c}$ **b)** $x = \dfrac{q}{p-q}$

  c) $x = \dfrac{y-z}{y+z}$ **d)** $x = \dfrac{d}{e-c}$

  e) $x = \dfrac{b^2+ac}{c-b}$ **f)** $x = \dfrac{p+pq}{p-1}$

  g) $x = \dfrac{rst}{s+t}$ **h)** $x = \dfrac{a^2+b}{ab}$

  i) $x = \dfrac{wz^2+y}{1-z^2}$ **j)** $x = \dfrac{-2c^2-d^2}{3c}$

  k) $x = \sqrt{\dfrac{p}{p^2-1}}$ **l)** $x = \sqrt{\dfrac{2a^2-b^2}{a^2-b^2}}$

3 $h = \sqrt{\left(\dfrac{A-\pi r^2}{\pi r}\right)^2 - r^2}$

4 a) $R = \dfrac{R_1 R_2}{R_1 + R_2}$ **b)** $R_1 = \dfrac{RR_2}{R_2 - R}$

5 a) $4xh + 2x^2$ **b)** $2\pi r^2 + 2\pi rh$

  c) $h = \dfrac{\pi r^2 - x^2}{2x - \pi r}$

Mixed exercise 3.5

1 a) $\dfrac{2}{3a}$ **b)** $\dfrac{2p(p+1)}{5}$ **c)** $\dfrac{x(y+1)}{y}$

  d) $\dfrac{4z(z+1)}{3}$ **e)** $\dfrac{3x+1}{x(x+1)}$ **f)** $\dfrac{2a-1}{a^2}$

g) $\dfrac{6c+b}{2abc}$ h) $\dfrac{4x-7}{(x+2)(2x-1)}$ i) $\dfrac{-5y-3}{y^2-1}$

j) $\dfrac{-6p+2q+7}{(q+2)(q-1)}$

2 a) $\dfrac{5x^2+9x+3}{(x+2)(x+1)}$ b) $x=-\dfrac{7}{6}$

3 a) $x=a(b+c)$ b) $x=\dfrac{p(1-r)}{q}$ c) $x=\dfrac{c}{e}+d$

d) $x=\dfrac{s+r}{s-r}$ e) $x=\sqrt{yz-w}$ f) $x=b(a-b)^2$

g) $x=\dfrac{p^2+q^2}{q-p}$ h) $x=z-\dfrac{y}{\sqrt{z}}$ i) $x=\dfrac{n}{m-n^2}$

j) $x=\sqrt{g^2-fh}$

4 a) $m=\dfrac{2E}{2gh+v^2}$ b) $v=\sqrt{\dfrac{2(E-mgh)}{m}}$

5 a) $25(G+10)$ b) $G=\dfrac{C-121}{14}$

c) $k=1.8,\ d=34$

6 a) Ask your teacher to check your answer

b) $r=\sqrt{\dfrac{A}{4-\pi}}$ c) $r=5.40$ m

7 a) 136.25 b) $h=\dfrac{R-r}{R-r-1}$

Chapter 4: Similarity and congruence

Exercise 4.1

1 a) $\dfrac{OA}{OC}=\dfrac{AB}{CD}=\dfrac{OB}{OD}$ b) $\dfrac{PQ}{ST}=\dfrac{PR}{RT}=\dfrac{QR}{RS}$

c) $\angle A=\angle X$ d) $\angle V=\angle Y$

2 a) $p=4\dfrac{1}{5}$ b) $q=1,\ r=1\dfrac{1}{3}$

c) $s=2\dfrac{1}{3}$

3 $x=6$ cm; 39 cm^2

4 7.5 m

5 CA = 6.125 m

6 a) Ask your teacher to check your answer
b) (i) DX = 2 (ii) CD = 65

7 Ask your teacher to check your answer

Exercise 4.2

1 a) yes, SSS b) no
c) yes, AAS d) yes, SAS
e) no f) yes, SSS
g) no
2 Ask your teacher to check your answer
3 Ask your teacher to check your answer
4 It is a rhombus
5 Ask your teacher to check your answer
6 Ask your teacher to check your answer
7 Ask your teacher to check your answer

Mixed exercise 4.3

1 e) is the only true statement
2 Ask your teacher to check your answer
3 a) Ask your teacher to check your answer
b) AB = 8.5 m
4 Ask your teacher to check your answer
5 a) 70° b) 10 cm
6 Ask your teacher to check your answer
7 The triangle formed is similar to triangle ABC
8 Ask your teacher to check your answer

Chapter 5: Statistics measures

Review exercise 5.1

1 a) 120
b) (i) 7 (ii) 7 (iii) 7.01 (2 d.p.)
2 a) Mode 0; median 1; mean 2
b) Ask your teacher to check your answer
3 Sheila is not correct (e.g. 1, 1, 5, 6, 7 has mode 1, mean 4 and median 5)
4 a) Discrete
b) Ask your teacher to check your answer
c) Median 44 mice approx.; IQR 21 mice approx.
d) 14 approx.
e) 5% approx.
f) 46 approx.
5 a) Continous
b) Ask your teacher to check your answer
c) Median 0.94 kg approx.; IQR 0.2 kg approx.
d) 27 approx.
e) 1.06 kg approx.
6 Mean 210 g; median 215 g;
modal class 220—240 g; range 120 g
7 a) Judge 1 mean 5.1; Judge 2 mean 5.1
b) Judge 1 range 0.4; Judge 2 range 1.2
c)

	A	B	C	D	E	F	G	H	I	J
Original score	5.2	5.1	4.9	5.1	5.0	5.3	5.0	5.3	5.1	5.0
– 5.1	0.1	0.0	-0.2	0.0	-0.1	0.2	-0.1	0.2	0.0	-0.1
× 3	0.3	0.0	-0.6	0.0	-0.3	0.6	-0.3	0.6	0.0	-0.3
Adjusted score: +5.1	5.4	5.1	4.5	5.1	4.8	5.7	4.8	5.7	5.1	4.8

d) Ask your teacher to check your answer
e) (i) F, A, H, D, B and G equal, I, J, E, C
(ii) F, A and H equal, D, B, I, G, J, E, C;
five (A, H, B, G, I)

Equivalence of standard deviation formulae (see page 56)

To show $\dfrac{\sum(x-\bar{x})^2}{n} = \dfrac{\sum x^2}{n} - \bar{x}^2$.

$$\frac{\sum(x-\bar{x})^2}{n} = \frac{\sum(x^2 - 2x\bar{x} + \bar{x}^2)}{n}$$

$$= \frac{\sum x^2 - \sum 2x\bar{x} + \sum \bar{x}^2}{n}$$

$$= \frac{\sum x^2}{n} - 2\bar{x}\frac{\sum x}{n} + \frac{\sum \bar{x}^2}{n}$$

$$= \frac{\sum x^2}{n} - 2\bar{x}.\bar{x} + n.\frac{\bar{x}^2}{n}$$

$$= \frac{\sum x^2}{n} - 2\bar{x}^2 + \bar{x}^2$$

$$= \frac{\sum x^2}{n} - \bar{x}^2$$

$\dfrac{\sum x}{n} = \bar{x}$

$\sum \bar{x}^2 = n\bar{x}^2$ since $\bar{x}^2$ is a constant

Exercise 5.2

1 a) (i) mean 5.5; standard deviation 2.87
      (ii) mean 15.5; standard deviation 2.87
      (iii) mean 105.5; standard deviation 2.87
   b) Ask your teacher to check your answer
2 a) (i) mean 5; standard deviation 5.63
      (ii) mean 50; standard deviation 56.3
      (iii) mean 2.5; standard deviation 2.81
   b) Ask your teacher to check your answer
3 a) (i) mean 3.69 (2 d.p.); standard deviation 1.37
         (2 d.p.)
      (ii) mean 3.69 (2 d.p.); standard deviation 1.96
         (2 d.p.)
   b) Ask your teacher to check your answer
4 a) Mean £24 000; standard deviation £9540.
      These answers are estimates because the actual
      value of each data item has been lost by
      grouping and the mid-point of the class interval
      is only an approximation to it.
   b) (i) $8\frac{1}{3}\%$ (ii) 34% approx.
5 a) 0.117 s
   b) (i) 2.72 s   (ii) 0.117 s
6 a) 6.47 cm
   b) Ask your teacher to check your answer
7 a) A: mean 60; B: mean 60
   b) A: standard deviation 5; B: standard deviation 15
   c) New mark = 60 + 3 (old mark − 60) giving
      66, 42, 48, 69, 45, 63, 39, 87, 66, 75
8 Ask your teacher to check your answer

Mixed exercise 5.3

1 a) False   b) True   c) False   d) True
2 a) Mean absolute deviation 2.4; standard
      deviation 2.83
   b) Mean absolute deviation 2; standard
      deviation 2.61

c) Mean absolute deviation 1.6; standard
      deviation 2.37
   d) Mean absolute deviation 2.67; standard
      deviation 2.94
   e) Mean absolute deviation 2.46; standard
      deviation 2.87
3 a) Mean 4   b) Standard deviation 2
4 a) £2300
   b) (i) £5010   (ii) £2300 to the nearest £100
5 a) Ask your teacher to check your answer
   b) 10.2 minutes. This is only an estimate because
      the actual length of each call has been lost by
      grouping and the mid-point of the class interval
      is only an approximation to it
   c) 3.4 minutes
   d) Ask your teacher to check your answer

Chapter 6: Trigonometry 1

Review exercise 6.1

1 a) 5.83 cm b) 4.47 cm c) 5.29 cm d) 8.06 cm
   e) 6.57 cm f) 11.1 cm   g) 8.69 cm h) 6.65 cm
2 a) 5.83   b) 5.83   c) 2.24   d) 7.07
3 139 m
4 2.99 m
5 a) 10.2 cm b) 9.29 cm c) 7.55 cm
   d) 9.64 cm e) 8.62 cm f) 6.71 cm
6 a) 3   b) 4.90
7 7.18 cm
8 3.46 cm

Exercise 6.2

1 a = 6.63 cm b = 6.63 cm c = 4.45 cm d = 8.58 cm
   e = 7.40 cm f = 7.88 cm g = 11.7 cm h = 6.43 cm
2 p = 41.4° q = 38.7° r = 64.6° s = 51.1°
   t = 54.5° u = 36.9°
3 a) 39.1 m   b) 6.37°
4 a) 24.6 km north, 17.2 km west
   b) 222.8°
5 a) 23.0°   b) 40.3°   c) 56.1°   d) 80.6°
6 61.1°
7 a) Ask your teacher to check your answer
   b) 40.5°

Exercise 6.3

1 Ask your teacher to check your answer
2 a) (i) 37°, 143°   (ii) 17°, 153°
      (iii) 192°, 348°
   b) They add up to a multiple of 180°
   c) Ask your teacher to check your answer
4 a) (i) 46°, 314°   (ii) 114°, 246°
      (iii) 143°, 217°
   b) They add up to 360°
   c) Ask your teacher to check your answer

5 a) Ask your teacher to check your answer
   b) (i) 24°, 66°   (ii) 44°, 46°
   c) They add up to 90°
   d) Ask your teacher to check your answer
8 a) (i) 11°, 191°   (ii) 27°, 207°
      (iii) 149°, 329°
   b) They have a difference of 180°

Exercise 6.4

1 a) 48.6°, 131.4°   b) 111.8°, 291.8°
   c) 35.9°, 324.1°   d) 199.9°, 340.1°
   d) 126.2°, 233.8°   f) 44.1°, 224.1°

2 a) $\sqrt{2}$

   b) $\sin 45° = \dfrac{1}{\sqrt{2}}$, $\cos 45° = \dfrac{1}{\sqrt{2}}$

   c) (i) −1   (ii) $\dfrac{1}{\sqrt{2}}$

   (iii) $-\dfrac{1}{\sqrt{2}}$ (iv) $-\dfrac{1}{\sqrt{2}}$

   (v) 1   (vi) $\dfrac{1}{\sqrt{2}}$

3 a) $\sqrt{3}$

   b) $\cos 30° = \dfrac{\sqrt{3}}{2}$, $\tan 30° = \dfrac{1}{\sqrt{3}}$

   c) $\sin 60° = \dfrac{\sqrt{3}}{2}$, $\cos 60° = \dfrac{1}{2}$, $\tan 60° = \sqrt{3}$

   d) (i) $\dfrac{1}{2}$ (ii) $-\dfrac{1}{2}$ (iii) $-\sqrt{3}$ (iv) $-\dfrac{\sqrt{3}}{2}$

   (v) $\dfrac{1}{\sqrt{3}}$ (vi) $\dfrac{\sqrt{3}}{2}$ (vii) $-\dfrac{1}{\sqrt{3}}$ (viii) $-\dfrac{\sqrt{3}}{2}$

   (ix) $-\dfrac{\sqrt{3}}{2}$

4 Ask your teacher to check your answer

Mixed exercise 6.5

1 $a = 56.5°$ $b = 4.94$ cm $c = 7.53$ cm $d = 8.35$ cm
   $e = 36.7°$ $f = 6.34$ cm $g = 5.09$ cm $h = 11.7$ cm
   $i = 51.2°$
2 a) 24.0°   b) 30.9m
3 a) 54.1°, 125.9°   b) 129.8°, 230.2°
   c) 58.0°, 238.0°   d) 21.6°, 338.4°
   e) 200.5°, 339.5°   f) 142.0°, 332.0°
4 a) 6.80 m   b) 31.0°
5 a) Ask your teacher to check your answer
   b) (i) Ask your teacher to check your answer
      (ii) 15.0 m
   c) 12.6 m

Chapter 7: Straight lines and curves

Exercise 7.1

1 a) gradient 2 intercept 3
   b) gradient 3 intercept −5
   c) gradient 5 intercept 4
   d) gradient −2 intercept −5
   e) gradient 1/2 intercept −3
   f) gradient 1/3 intercept −4/3
2 a) $y = 5x + 3$ b) $y = 4x − 1$
   c) $y = −3x − 2$ d) $2y = x + 10$
   e) $y = 2x + 1$ f) $y = −x − 1$
3 a) $y = 2x + 5$ b) $y = 3x + 3$
4 a) £80   b) £210   c) £$(50 + 10n)$
5 a) $2y = x$ b) $2y = x − 2$
6 b) $a = 0.08$, $b = 200.6$
   c) b is the length of the rod at 0° C, a is the expansion of the rod per °C of temperature
7 a) £12 000   b) £800   c) £$(11 200 + 800n)$
   d) £13 600   e) By stepping

Exercise 7.2

1 c) (i) $y = 3x^2 + 7$ (ii) $y = 4x^3 + 2$
      (iii) $y = 0.1x^2 + 4$ (iv) $y = 0.5\,x^2 + 7$
      (v) $y = 0.5x^3 − 3.5$
2 $a = 24$, $b = 11$
3 $a = 36$, $b = 9$
4 a) $C = 5x^2 + 3$ where x is length of side in metres
   b) £4.25
5 a) $\dfrac{d}{v} = a + bv$ d) $a = 1$, $b = 1/20$

Exercise 7.3

1 b) (i) 193 00   (ii) 26 000
   c) (i) 2.3 years   (ii) 4.6 years
   e) 2 021 000
2 b) (i) 39 units   (ii) 21.9 units
   c) (i) 2.4 hours   (ii) 5.6 hours
   d) $a = 60$, $b = 0.75$
3 b) (i) £5584   (ii) £6142
   c) (i) 2.35 years   (ii) 6.6 years
   d) $A = 4000(1.1)^t$
   e) £26 910
4 a) 0.9
   b) (i) 98   (ii) 89
   d) (i) 1.73   (ii) 3.85
5 b) 1.2   c) 7.45 years
6 b) After 6 hours
   c) Dose at 12 hours should be the last (98.85 milligrams)

Exercise 7.4

1. a) $30°$ $150°$
   b) $60°$ $300°$
   c) $0°$ $180°$ $360°$
2. b) 9 m, 5 m
   c) 3 am
   d) Between 1 am and 5 am and between 1 pm and 5 pm
3. a) (i) $t = 3$ (ii) $t = 9$
   b) (i) 8 m (ii) 2 m
   c) between $t = 7$ and $t = 11$
   d) before $t = 1$ and after $t = 5$
4. a) (i) 2.5 million gallons
      (ii) 1.5 million gallons
   b) between $t = 5$ (May) and $t = 7$ (July)

Mixed exercise 7.5

1. b) (2, 8.9)   c) Yes   d) $L = 0.86W + 8$
2. a) $a = 700$, $b = 50$ b) 14 mins
3. b) $y = 5 - 0.05x^2$
4. b) $P = 5$, $V = 7.2$ c) $P = 36/V$
5. b) $V = 70$, $R = 109$ c) $R = 1.2 V + 25$
6. c) $H = 50\,T - 5T^2$
7. $K = \dfrac{1}{20}$
8. b) $A = 50(0.7)^t$
9. b) 1.6 m, 1.2 m   c) 1.5 m
   d) $t = 6$ e) 5
10. a) 6 m, 2 m   b) 5 m
    c) 5 am   d) 6.15 am
    e) 9

Chapter 8: Transformations

Exercise 8.1

1. Ask your teacher to check your answer
2. a) (3, 4), $x = 3$ b) (−1, −1), $x = −1$
   c) (−0.5, 2.3), $x = −0.5$ d) ($\frac{5}{2}$, −7), $x = \frac{5}{2}$
3. a) $y = (x − 1)^2 + 3$, $y = (x + 2)^2 − 4$, $y = (x + 3)^2 + 2$
   b) $y = x^2 − 2x + 4$, $y = x^2 + 4x$, $y = x^2 + 6x + 11$

Exercise 8.2

1. Ask your teacher to check your answer
2. Ask your teacher to check your answer
3. a) max (0, 8), $x = 0$ b) min (−1, −3), $x = −1$
   c) min (6, −12), $x = 6$ d) max (−10, 10), $x = −10$
4. a) 1 m   b) 17 m
   c) 40.6 m   d) $y = 19 − \dfrac{1}{25}(x − 20)^2$
   e) 41.8 m

Exercise 8.3

1. Ask your teacher to check your answer
2. a) Reflection in the x axis and a one-way stretch with scale factor $\dfrac{3}{2}$ and invariant line the x axis (either way round). $y = -\dfrac{3}{2} \cos x$
   b) One-way stretch with scale factor 2 and invariant line the y axis. $y = \cos \dfrac{x}{2}$
   c) A one-way stretch with scale factor $\dfrac{2}{3}$ and invariant line the y axis and a one-way stretch with scale factor $2\dfrac{1}{2}$ and invariant line the x axis (either way round). $y = \dfrac{5}{2} \cos \dfrac{3}{2} x$
3. a) max $d = 10$ m, min $d = 6$ m
   b) 6 hours

Exercise 8.4

1. Ask your teacher to check your answer
2. a) $y = x^3 + 10$ b) $y = -x^3$
   c) $y = (x − 2)^3$
   d) $y = (x − 2)^3 + 10$ e) $y = 3x^3$
3. a)

x	0.1	0.2	0.3	0.4	0.5	0.6	0.7	0.8	0.9	1.0
y	20	10	6.67	5	4	3.33	2.86	2.5	2.22	2

   c) (i) translation $\begin{pmatrix} 0 \\ 5 \end{pmatrix}$
      (ii) one-way stretch, scale factor $\dfrac{1}{2}$, invariant line $y = 0$
      (iii) one-way stretch, scale factor 2, invariant line $y = 0$, followed by reflection in the x axis
      (iv) translation $\begin{pmatrix} 0.5 \\ 5 \end{pmatrix}$

Mixed exercise 8.5

1. a) Ask your teacher to check your answer
   b) Reflection in x axis
   c) One-way stretch, scale factor 2, invariant line x axis
   d) Translation $\begin{pmatrix} 1 \\ 0 \end{pmatrix}$

2.

	A	B	C	D	Equation
a)	(−1,−6)	(0,0)	(1,0)	(2,0)	$y = x(x − 1)(x − 2)$
b)	(0,6)	(1,0)	(2,0)	(3,0)	$y = -(x − 1)(x − 2)(x − 3)$
c)	(0,−12)	(1,0)	(2,0)	(3,0)	$y = 2(x − 1)(x − 2)(x − 3)$

3. Ask your teacher to check your answer
4. a) cuts at $x = 1$ and $x = 5$
   b) $\dfrac{a + 2}{2}$ c) $y = x^2 + 2x − 3$
5. Ask your teacher to check your answer
6. $a = 2$, $b = −90°$ or $270°$

7 a) $p = 2$

b) Ask your teacher to check your answer

8 $q = \dfrac{4a - b^2}{4a^2}$

Chapter 9: Probability

Review exercise 9.1

1 a) (i) $\dfrac{1}{2}$ (ii) $\dfrac{1}{6}$ (iii) $\dfrac{1}{4}$ (iv) $\dfrac{1}{13}$

b) all calculated

2 a) $\dfrac{1}{2}$ b) 1 c) 0 d) 1

3 a) (i) $\dfrac{1}{37}$ (ii) $\dfrac{36}{37}$ (iii) $\dfrac{18}{37}$

b) Expected number of wins = 5.4
5 wins she loses £900, 5 wins she loses £280

4 a) (i) $\dfrac{4}{30} = \dfrac{2}{15}$ (ii) 0 (iii) $\dfrac{1}{30}$

(iv) $\dfrac{7}{30}$ (v) $\dfrac{13}{30}$

b) There are 5 'o's : $\dfrac{5}{30} = \dfrac{1}{6}$. False statement

5 a) (i) A (ii) $\dfrac{8}{30} = \dfrac{4}{15}$

b) B; the HT sequence is too good to be true

6 a) $\dfrac{1}{4}$ b) (i) $\dfrac{27}{64} \approx 0.422$ (ii) $\dfrac{37}{64} \approx 0.578$

7 a) Ask your teacher to check your answer

b) (i) $\dfrac{1}{2}$ (ii) $\dfrac{1}{6}$ (iii) $\dfrac{1}{12}$ (iv) $\dfrac{7}{12}$

8 a) Ask your teacher to check your answer

b) (i) $\dfrac{1}{8}$ (ii) $\dfrac{1}{2}$

c) A child is equally likely to be a boy or a girl

9 a) Ask your teacher to check your answer

b) (i) $\dfrac{1}{36}$ (ii) $\dfrac{35}{36}$

(iii) $\dfrac{6}{36} = \dfrac{1}{6}$ (iv) $\dfrac{8}{36} = \dfrac{2}{9}$

c) The probability that each number comes up is the same

10 a) (i) $\dfrac{1}{16}$ (ii) $\dfrac{9}{16}$ (iii) $\dfrac{6}{16} = \dfrac{3}{8}$

b) 1. They cover all the possible outcomes

11 a) Ask your teacher to check your answer

b) (i) $\dfrac{1}{6}$ (ii) $\dfrac{1}{3}$ (iii) $\dfrac{1}{2}$

c) They cover all possible cases and so should add to 1

Exercise 9.2

1 a) $\dfrac{3}{4}$ b) 15

2 a) Ask your teacher to check your answer

b) $\dfrac{1}{3}$ c) About 10

3 a) (i) $\dfrac{1}{10}$ (ii) $\dfrac{9}{10}$

b) Ask your teacher to check your answer

c) (i) $\dfrac{1}{110}$ (ii) $\dfrac{1}{11}$ (iii) $\dfrac{1}{11}$ (iv) $\dfrac{89}{110}$

4 $\dfrac{470}{870} = \dfrac{47}{87}$

5 $\dfrac{5}{12}$

6 a) Ask your teacher to check your answer

b) 0.15

7 a) (i) $\dfrac{9}{30} = \dfrac{3}{10} = 0.3$ (ii) $\dfrac{28}{123} \approx 0.23$

(iii) $\dfrac{142}{365} \approx 0.39$

b) Either May to Sept (inclusive) or June to October (inclusive)

c) No. The weather on any day is random

8 a) $\dfrac{66}{84} = \dfrac{11}{14}$ b) $\dfrac{66}{70} = \dfrac{33}{35}$

c) $\dfrac{22}{150} = \dfrac{11}{75}$

Mixed exercise 9.3

1 a) 0.7 b) 0.15

2 a) 0.343 b) 2

3 a) (i) $\dfrac{1}{25}$ (ii) $\dfrac{1}{5}$ b) (i) 0.28 (ii) 0.228

4 a) 0.02 b) 0.64

5 a) 700 b) 0.42 c) 0.18 d) 0.91

6 a) $\dfrac{2}{3}$ b) $\dfrac{1}{5}$ c) $\dfrac{40}{48} = \dfrac{5}{6}$

7 a) Ask your teacher to check your answer

b) (i) 0.285 (ii) 0.644

(iii) 0.929 (iv) 0.071

Chapter 10: Vectors

Exercise 10.1

1 a) $\begin{pmatrix} 2 \\ 2 \end{pmatrix}$, $2\mathbf{i} + 2\mathbf{j}$ b) $\begin{pmatrix} -2 \\ 4 \end{pmatrix}$, $-2\mathbf{i} + 4\mathbf{j}$

c) $\begin{pmatrix} 0 \\ -2 \end{pmatrix}$, $-2\mathbf{j}$

2 a) $\overrightarrow{AB}$ and $\overrightarrow{FE}$ b) CD and HG

c) B to F

3 a) (i) $\begin{pmatrix} 2 \\ 1 \end{pmatrix}$, $2\mathbf{i} + \mathbf{j}$ (ii) $\sqrt{5}$ at 26.6°

   b) (i) $\begin{pmatrix} -2 \\ 1 \end{pmatrix}$, $-2\mathbf{i} + \mathbf{j}$ (ii) $\sqrt{5}$ at 153.4°

   c) (i) $\begin{pmatrix} 1 \\ -3 \end{pmatrix}$, $\mathbf{i} - 3\mathbf{j}$

      (ii) $\sqrt{10}$ at −71.6° (or 288.4°)

4 a) $\sqrt{32}$ at 45°   b) $\sqrt{20}$ at 206.6°

   c) $\sqrt{80}$ at 206.6°   d) 5 at 0°

5 a) $\begin{pmatrix} 10 \\ 10 \end{pmatrix}$, $10\mathbf{i} + 10\mathbf{j}$ b) $\begin{pmatrix} -2.27 \\ 4.46 \end{pmatrix}$, $-2.27\mathbf{i} + 4.46\mathbf{j}$

   c) $\begin{pmatrix} -1 \\ -1.73 \end{pmatrix}$, $-\mathbf{i} - 1.73\mathbf{j}$ d) $\begin{pmatrix} 3.46 \\ -2 \end{pmatrix}$, $3.46\mathbf{i} - 2\mathbf{j}$

Exercise 10.2

1 a) $\begin{pmatrix} 6 \\ 8 \end{pmatrix}$ b) $\begin{pmatrix} 0 \\ 0 \end{pmatrix}$

   c) $\begin{pmatrix} 7 \\ 7 \end{pmatrix}$ d) $\begin{pmatrix} -2 \\ -12 \end{pmatrix}$

   e) $\mathbf{i} + \mathbf{j}$

2 a) $\begin{pmatrix} -4 \\ 4 \end{pmatrix}$ b) $\begin{pmatrix} -3 \\ 18 \end{pmatrix}$

   c) $\begin{pmatrix} 11 \\ 10 \end{pmatrix}$ d) $\begin{pmatrix} 4 \\ -4 \end{pmatrix}$

   e) $\begin{pmatrix} 25 \\ -6 \end{pmatrix}$

3 a) (ii) $\begin{pmatrix} 2 \\ -2 \end{pmatrix}$ b) (ii) $\begin{pmatrix} 5 \\ -2 \end{pmatrix}$

   c) (ii) $\begin{pmatrix} -4 \\ -6 \end{pmatrix}$ d) (ii) $\begin{pmatrix} 6 \\ 4 \end{pmatrix}$

4 a) (i) $\begin{pmatrix} 2 \\ -1 \end{pmatrix}$ (ii) $\begin{pmatrix} 0 \\ 1 \end{pmatrix}$

     (iii) $\begin{pmatrix} 2 \\ 1 \end{pmatrix}$ (iv) $\begin{pmatrix} -3 \\ 1 \end{pmatrix}$

   b) (i) 1 at 0° (i.e., in **i** direction)

     (ii) 0, no direction

5 a) Ask your teacher to check your answer
   b) They all end up at the same place
6 a) **l** : 5 at 53.1°; **m**: 5 at −36.9° (or 323.1°)
   b) 90°

   c) (i) $\begin{pmatrix} 25 \\ 0 \end{pmatrix}$ (ii) $\begin{pmatrix} 0 \\ 25 \end{pmatrix}$

   d) (i) $\frac{3}{25}\mathbf{l} + \frac{4}{25}\mathbf{m}$ (ii) $\frac{4}{25}\mathbf{l} - \frac{3}{25}\mathbf{m}$

7 a) Ask your teacher to check your answer
   b) $0\mathbf{i} + 0\mathbf{j}$
8 a) (i) $2\mathbf{p} + \mathbf{q}$ (ii) $4\mathbf{p} + 2\mathbf{q}$
     (iii) They form a triangle
   b) AB and DC are parallel : ABCD is a trapezium
   c) OM = $4\mathbf{p} + 2\mathbf{q}$
   d) Both are parallelograms

Exercise 10.3

1 11.5 knots at 131°
2 468 knots at 064°
3 114 knots at 093°
4 4.5 knots at 081°
5 44 km hr⁻¹ at 047°
6 a) Peter 208.9 N, Queenie 215N, Ros 211.0; Queenie
   b) (i) $630\mathbf{i} - 20\mathbf{j}$
     (ii) 630.3, 1.8° from forward direction
   c) 99.95%
7 a) $\begin{pmatrix} 12 \\ 4 \end{pmatrix}$, $\begin{pmatrix} 24 \\ 8 \end{pmatrix}$, $\begin{pmatrix} 36 \\ 12 \end{pmatrix}$ b) $\begin{pmatrix} 27 \\ 2 \end{pmatrix}$, $\begin{pmatrix} 9 \\ 12 \end{pmatrix}$, $\begin{pmatrix} -9 \\ 24 \end{pmatrix}$
   c) No but they are close at $t = 1.5$
8 a) Usually the wind gusts so this is probably an average velocity.
   b) (ii) $(80, 140), \frac{1}{2}$ (iii) 1400 hours
   c) (80, 200)
   d) $\begin{pmatrix} -20 \\ -140 \end{pmatrix}$. The speed is the same as that from Aberdeen to the oil rig but greater than that from the rig to the supply ship.

Exercise 10.4

1 a) $\begin{pmatrix} 5 \\ 0 \end{pmatrix}$, $\begin{pmatrix} 3 \\ 4 \end{pmatrix}$ b) $\begin{pmatrix} 8 \\ 4 \end{pmatrix}$, (8, 4)
   c) 5, 5 : Rhombus

2 a) (i) to (iv) all $\begin{pmatrix} 3 \\ 1 \end{pmatrix}$ same length and parallel

   b) DF = OB = $\begin{pmatrix} 8 \\ 1 \end{pmatrix}$

   c) (i) T   (ii) F   (iii) T   (iv) T

3 a) Q (12, 6), R (18, 17), S (6, 12)

   b) 13 and $\sqrt{125} \approx 11.2$

   c) (i) PM $= \begin{pmatrix} 8 \\ 8 \end{pmatrix} = \frac{1}{2}\begin{pmatrix} 16 \\ 16 \end{pmatrix}$ (ii) SM $= \begin{pmatrix} 4 \\ -3 \end{pmatrix} = \frac{1}{2}\begin{pmatrix} 8 \\ -6 \end{pmatrix}$

4 a) $\begin{pmatrix} 3 \\ -8 \end{pmatrix}$ b) isosceles triangle

5 a) $(-1, 7)$ b) $\begin{pmatrix} 1 \\ 7 \end{pmatrix}, \begin{pmatrix} -7 \\ 1 \end{pmatrix}$

  c) $\sqrt{50}$ at $81.9°$ to x axis

     $\sqrt{50}$ at $8.1°$ to negative x axis

  d) They are at right angles

6 a) $90°$

  b) OA $= \sqrt{5}$ at $63.4°$: OB: $\sqrt{5}$ at $153.4°$

  c) **u**, **v** are parallel; the magnitude of **v** is 6 times that of **u**.

  d) **v** and **w** are perpendicular: the magnitude of **v** is 6 times that of **w**.

7 a) (i) **b** – **a**   (ii) $2(\mathbf{b} - \mathbf{a})$

  b) These are parallel; the length of FC is twice that of AB.

8 a) **b** – **a**   b) $\frac{1}{2}\mathbf{b} - \frac{1}{2}\mathbf{a}$

  b) LM is parallel to AB and half its length

9 a) (i) $2\mathbf{a}$ (ii) $2\mathbf{b}$

    (iii) **b** – **a**   (iv) **a** + **b**

  b) It is a parallelogram

10 a) $\begin{pmatrix} 15 \\ 0 \end{pmatrix}$ b) P is $(10, 6)$

  c) $(10, 6)$

  d) $(10, 6)$, P, Q, R are the same point

Mixed exercise 10.5

1 a) (i) $\sqrt{13}$ at $56.3°$

    (ii) 5 at $-53.1°$ (or $306.9°$)

    (iii) $\sqrt{125}$ at $153.4°$

    (iv) $\sqrt{2}$ at $225°$

  b) (i) $\begin{pmatrix} 0 \\ 2 \end{pmatrix}$, $2\mathbf{j}$

    (ii) $\begin{pmatrix} 5 \\ 8.66 \end{pmatrix}$, $5\mathbf{i} + 8.66\mathbf{j}$

    (iii) $\begin{pmatrix} -5.66 \\ -5.66 \end{pmatrix}$, $-5.66\mathbf{i} - 5.66\mathbf{j}$

    (iv) $\begin{pmatrix} 6 \\ -10.4 \end{pmatrix}$, $6\mathbf{i} - 10.4\mathbf{j}$

2 a) (i) $\begin{pmatrix} -2 \\ 6 \end{pmatrix}$ (ii) $\begin{pmatrix} -1 \\ 3 \end{pmatrix}$

    (iii) $\begin{pmatrix} 3 \\ 0 \end{pmatrix}$ (iv) $\begin{pmatrix} 2 \\ 3 \end{pmatrix}$

  b) Trapezium, OC is parallel to AB

  c) 16.09 units

3 c) Using directions $\begin{pmatrix} \text{East} \\ \text{North} \end{pmatrix}, \begin{pmatrix} 2.5 \\ 4.33 \end{pmatrix}, \begin{pmatrix} -6 \\ 0 \end{pmatrix}, \begin{pmatrix} 2 \\ -3.46 \end{pmatrix}$

  d) $\begin{pmatrix} -1.5 \\ 0.87 \end{pmatrix}$

  e) 1.73 miles, $300°$

4 a) Ask your teacher to check your answer

  b) $-\mathbf{p} + \mathbf{q}$

5 b) 126.9 mph, $083°$

6 a) (i) **a**   (ii) **b** – **a**

    (iii) $2\mathbf{b}$ (iv) **b**

    (v) $3\mathbf{b}$ (vi) $2\mathbf{b} - \mathbf{a}$

    (vii) $2\mathbf{b} - 2\mathbf{a}$ (viii) $3\mathbf{b} - 2\mathbf{a}$

  b) (i) $\overrightarrow{CD} = 2\overrightarrow{AB}$

    (ii) $\overrightarrow{CE}$ is not a multiple of $\overrightarrow{AB}$

7 a) (i) **b** – **a**   (ii) $k\mathbf{b} - 4\mathbf{a}$

  b) 4

8 a) (i) **a** + **c**   (ii) $\frac{1}{2}\mathbf{a}$

    (iii) $\mathbf{c} - \frac{1}{2}\mathbf{a}$

  b) (i) $\frac{2}{3}\mathbf{c} - \frac{1}{3}\mathbf{a}$ (ii) $\frac{2}{3}\mathbf{a} + \frac{2}{3}\mathbf{c}$

  c) It is $\frac{2}{3}$ of the way along the line from O to B.

9 a) $\begin{pmatrix} 3 \\ 0 \end{pmatrix}$

  b) (i) **p** + **q**   (ii) $\mathbf{p} + 2\mathbf{q}$

    (iii) $\frac{1}{2}\mathbf{q}$ (iv) $\frac{1}{3}\mathbf{p} - \frac{1}{6}\mathbf{q}$

    (v) $21\mathbf{p} - 34\mathbf{q}$

  c) Yes

  d) Not if the two vectors are parallel

Chapter 11: Trigonometry 2

Exercise 11.1

1 a) 7.93 cm   b) 5.28 cm

  c) 6.45 cm   d) 6.16 cm

2 a) $17.4°$ b) $77.0°$ or $103.0°$

  c) $33.4°$ d) $95.9°$

3 a) Ask your teacher to check your answer

  b) 1.52 km and 3.34 km

Exercise 11.2

1 a) 7.50 cm   b) 8.18 cm

  c) 5.73 cm   d) 6.97 cm

2 a) $33.1°$ b) $93.8°$

  c) $134.6°$ d) $39.3°$

3 3) AC = 4.25 cm, $\angle$BAC = $50.5°$, $\angle$BCA = $74.5°$

    $\angle$YXZ = $46.7°$, $\angle$YZX = $29.3°$, XY = 4.04 cm

4 Ask your teacher to check your answer

Exercise 11.3

1 4.51 km, bearing 344.3°
2 a) (i) $\sqrt{149}$ (ii) $\sqrt{125}$ (iii) $\sqrt{74}$
   b) 42.9°
3 74.1°
4 a) 5.26 m   b) 46.9 m
5 A = 57.6°, B = 107.0°, C = 93.4°

Exercise 11.4

1 a) 9.99 cm²   b) 17.82 cm²
   c) 5.82 cm²   d) 23.17 cm²
2 a) 146.1 m   b) 122.7°
   c) 6971 m²
3

	∠A	∠B	∠C	*a*	*b*	*c*	Area
a)	40°	32.4°	107.6°	6 cm	5 cm	8.90 cm	14.3 cm²
b)	95.2°	58°	26.8°	8.84 cm	7.53 cm	4 cm	15 cm²
c)	25.0°	81.0°	74°	3 cm	7 cm	6.81 cm	10.1 cm²
d)	48.6°	48.1°	83.3°	6.04 cm	6 cm	8 cm	18 cm²

Mixed exercise 11.5

1 a) 8.89 cm   b) 8.16 cm
   c) 10.73 cm   d) 7.31 cm
2 a) 81.8°   b) 87.7° or 92.3°
   c) 44.3°   d) 55.8°
3 a) 23.8 cm²   b) 24.6 cm²
4 a) 33.3 cm   b) 44.3 cm
5 58.1° or 121.9°
6 a) Ask your teacher to check your answer
   b) 2.17 or –3.84   c) 4.46cm

Chapter 12: Polar co-ordinates

Review exercise 12.1

1 a) 2.54 m   b) 1.59 m
2 a) 100 m   b) 70.71 m
   c) 87.41 m; 22.6°
3 a) Reflection in *x* axis
   b) Rotation 90° anti-clockwise about the origin
   c) Reflection in *y = x*
4 Ask your teacher to check your answer
5 a) Ask your teacher to check your answer
   b) (i) 12 sq units   (ii) 48 sq units
      (iii) 1: 4

Exercise 12.2

1 a) (5.52, 2.34)   b) (–9.99, 13.75)
   c) (–6.95, –7.19)   d) (2.40, –3.56)
   e) (–100, –188)   f) (–19.8, 19.8)
2 a) (13, 67.4°)   b) (17, 118°)
   c) (41, 257.3°)   d) (61, 280.4°)
   e) (29, 133.6°)   f) (65, 255.75°)

3 a) (9, 0°)   b) (9, 45°)
   c) (9, 90°)   d) (9, 225°)
4 a) (i) 30°   (ii) 5°
   b) (i) (3, 0°), (5, 90°)   (ii) (3, 300°), (5, 90°)
   (iii) (3, 255°), (5, 270°)
   (iv) (3, 220°), (5, 210°)

Exercise 12.3

1 a) (6, 50°)   b) (6, 170°)
   c) (6, 150°)   d) 120° anticlockwise
2 a) A′ (3, 45°) B′ (4, 45°) C′ (5, 75°)
   b) A″ (3, 135°) B″ (4, 135°) C″ (5, 105°)
   c) A‴ (3, 265°) B‴ (4, 265°) C‴ (5, 295°)
   d) 95° anticlockwise
3 A′ (6, 60°) B′ (6, 80°) C′ (12, 70°)
4 θ = 60°
5 a) 5/2   b) 30° anticlockwise

Exercise 12.4

1 a) 65   b) 31   c) 13   d) 31
2 a) 9100 m
   b) Ask your teacher to check your answer
   c) (8500, 110°)   d) 1100 m
3 a) 81, bearing 206°   b) 7, bearing 332°
   c) 8.49, bearing 270°
   d) 66, bearing 109°

Mixed exercise 12.5

1 a) (45.4, 89.1)   b) (–11.5, 3.3)
   c) (–1.05, –20)   d) (10.4, –48.9)
2 a) (11.7, 31°)   b) (11.2, 349.7°)
   c) (9.85, 246°)   d) (3.16, 108.4°)
3 Place Fell   (7, 48°)
   Hellvelyn   (4, 117°)
   Nethermost Pike   (3, 124°)
   Dollywaggon Pike   (2, 139°)
   Seat Sandal   (1.5, 186°)
   Great Rigg   (1.5, 251°)
   Dove Crag   (1.6, 328°)
   Hart Crag   (1.2, 341°)
   High Street   (8, 354°)
4 a) (6, 240°)   b) (6, 180°)
   c) (6, 90°)   d) (6, 0°)
5 a) (6, 90°) (9, 120°) (5, 150°)
   b) (6, 270°) (9, 240°) (5, 210°)
   c) (6, 270°) (9, 300°) (5, 330°)
   d) 90° anticlockwise
6 (10, 90°) (20, 110°) (30, 130°)
7 θ = 90°
8 a) 3.5   b) 50° anticlockwise
9 OA = OB
   OR = OS
   AÔB = BÔS = 60°
   ∴ triangles SOB and ROA are congruent

Chapter 13: Review: Arithmetic

Review exercise 13.1

1 About 170 litres
2 £100 approximately
3 a) (i) $2 \times 2 \times 3 \times 5$
     (ii) $3 \times 3 \times 3 \times 5$
   b) 15   c) 540
4 a) –1   b) –5   c) –36
   d) –7   e) 7   f) –9
   g) 1   h) –2
5 a) 35   b) 23   c) 23
   d) 1   e) –7   f) 4
   g) 22   h) 15
6 a) $3\frac{7}{16}$ b) $3\frac{9}{10}$ c) $1\frac{17}{24}$
   d) $27\frac{7}{12}$ e) $8\frac{2}{3}$ f) $25\frac{5}{16}$
   g) $1\frac{13}{16}$ h) 6
7 a) 4.55   b) 4.37   c) 13.53
   d) 0.115   e) 38.44   f) 29
   g) 0.025   h) 100
8 a) $0.09, \frac{1}{11}, 0.1, \frac{1}{9}, 0.9$
   b) $0.6666, \frac{2}{3}, 0.667, 0.67, \frac{17}{25}$
9 a) (i) 20%   (ii) $33\frac{1}{3}\%$ b) Greek
   c) 30
10 £378.05
11 a) $1:2$ b) $5:2$ c) $24:7$
   d) $1:20\,000$ e) $7:5$ f) $8:3$
12 a) £270, £360   b) £1225, £735, £490
13 £121
14 £1.98
15 £59 400

Review exercise 13.2

1 £36
2 £132
3 a) £11 951.68   b) £12 950
4 a) £61.80   b) $(1.07)^3$
5 a) £2458.91   b) 7.18% (2 d.p.)
6 £31.25
7 a) 40%   b) 216
   c) £196 800 000
8 a) 2.4 m   b) 1.92 m   c) 4

Review exercise 13.3

1 2167.5 m, 2152.5 m
2 210 g, 200 g
3 a) 20.5 kg, 19.5 kg
   b) 1.15 kg

4 a) (i) 35   (ii) 65
   b) 2925
   c) 0.538
   d) 1.29
5 a) (i) 0.615 kg   (ii) 0.625 kg
   b) (i) 30.75 kg   (ii) 31.25 kg
   c) ±0.25 kg
   d) ±2.5 kg
6 Ask your teacher to check your answer
7 6.25
8 a) 17.15 m
   b) (i) 3.25 km   (ii) 0.3 km^2

Mixed exercise 13.4

1 a) 3.1   b) 3.072   c) 0.42
   d) 0.000 985, 0.001 6, 0.002, 0.01
2 a) $\frac{5}{9}$ b) 180 hectares
3 Ask your teacher to check your answer
4 a) (i) $2 \times 2 \times 2 \times 3 \times 3$
     (ii) $2 \times 2 \times 2 \times 2 \times 5$
   b) 12 minutes
5 1.094 yards
6 £334.54
7 0.209 (3 d.p.)
8 a) 32
   b) (i) $\frac{1}{12}$ (ii) 36
9 a) 21%   b) 19%
10 7500 mm^2
11 a) 12.5% increase   b) £172.82
12 a) $n = 3, p = 37$ b) 111
13 £5593
14 85 kg
15 a) 11.5 pounds
   b) (i) 5.613 636 4   (ii) 6
   c) Ask your teacher to check your answer
16 a) Anti-clockwise   b) (i) 4   (ii) 2
17 a) –32.3
   b) Ask your teacher to check your answer
18 a) 17 cm   b) 4437.5 cm^2

Chapter 14: Review: Equations and formulae

Review exercise 14.1

1 a) $x > 3$ b) $x \geq -2$
   c) $-4 < x < 4$ d) $x \geq 4$
   e) $x > -\frac{2}{3}$ f) $x > 2$ or $x < -2$
   g) $x \leq 2$ h) $x < 5.5$
   i) $x \geq 1.2$ j) $x \leq \frac{17}{23}$

2 a) $x < 1.4$
   b) Ask your teacher to check your answer
   c) Ask your teacher to check your answer
3 a) C   b) B
   c) $250 < n < 350$
4 a) If the lengths of the two shorter sides are greater than or equal to the longest side, a triangle cannot be drawn.
   b) $x < 2.5$

Review exercise 14.2

1 a) $x = 2, y = 3$ b) $a = 4, b = -2$
   c) $p = 3, q = -1$ d) $c = -1, d = -2$
   e) $g = 1, h = 5$ f) $x = 2, y = 2$
   g) $w = -2, z = 3$ h) $p = 2, q = -1$
   i) $s = 5, t = 2$ j) $a = 3, b = -2$
2 a) $(1.5, 7)$
   b) $(2, 4)$
   c) $(3, -1)$
3 A bar of chocolate costs 43p
   A packet of crisps costs 26p
4 $a = 2, b = -5$
5 a) $k + 4m = 117$, $k + 6m = 149$
   b) $m = 16$

Review exercise 14.3

1 a) $(x + 2)(x + 5)$ b) $(x - 3)(x - 2)$
   c) $(x + 4)(x - 1)$ d) $(x + 3)(x - 3)$
   e) $(2x + 1)(x + 5)$ f) $(3x - 2)(x + 2)$
   g) $(4x - 1)(x - 3)$ h) $(3x - 2)(2x + 3)$
   i) $(6x - 5)(x + 2)$ j) $(2x - 1)^2$
   k) $(4x - 3)(2x - 5)$ l) $(6x + 1)(2x + 3)$
2 a) $x = 4$ or 3 b) $x = -2$ or 6
   c) $x = 0.5$ or -4 d) $x = 1$
   e) $x = -\dfrac{1}{3}$ or 4 f) $x = 3$ or -3
   g) $x = 2.5$ or -0.5 h) $x = 0.6$ or -1.5
   i) $x = 2.5$ j) $x = 0.625$ or -1
   k) $x = \dfrac{5}{3}$ or -0.75 l) $x = \dfrac{11}{12}$ or -2
3 a) $x = 0.732$ or -2.732 b) $x = 2.618$ or 0.382
   c) $x = -0.219$ or -2.281 d) no solutions
   e) $x = 2.158$ or -1.158 f) $x = 0.883$ or -1.133
   g) $x = -0.791$ or 3.791 h) no solutions
   i) $x = 0.219$ or 2.281 j) $x = 0.643$ or -1.243
   k) $x = 0.843$ or -0.593 l) $x = -0.264$ or 1.264
4 a) $x = 0.303$ or -3.303 b) $x = -2$ or $\dfrac{1}{3}$
   c) $x = 3.828$ or -1.828 d) $x = 1.569$ or -0.319
   e) $x = 1$ or -4 f) $x = 1.707$ or -0.293
   g) $x = 1.816$ or 0.184 h) $x = 1.344$ or -0.744
5 6.73 cm and 3.27 cm
6 80 km/h

Review exercise 14.4

1 a) $4n - 1$ b) $3n + 2$
   c) $n^2 - 1$ d) $14 - 2n$
   e) $n(n - 1)$ f) $2n^2$
   g) $6n + 1$ h) $(n - 1)(n + 2)$
2 a) 2^n b) $2 \times 3^{n-1}$
   c) $128 \times \left(\dfrac{1}{2}\right)^n$ or $64 \times \left(\dfrac{1}{2}\right)^{n-1}$
   d) $(-4)^{n-1}$
3 a) 3^{n-1} b) $n^2 + 1$
   c) $2 \times 5^{n-1}$ d) $4n - 2$
   e) $n(n + 2)$ f) n^3
4 $m = 2t + 1$
5 $r = \left(\dfrac{b - 1}{2}\right)^2$
6 a) 3, 9, 18, 30, 45, 63
   b) $\dfrac{3}{2}n(n + 1)$
7 a) (i) 1   (ii) 3   (iii) 6
   b) $\dfrac{1}{2}n(n + 1)$ c) 20 dots
8 a) 3
   $4^2 = 3^2 + 4 + 3$
   $10^2 = 9^2 + 10 + 9$
   $n^2 = (n - 1)^2 + n + (n - 1)$
   b) $(n - 1)^2 + n + (n - 1) = n^2 - 2n + 1 + n + n - 1 = n^2$
9 a) 1, 5, 13, 25, 41, 61
   b) $2n^2 - 2n + 1$

Mixed exercise 14.5

1 a) $x = -0.2$ b) $x = -7/3$
   c) $x = -11$ d) $x = 0.25$
   e) $x = 37/9$ f) $x = 1.25$
   g) $x = 1/11$ h) $x = -1.4$
2 a) $x > 1.75$ b) $x \geq 6$
   c) $x \geq 3$ or $x \leq -3$ d) $x > -10/7$
   e) $x < 2.6$ f) $-1 < x < 1$
   g) $x < -9/7$ h) $x \geq 1.2$
   i) $x \leq 23/7$ j) $x \leq 7/5$
3 a) $a = 3, b = 1$ b) $x = 2, y = -0.5$
   c) $p = -1, q = -2$ d) $c = -2, d = -4$
   e) $x = -2, y = -4$ f) $s = 4, t = 1$
   g) $p = 3, q = 6$ h) $a = -3, b = 1$
4 a) $x = 3$ or -5 b) $x = 1.5$ or 2
   c) $x = 1.193$ or -4.193 d) no solutions
   e) $x = 0.351$ or -2.851 f) $x = -2$ or 3
   g) $x = 6.606$ or -0.605 h) $x = 0.225$ or -2.225
   i) no solutions   j) $x = 2$ or -0.5
5 a) $3n + 1$ b) $n^2 + 4$
   c) 2×3^n d) $\dfrac{1}{2}n + 2$
   e) $3n^2$ f) $3 \times 5^{n-1}$
   g) $5 - 2n$ h) 2^{n+1}

6 a) $a = 52\,000$, $b = 6$

b) They must sell at least $13\,000$

7 a) $\dfrac{20}{x} + \dfrac{20}{x-2} = 4$

b) $x = 11.1$ or 0.9

c) x cannot be 0.9 or the speed on the way back would be negative.

d) Ask your teacher to check your answer

8 a) (i) 50th term = $2 + 3 \times 49 = 149$

    (ii) nth term = $2 + 3(n-1)$

b) (i) 199   (ii) $4n - 1$

9 $5n + 1$

10 a) (i)

Position	1st term	2nd term	3rd term	4th term	5th term	6th term
Sequence	1	7	19	37	61	91
1st differences		6	12	18	24	30
2nd differences			6	6	6	6

    (ii) 127, 169

b) (i) Ask your teacher to check your answer

    (ii)

Position	1st term	2nd term	3rd term
Sequence	$a+b+c$	$4a+2b+c$	$9a+3b+c$
1st differences		$3a+b$	$5a+b$
2nd differences			$2a$

c) $a = 3$, $b = -3$, $c = 1$

11 a) $5n(n+1)$

b) Ask your teacher to check your answer

Chapter 15: Review : Area and volume

Review exercise 15.1

1 a) Perimeter = 42 cm, area = 71 cm^2

b) Perimeter = 21.1 cm, area = 21 cm^2

c) Perimeter = 22.0 cm, area = 38.5 cm^2

d) Perimeter = 22.6 cm, area = 28 cm^2

e) Perimeter = 30.0 cm, area = 48 cm^2

f) Perimeter = 36.9 cm, area = 87.3 cm^2

2 a) Perimeter = 27.0 cm, area = 45.3 cm^2

b) Perimeter = 10.6 cm, area = 5.17 cm^2

c) Perimeter = 40.9 cm, area = 86.7 cm^2

3 a) 54 cm^2 b) 5.56 cm^2

4 52.4 cm^2

5 a) 250 m^2 b) 70.0 m

6 11.8 cm

7 742.7 m^2

8 1.86 cm^2

Review exercise 15.2

1 a) 180 cm^3 b) 88.0 cm^3 c) 904.8 cm^3

   d) 75.4 cm^3 e) 26.7 cm^3 f) 54 cm^3

2 a) 216 cm^2 b) 113.1 cm^2 c) 452.4 cm^2

   d) 108.8 cm^2 e) 59.1 cm^2 f) 112.9 cm^2

3 a) 327.68 cm^3 b) 33.75 cm^3

4, 5

Length	Area	Volume	None of these
$p + q + r$ (F)	$\pi p(p + r)$ (B)	$\frac{4}{3}\pi p^3$ (E)	$pq^2 r$
$2\pi p$ (C)	πp^2 (C)	$\frac{1}{3}p^2 q$ (G)	$pq + pr$
	$\frac{1}{2}pq$ (F)	πpq^2 (D)	
	$2\pi q(p + q)$ (D)	$\frac{1}{3}\pi p^2 q$ (B)	
	$4\pi p^2$ (E)	pqr (A)	
	$2(pq + qr + pr)$ (A)		

6 a) 33.7°   b) 904.8 cm^3

7 a) 2790 cm^3 b) 910 cm^2

8 a) 339.3 cm^3

   b) (i) 50   (ii) 4635 cm^3

9 a) 1005 m^3 b) 427.3 m^2 c) 1276 tonnes

10 a) 2027 cm^3 b) 868 cm^2

Mixed exercise 15.3

1 a) Area = 32 cm^2, Perimeter = 26 cm

b) Area = 15 cm^2, Perimeter = 20.8 cm

c) Area = 28.3 cm^2, Perimeter = 18.8 cm

d) Area = 66.5 cm^2, Perimeter = 33.9 cm

2 a) Volume = 226.2 cm^3, surface area = 207.3 cm^2

b) Volume = 381.7 cm^3, surface area = 254.5 cm^2

c) Volume = 35.7 cm^3, surface area = 66.8 cm^2

d) Volume = 165 cm^3, surface area = 186.0 cm^2

e) Volume = 20 cm^3, surface area = 49.0 cm^2

f) Volume = 146.6 cm^3, surface area = 164.3 cm^2

3 a) Area   b) Volume   c) Length

   d) None   e) Volume   f) Area

4 a) 29.8°   b) 196 cm^2

5 a) Medium 675 g, large 1318 g

b) Medium 337.5 cm^2, large 527.3 cm^2

6 0.991 m^3

7 a) 0.157 m^3 b) 176.7 m^2

8 Large – height 11.7 cm, area of base = 41.0 cm^2

   Extra-large – height 12.6 cm, area of base = 47.6 cm^2

9 a) 41.9 cm   b) 6.67 cm   c) 27

10 a) 31.5 m^2

11 a) 0.916 cm^3 b) 13.0 cm^2

12 a) 6.27%   b) 9.54%

Chapter 16: Review : Geometry

Review exercise 16.1

1 $d = 82°$, $e = 50°$, $f = 46°$, $g = 84°$

2 80°

3 125°

4 3, 4, 6, 8, 9, 12, 18, 24, 36, 72

5 a) (i) 108°   (ii) Yes, 10

   b (i) yes, 6

    (ii) Not a closed ring

6 22 to 25 inclusive

Review exercise 16.2

1 a) Ask your teacher to check your answer
   b) Ask your teacher to check your answer.
       PQ = 12.1 cm
2 Ask your teacher to check your answer
3 Ask your teacher to check your answer
4 a) Ask your teacher to check your answer
   b) Slower
   c) 0.72 : 1

Review exercise 16.3

1 Ask your teacher to check your answer
2 Ask your teacher to check your answer
3 Ask your teacher to check your answer
4 Ask your teacher to check your answer
5 Ask your teacher to check your answer
6 a) $s = 50°$, $t = 40°$ b) $v = 60°$
   c) $w = 57°$, $x = 13°$ d) $y = 58°$
   e) $m = 42°$, $n = 76°$ f) $e = 57°$, $f = 57°$, $g = 62°$,
                                    $h = 56°$
7 Ask your teacher to check your answer
8 Ask your teacher to check your answer
9 Ask your teacher to check your answer
10 Ask your teacher to check your answer
11 a) $\angle ABT = x$, $\angle BCT = 2x$
   b) Ask your teacher to check your answer
   c) Ask your teacher to check your answer

Review exercise 16.4

1 Ask your teacher to check your answer
2 e) Enlargement, centre $(-5,4)$, scale factor $-\frac{1}{2}$
3 b) Enlargement, centre $(0,0)$, scale factor 2
4 Ask your teacher to check your answer
5 a) Translation $\begin{pmatrix} 2x \\ 0 \end{pmatrix}$
   b) (i) and (ii); translation as before
   c) Translation $\begin{pmatrix} -2x \\ 0 \end{pmatrix}$
   d) Rotation

Mixed exercise 16.5

1 a) Ask your teacher to check your answer
   b) (i) 60°   (ii) 150°
   c) (i) Equilateral
       (ii) Ask your teacher to check your answer
2 12
3 a) Ask your teacher to check your answer
   b) Ask your teacher to check your answer
   c) (i) 6.5 km   (ii) 7.5 km
4 Ask your teacher to check your answer
5 a) Ask your teacher to check your answer
   b) 36.1 cm

6 a) 32°   b) 64°
   c) 90°   d) 58°
7 a) $\angle TAC$ is the angle between the tangent and the
       radius at the point of contact. $\angle ABC$ is an angle
       in a semi-circle.
   b) (i) 32° (ii) 58°   (iii) 58°   (iv) 122°
8 a) (i) 40° b) (i) 35°   (ii) $70° + 40° \neq 180°$
9 a) Ask your teacher to check your answer
   b) Ask your teacher to check your answer
   c) Enlargement centre $(2,0)$ scale factor $-\frac{1}{3}$.
10 a) Ask your teacher to check your answer
   b) Rotation through 90° anticlockwise, centre $(1,3)$

Chapter 17: Review: Statistics

Review exercise 17.1

1 a), b) Ask your teacher to check your answers
2 a) numerical, continuous
   b) categorical
   c) numerical, continuous
   d) numerical, discrete
3 a) Your table might look like this

Store	No. of beds sold in first quarter	
	Current year	Previous year
A	150	120
B	120	120
C	100	80
D	80	40

   b), c) Ask your teacher to check your answers
4 a) 6.7% (1 d.p.)   b) 73.3% (1 d.p.)

Review exercise 17.2

1 a) One possibility is 63, 576, 92, 241, 589, 203,
       56, 672, 841, 399
   b) One possibility is 635, 2241, 305, 460, 1029,
       4472, 1803, 1132, 3258, 4981
2 a), b), c) Ask your teacher to check your answers
3 a) Lower 49, middle 36 and upper 15
   b) Ask your teacher to check your answer
4 a) Ask your teacher to check your answer
   b) 15
5 a), b), c), d) Ask your teacher to check your
       answers
6 a), b) Ask your teacher to check your answers
7 a), b) Ask your teacher to check your answers

Review exercise 17.3

1 Ask your teacher to check your answers
2 a), c), d), e) Ask your teacher to check your
       answers
   b) Moderate positive linear correlation

3 a), b), d) Ask your teacher to check your answer
   c) Brenda

Review exercise 17.4

1 Ask your teacher to check your answer
2 Ask your teacher to check your answer
3 Ask your teacher to check your answer
4 a) The missing frequencies are 70, 58, 60, 44, 16
   b) The missing frequency densities are $0.4x$, $0.5y$

Mixed exercise 17.5

1 Ask your teacher to check your answer
2 Ask your teacher to check your answer
3 Ask your teacher to check your answer
4 a) Ask your teacher to check your answer
   b) Take 3, 8, 12, 14 and 3 patients from the age groups listed

Index